Business Analyst™ Guidebook

Note: The calculator keystrokes and descriptions used in this book were based on the Student Business Analyst™ financial calculator. The facts and information included will be generally useful when working with other specially dedicated business calculators, but the keystroke sequences described will only apply directly to the Student Business Analyst™ calculator.

This book was developed by:

Elbert B. Greynolds, Jr., Ph.D., CPA
Associate Professor of Accounting
Edwin L. Cox School of Business
Southern Methodist University

James M. Davenport, Ph.D.
Associate Professor of Mathematics
Texas Tech University

Stephen M. Scariano
Department of Mathematics
Texas Tech University

and

Kathy A. Kelly

Robert E. Whitsitt, II

Yvonne Lelko

Mahendra P. Agrawal

With contributions by:

Benjamin S. Duran
Texas Tech University

Patrick A. Hays
Texas Tech University

John W. Kensinger
Southern Methodist University

Jonathan A. Scott
Southern Methodist University

Norma Bohannon

Lane L. Douglas

Judy Lipsett

Charles L. McCollum

William J. Mullican

Samir W. Rizk

ISBN 0-89512-053-4
Library of Congress Catalog Card Number: 82-60168

Table of Contents

(continued)

(Table of Contents–Continued)

(continued)

Table of Contents

(continued)

(Table of Contents–Continued)

(continued)

Table of Contents

(continued)

(Table of Contents–Continued)

                                                       (continued)

Table of Contents

(Table of Contents–Continued)

(continued)

(Table of Contents–Continued)

Section I
INTRODUCTION

Introduction

Hand-held calculators have made business mathematics easier. A new speed, confidence, and accuracy are now possible in handling the arithmetic parts of our lives and studies. As hand-held calculators continue their rapid evolution, machines handling increasingly complicated mathematics are becoming available. Many techniques that previously required large volumes of tables, tedious calculations, or access to a large computer center can now be carried out with a few keystrokes on hand-held units such as the Student Business Analyst™ calculator.

This book discusses how the Student Business Analyst™ calculator makes your finance, statistics, and accounting course work easier, concentrating on how to use the statistical, mathematical, and financial functions in a straightforward manner with examples and keystroke solutions. The book and calculator are designed with the business and statistics student in mind. The book describes the use and need for financial and statistical functions. The calculator makes the arithmetic simple so you can concentrate on the theory.

The Story of Calculators

Throughout the centuries, businessmen have looked for tools to help them handle the "numbers" part of their business more quickly and accurately. Your calculator represents one link in what has been and probably will continue to be an explosive evolution in technology. To a large extent, this evolution has been brought about by real and practical business needs.

Introduction

As a human institution, business goes back quite a long way in history. As soon as Man began to trade the products of his labors for those of his neighbors, business was born. Very early, simple counting systems were developed for record-keeping purposes in these transactions, using tally sticks or some other small counters such as pebbles—with one counter representing one unit of the commodity. Historians usually consider the abacus, which originated in the Orient more than 5,000 years ago (and is still in use today), to be the first calculating device. For many centuries, there was little change in these simple devices, but by the 17th century, the evolution had begun to move again.

In 1642, the French scientist-philosopher, Blaise Pascal invented the first actual "adding machine." Pascal's work in this area began the evolution of the mechanical calculator. The first machines handled calculations rather slowly with the aid of complex entanglements of whirling gears, whizzing cranks, wheels, and windows. This evolution continued on up through 1890, when the punched card helped to take the 1890 U.S. Census. This led the way to later electric relay devices which continued to evolve into large-scale computers.

A few years ago, people working in the electronics industry made several breakthroughs that resulted in Texas Instrument's creation of the integrated circuit (IC). Integrated circuits made it possible to process and store large amounts of information in very small spaces with little power and at low cost. These devices, coupled with the development of inexpensive miniature displays, made hand-held calculators a reality. Recent advances in integrated circuits are continuing to increase the amount of information storage and processing that can be handled on a single "IC chip." (The term "IC chip" refers to the tiny piece of silicon upon which an integrated circuit is fabricated.)

New highly versatile IC chips make today's advanced statistical and business hand-held calculators possible. With these advanced machines, highly complex mathematical calculations can be executed rapidly and accurately with the touch of a key.

The "Business Analyst Guidebook"

Mathematics is part of many everyday, statistical, and business activities that you are studying. Your calculator can quickly and accurately handle the mathematics side of your life and courses. This book has been designed to show you how.

Your *Business Analyst Guidebook* gives compact, accessible, step-by-step techniques enabling you to take a variety of situations and analyze them with keyboard solutions. The book was designed to help you with your courses and to work directly with the calculator, so be sure to use them together.

An important first step is to get thoroughly acquainted with your calculator. Chapter 2 of this book is a quick explanation of all the features and keys of the calculator, along with brief examples illustrating the use of each feature. Chapter 2 is divided into six major sections.

Section 1—Getting Acquainted

Section 2—Basic Operation Keys

Section 3—Algebraic Keys

Section 4—Statistical Keys

Section 5—Financial Keys

Section 6—Memory Keys

The subsequent chapters in the book give examples that illustrate how you can use your calculator in your statistics and business courses. In each case the theory, application, and solution of a real-life business, statistical, or mathematical situation is described for you.

Most examples are broken into the following segments with each identified by its own graphic symbol, as shown:

Concepts: A statement of what types of calculation are used to analyze the problem, and how to begin implementing the calculation. This includes the theory and equations necessary to arrive at solutions.

Example: A sample showing the use of the concepts previously developed. Sample keystrokes to execute the solution (using the data given in the example statement), along with what you'll see in the display at key points in the calculation are included.

Review: A simple reference outlining the keystrokes necessary to the solution of the kind of problem shown in the example.

While you are using your calculator, remember that even though it has the latest in solid state technology, it still qualifies as a great toy for children of all ages. Play with it! Use it for exploring and "what iffing," as well as just idle doodling on the keys. You may just find yourself exploring patterns and relationships which can lead you to a new appreciation of the beautiful side of numbers and mathematics.

Chapter 2

STUDENT BUSINESS ANALYST™ KEYTOUR

INTRODUCTION

This chapter explains the basic features and key functions of your Student Business Analyst™ calculator. Completely read the section to become familiar with the calculator, and work some of the problems in the remaining chapters of the book to practice using the keys.

Getting Acquainted

Understanding the Keyboard

The Student Business Analyst™ calculator is designed for undergraduate and graduate students enrolled in number-intensive business courses. It is programmed with functions that can help the business school student with numerous statistical and financial calculations.

The calculator keyboard is divided into sections which group together related keys.

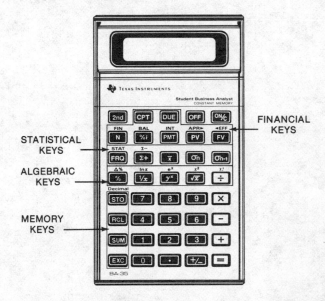

The top section contains the financial keys, while the next section is composed of the keys used in statistical calculations. The section below the statistics keys contains the calculator's algebraic keys. Keys associated with the memory function of the calculator are located on the lower left side of the keyboard. To the right of the memory keys are the usual number entry and arithmetic keys.

This method of grouping and marking the calculator keyboard lets you quickly locate the keys you need in your business course calculations.

INTRODUCTION

(Getting Acquainted–Continued)

Reading the Display

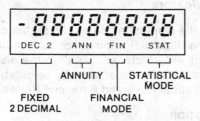

A maximum of eight digits may be entered in the liquid crystal display (LCD). A maximum of seven digits may be entered to the right of a decimal point. A zero appears to the left of the decimal point for numbers less than one and greater than minus one.

Extended Display Range (Scientific Notation)

The normal display range of your calculator is between 0.0000001 and 99999999 (positive or negative). A number outside this range can be shown in the display using a method called scientific notation. The calculator automatically changes to this method of display when a calculation results in a number smaller or larger than the normal range. Scientific notation can be identified by the special display format which contains 2 digits on the right side of the number (power-of-ten exponent) and 5 digits on the left side (mantissa). Either of the values may be a positive or negative number. For example, the result of the calculation:

$$-0.0065718 \div 10000000 =$$

is -6.5718×10^{-10} and is shown in the display as:

$$-6.5718 -10$$

(mantissa) (exponent)

In scientific notation, a positive exponent indicates the number of places to the right the decimal should be shifted. If the exponent is negative, the decimal should be moved to the left. In the above example, move the decimal 10 places to the left to express the number in algebraic form.

$$-0.\underset{\text{10 places left}}{0000000006}5718$$

(Getting Acquainted–Continued)

Display Indicators

"STAT" in the display indicates the statistical mode; "FIN" indicates the financial mode. "DEC 2" indicates a fixed decimal point at two places. "ANN" in the display indicates that the payment value in an annuity calculation is not zero. (See the Statistical Keys and Financial Keys sections.)

Error Indication

"Error" appears in the display when an overflow or underflow occurs or when you attempt an inappropriate operation or key sequence. When "Error" appears, no entry from the keyboard (except OFF) is accepted until ON/C is pressed. (See Appendix C for a list of error condition causes.)

Constant Memory™ Feature

The Constant Memory feature saves the memory content, the decimal setting, the mode, and all values entered in that mode (statistical or financial) when the calculator is turned off. The Constant Memory feature is not maintained if the batteries are discharged or removed.

Automatic Power Down (APD™) Feature

All calculations in progress are lost when the calculator automatically turns off after 15 to 35 minutes of nonuse. The effect is the same as if you press OFF. Press ON/C to turn the calculator on again. Because of the Constant Memory feature, the memory content, decimal setting, mode, and values entered in mode registers are retained.

Basic Operation Keys

On and Off Keys

[ON/c] —Press [ON/c] once to turn on the calculator. A "0" and the mode indicator appear in the display. "DEC 2" also appears if the calculator is in the fixed decimal point format. The first time the calculator is turned on, and after the batteries are replaced, you must clear all mode and memory registers. Press [OFF], [ON/c], [STO], [2nd] FIN , [2nd] STAT .

The [ON/c] key also serves as a clearing key. Before pressing any function or operation key, press [ON/c] once to clear the last number entered in the calculator. Pressing [ON/c] after a function or operation key (including [=]) clears the display and any pending calculation.

Pressing [ON/c] twice always clears the display and any pending calculation. This does not affect the memory and mode registers.

[OFF] —Press this key to turn off the calculator and clear any incomplete calculation. Pressing this key does not affect the memory and mode registers.

Second Function Key

[2nd] —To provide the maximum number of calculator features, some keys have more than one function.

The first function is printed on the key. To use the first function, just press the key. The second function is printed directly above the key. To use the second function, press the [2nd] key (located in the upper left corner of the keyboard) and then the function key. When [2nd] is pressed twice, the calculator performs the first function operation. If [2nd] is pressed before a digit key, [+/−], [·], [X], [−], [+], [=], [SUM], [EXC], [x̄], [σn], or [σn-1], the [2nd] operation is ignored.

In this book, keys with a black background indicate second functions. For example, to use the second function square of x, press [2nd] x^2 .

(Basic Operation Keys–Continued)

Number Entry Keys

Numbers are entered into the calculator with the entry keys ⌈0⌋ to ⌈9⌋, ⌈·⌋, and ⌈+/−⌋. As you enter any number, the decimal point is assumed (but not displayed) to the right of your entry until the decimal point key is pressed. After pressing the decimal key, the fractional part of the number is entered, and the decimal point "floats" to the left. To change the sign of a number in the display, press the change-sign key, ⌈+/−⌋. Press the key a second time to change the sign again.

Fixed Decimal Key

The calculator operates with a floating decimal point or a decimal point fixed at two places. "DEC 2" appears in the display when using the fixed decimal. To change from one decimal point format to the other, press ⌈2nd⌋ ⌈Decimal⌋ . For numbers smaller than .005, the fixed decimal point is ignored even though "DEC 2" is still shown in the display.

(Basic Operation Keys–Continued)

Arithmetic Keys

Basic arithmetic uses five operation keys: ⊞, ⊟, ⊠, ⊞, and ⊜. Since the calculator uses chain arithmetic, each time you press an operation key (including the algebraic keys [2nd]△% and [yˣ]) the previous operation is completed. All of the basic operation keys can be used in both the statistical and financial modes.

⊞   Adds the next entered number and the displayed number.

⊟   Subtracts the next entered number from the displayed number.

⊠   Multiplies the displayed number and the next entered number.

⊞   Divides the displayed number by the next entered number.

⊜   Completes all entered operations, including both intermediate and final results.

Operation entry errors can be corrected easily by pressing the correct arithmetic operation key, [yˣ], or [2nd]△% immediately after the incorrect operation. Number entry errors can be corrected by using the clear-entry function of the [ON/c] key.

Example: Calculate 7 ≠ x 8 ≠ + ≴ 1 = 57.

Press [2nd] [Decimal] as necessary to remove "DEC 2" from the display.

Procedure	Press	Display
1. Clear calculator.	[ON/c]	0
2. Enter 7 and change + to ×.	7 ⊞ ⊠	7
3. Enter 8 and change – to +.	8 ⊟ ⊞	56
4. Enter 5.	5	5
5. Change 5 to 1.	[ON/c] 1	1
6. Calculate result.	⊜	57

Algebraic Keys

Square, Square Root, and Reciprocal Keys

These three keys immediately act on the number in the display (called x) and do not affect any calculations in progress.

[2nd] x^2—Multiplies the displayed number (x) by itself and shows the result.

[$\sqrt{x}$]—Finds the number that, when multiplied by itself, produces the displayed number (x). X cannot be negative.

[$1/x$]—Divides the displayed number (x) into one. X cannot be zero.

Factorial Key

[2nd] [$x!$]—The factorial key acts only on the number in the display and does not affect any calculations in progress. It calculates and displays the factorial of the displayed number. The factorial of any integer is written as x! and is equal to $1 \times 2 \times 3 \times . . . \times X$. 0! is equal to 1 by definition. The largest possible factorial you can calculate with this calculator is 69.

Example: Find the factorial of 5.001. (This example shows that the factorial key acts only on the displayed value.)

Press [2nd] [Decimal] as necessary to remove "DEC 2" from the display.

Procedure	Press	Display
1. Clear calculator.	[ON/C]	0
2. Enter 5.001.	5.001	5.001
3. Calculate factorial.	[2nd] [$x!$]	Error
4. Clear error condition.	[ON/C]	0
5. Reenter 5.001.	5.001	5.001
6. Select fixed decimal point.	[2nd] [Decimal]	5.00 DEC 2
7. Calculate factorial.	[2nd] [$x!$]	120.00 DEC 2

(Algebraic Keys-Continued)

Percent and Percent Change Keys

The symbol "%" means percent, which is "one hundredth." For instance, the term 75% also can be written as .75, 75/100, or 3/4.

⌐%⌐—Converts a displayed percentage to its decimal equivalent (divided by 100). If you enter 36.9 and press ⌐%⌐, 0.369 is displayed.

When you use the percent key with an operation key, you can solve "mark up," "mark down," and other percentage problems.

⌐+⌐ n ⌐%⌐⌐=⌐ Adds n% of the number to the originally displayed number.

⌐−⌐ n ⌐%⌐⌐=⌐ Subtracts n% of the number from the originally displayed number.

⌐×⌐ n ⌐%⌐⌐=⌐ Multiplies the originally displayed number by n%.

⌐÷⌐ n ⌐%⌐⌐=⌐ Divides the originally displayed number by n%.

⌐2nd⌐ ⌐Δ%⌐—Calculates the percentage change between two values, X_1 and X_2, where

$$\Delta\% = \frac{X_1 - X_2}{X_2} \times 100$$

where X_2 is the reference value (old value) and X_1 is the new value.

(Algebraic Keys–Continued)

Example: You've been getting 18.9 miles per gallon of gasoline from your car. After you have the car tuned, the mileage rises to 22.3 MPG. Calculate the percentage increase.

Press ⟨2nd⟩ ⟨Decimal⟩ as necessary to remove "DEC 2" from the display.

Procedure	Press	Display
1. Clear calculator.	⟨ON/c⟩	0
2. Enter new mileage (X₁).	22.3 ⟨2nd⟩ ⟨Δ%⟩	22.3
3. Enter old mileage (X₂).	18.9	18.9
4. Calculate percentage change.	⟨=⟩	17.989418

Universal Power Key

⟨yˣ⟩—This key lets you raise a positive number to a power. To use the ⟨yˣ⟩ key, follow these steps:

- Enter the number (y) you want to raise to a power.
- Press ⟨yˣ⟩.
- Enter the power (x).
- Press ⟨=⟩ or any basic operation key.

To take the "x^{th}" root of any number y ($^x\sqrt{y}$):

- Enter the number (y) whose root you want to find.
- Press ⟨yˣ⟩.
- Enter the root (x).
- Press ⟨1/x⟩.
- Press ⟨=⟩ or any basic operation key.

(Algebraic Keys–Continued)

The variable y must always be a positive number. Also, attempting to take the 0th root of a number results in an "Error" condition.

Example: Calculate 9^3.

Press 2nd Decimal as necessary to remove "DEC 2" from the display.

Procedure	Press	Display
1. Clear calculator.	ON/c	0
2. Enter y.	9 y^x	9
3. Enter x.	3	3
4. Calculate result.	=	729

Logarithm Keys

Both of these key sequences immediately act on the number in the display. They do not affect any calculations in progress.

2nd lnx —Natural logarithm key. This key displays the natural logarithm (base e) of the number (x) in the display. X cannot be negative or zero.

2nd e^x —Natural antilogarithm (e to the power x). This key calculates the natural antilogarithm (base e) of the number (x) in the display. The value of e is approximately 2.7182818.

Example: Calculate the natural logarithm of 5.7 and the natural antilogarithm of 5.75.

Press 2nd Decimal as necessary to remove "DEC 2" from the display.

Procedure	Press	Display
1. Clear calculator.	ON/c	0
2. Calculate logarithm of 5.7.	5.7 2nd lnx	1.7404662
3. Calculate antilogarithm of 5.75.	5.75 2nd e^x	314.19066

Statistical Keys

Selecting and Clearing Statistical Mode

[2nd] [STAT] —Press this key sequence to enter the statistical mode. The "STAT" indicator appears in the display. If the calculator is already in the statistical mode, this key sequence clears the mode registers.

Statistical Data Entry and Removal Keys

These keys are only functional when the calculator is in the statistical mode. Press [2nd] [STAT] and "STAT" appears in the display.

[Σ+] —Enters data points for statistical calculations. After you enter a data point, the calculator displays the current total number (n) of data points entered.

[2nd] [Σ-] —Removes unwanted data points from the stored data sequence. After a data point is removed, the calculator displays the current total number (n) of stored data points.

[FRQ] —Used when several identical data points are to be entered. Enter them using the following key sequence: (data point), [FRQ], (number of data points), [Σ+]. Remove identical data points with this sequence: (data point), [FRQ], (number of data points), [2nd] [Σ-].

The mode registers retain all entered data even after you turn off the calculator. This means you can add data points to a previously entered data sequence without having to reenter the data.

(Statistical Keys–Continued)

Use the following procedures to enter and remove a sequence of single-variable data (data involving one variable).

1. To enter data points:
   • Enter the first data point.
   • Press $\boxed{\Sigma+}$.
   • Repeat for all data points.
2. To remove data points:
   • Press $\boxed{\text{ON/C}}$.
   • Enter the unwanted data point.
   • Press $\boxed{\text{2nd}}\boxed{\Sigma-}$.
   • Repeat for other unwanted data points.

Once entered, the data is used to calculate the mean, standard deviation, and variance by pressing the appropriate
keys.

IMPORTANT: Since the calculator can hold statistical data
in the mode registers even when it is turned off, always clear
the registers with $\boxed{\text{2nd}}\boxed{\text{STAT}}$ before entering a new set of
statistical data.

Mean, Standard Deviation, and Variance Keys

These keys may be used only in the statistical mode after
data has been entered as previously described.

$\boxed{\bar{x}}$—Calculates the mean (average) of the entered data.

When you are calculating the standard deviation or
variance, the keys you use depend on whether your data
represents an entire population or a sample portion of the
population.

$\boxed{\sigma n}$—Calculates the standard deviation with n weighting
(for population data).

(Statistical Keys–Continued)

$\boxed{\sigma_{n\text{-}1}}$—Calculates the standard deviation with $n-1$ weighting (for sample data).

$\boxed{\sigma_n}$ $\boxed{\text{2nd}}$ $\boxed{x^2}$—Calculates the variance of a population (with n weighting).

$\boxed{\sigma_{n\text{-}1}}$ $\boxed{\text{2nd}}$ $\boxed{x^2}$—Calculates the variance of a sample (with $n-1$ weighting).

NOTE: If you enter more than 30 data points, the difference between the standard deviation with n weighting and the standard deviation with $n-1$ weighting becomes very small.

Example: Enter the three data points 96, 85, and 57, and find the mean.

Press $\boxed{\text{2nd}}$ $\boxed{\text{Decimal}}$ as necessary to remove "DEC 2" from the display.

Procedure	Press	Display
1. Clear calculator and mode registers.	$\boxed{\text{ON/C}}$	0
2. Select statistical mode ("STAT" shows in display).	$\boxed{\text{2nd}}$ $\boxed{\text{STAT}}$	0 _{STAT}
3. Enter first data point.	96 $\boxed{\Sigma+}$	1 _{STAT}
4. Enter second data point incorrectly.	88 $\boxed{\Sigma+}$	2 _{STAT}
5. Remove incorrect data point.	88 $\boxed{\text{2nd}}$ $\boxed{\Sigma-}$	1 _{STAT}
6. Enter second data point correctly.	85 $\boxed{\Sigma+}$	2 _{STAT}
7. Enter third data point.	57 $\boxed{\Sigma+}$	3 _{STAT}
8. Compute mean.	$\boxed{\bar{x}}$	79.333333 _{STAT}

Financial Keys

Selecting and Clearing Financial Mode

[2nd] [FIN] —Press this key sequence to enter the financial mode. The "FIN" indicator appears in the display. If the calculator is already in the financial mode, this key sequence clears the mode registers.

Compound Interest Calculation Keys (Single Sum)

When performing compound interest calculations, select the financial mode by pressing [2nd] [FIN]. "FIN" appears in the display. The four basic elements of compound interest computations are:

[N]—the total number of compounding periods. (Entries and results are automatically rounded to four significant digits with this key.)

[%i]—the percent interest per compounding period.

[PV]—the present value (what your money is worth today).

[FV]—the future value (what your money will be worth in the future).

Enter the three known values. Then press [CPT] and the key for the unknown value. The calculator solves the compound interest problem for you. For compound interest calculations, the payment must be zero. If "ANN" appears in the display, it indicates that the payment value is not zero and the compound interest calculation is incorrect.

A financial value can be recalled by pressing [2nd] [RCL] and the key for the desired value ([N], [%i], [PMT], [PV], or [FV]).

(Financial Keys–Continued)

Annuity Problems (Series of Equal Payments)

The basic elements of an annuity problem are:

[N]—the total number of payment periods. (Entries and results are automatically rounded to four significant digits with this key.)

[%i]—the percent interest per payment period.

[PMT]—the amount of the regular payment ("ANN" appears in the display to indicate that the payment value for an annuity calculation is not zero.)

[PV]—the present value of a series of payments when considering savings or the loan amount when considering loans.

[FV]—the future value of a series of payments.

[CPT]—the key used to compute an ordinary annuity.

[DUE]—the key used to compute an annuity due.

Your calculator recognizes an annuity calculation when the payment key ([PMT]) is used with the other financial keys. When you enter any four of the known values, the calculator solves for the unknown value in ordinary annuity or annuity due computations. (Ordinary annuities are situations where equal payments are made at the end of a specified period. Annuities due occur when equal payments are made at the beginning of the period.) To compute annuity calculations, your calculator must be in the financial mode. Press [2nd] [FIN] for "FIN" to appear in the display.

The calculator is capable of directly solving annuity problems involving present and future value. When payments are compounded forward (future value is given or is being computed—PV = 0), enter the payment as a negative value. When payments are discounted back (present value is given or is being computed—FV = 0), enter the payment as a positive value. In more general annuity cases involving both PV and FV values, these rules do not apply.

After you enter the four known values, solve for the unknown by pressing [CPT] (to compute an ordinary annuity) or [DUE] (to compute an annuity due), followed by the key for the variable you are computing.

(Financial Keys–Continued)

IMPORTANT: The calculator clears the display of all information except the indicators while performing calculations. Keyboard entries are ignored when the display is blank. The computation for %i typically may take five to 30 seconds. If unrealistic values are entered for computation of %i, the calculating time may be minutes or even hours. If this occurs, press [OFF] once and then [ON/C] twice to go on to another calculation.

Interest Key

[2nd] [INT] or [DUE] [2nd] [INT] —To calculate the interest paid in a given payment of an ordinary annuity (payments made at the end of the payment period), enter the payment number and press [2nd] [INT]. To calculate the interest amount of annuities due (payments made at the beginning of the payment period), enter the payment number and press [DUE] [2nd] [INT]. The calculator must be in the financial mode ("FIN" shows in the display) for calculations involving this key sequence, and PV, PMT, %i, and FV must be entered. PV or FV may be zero depending upon type of annuity situation.

Loan Balance Key

[2nd] [BAL] or [DUE] [2nd] [BAL] —To calculate the remaining balance of the principal of an ordinary annuity (end-of-period payments), enter the payment number and press [2nd] [BAL]. To calculate the balance of annuities due (beginning-of-period payments), enter the payment number and press [DUE] [2nd] [BAL]. When you use this key sequence, the calculator must be in the financial mode ("FIN" shows in the display), and PV, PMT, %i, and FV must be entered. PV or FV may be zero depending upon annuity situation.

(Financial Keys–Continued)

Follow this procedure to calculate the accumulated interest from the Mth through the Nth payments.

- Enter the interest rate per payment period, the payment amount, present value, and future value with `%i`, `PMT`, `PV`, and `FV`.
- Enter Mth payment number, press `2nd` `BAL`*, wait for result, then press `STO`.
- Enter Nth payment number, press `2nd` `BAL`*, wait for result, then press `+/-` `SUM` to calculate and store accumulated principal.
- Enter Nth payment number, press `-`, enter Mth payment number, then press `=` `X` `2nd` `RCL` `PMT` `=` to calculate total payment amount from the Mth through the Nth payments.
- Press `-` `RCL` `=` to calculate accumulated interest from the Mth through the Nth payments.

Annual Percentage Rate Key

`2nd` `APR▶`—This key sequence converts annual percentage rates to annual effective rates. Enter the number of compounding periods per year. Press `2nd` `APR▶`, then enter the annual percentage rate, and press `=` to calculate the annual effective rate. The calculator must be in the financial mode ("FIN" shows in the display) to use this key sequence.

Annual Effective Rate Key

`2nd` `◀EFF`—This key sequence converts annual effective rates to annual percentage rates. Enter the number of compounding periods per year for the annual percentage rates. Press `2nd` `◀EFF`, then enter the annual effective rate, and press `=` to calculate the annual percentage rate. The calculator must be in the financial mode ("FIN" shows in the display) to use this key sequence.

*Use `DUE` `2nd` `BAL` for annuity due situations.

Memory Keys

The memory in your calculator is a special storage register that can hold a number you may need to use in other problems. You can store numbers and add to the value in memory without affecting any other calculations in progress. The memory content is not changed by any key except STO, SUM, or EXC. The memory remains in effect even when the calculator is turned off.

STO—Stores the displayed number in memory without removing it from the display. Any number previously stored in memory is lost. Press ON/C STO to clear the memory by storing a zero.

RCL—Causes a number which is stored in memory to reappear in the display. The number then can be used in operations and calculations. It remains in the memory after you press the RCL key and can be recalled as often as you need until you alter it with one of the other memory keys.

If you are using only the arithmetic or algebraic functions of the calculator, you have five additional memories. First, the "FIN" indicator must be in the display. Then you may store values in memories N, %i, PMT, PV, and FV and recall the values by pressing 2nd RCL followed by N, %i, PMT, PV, or FV. Values stored in the N memory may contain only four significant digits.

SUM—Allows you to add the number in the display and the value in the memory, without affecting any calculation in progress. You can use the SUM key when you want to keep a running total (on your expense account, for example), and keep the rest of the calculator clear for other uses.

To ensure that the memory content does not affect your calculation, always use STO to store the first quantity of a new problem, or press ON/C STO to clear the memory.

EXC—Exchanges the value stored in memory with the number in the display. The display value is stored, and the stored number is recalled.

Student Business Analyst™ Keytour

(Memory Keys–Continued)

Example: Store 50 in memory and add 14.8. Enter 84.42, and exchange it with the result in memory. Recall 84.42.

Press **2nd** **Decimal** as necessary for "DEC 2" to appear in the display.

Procedure	Press	Display	Memory
1. Clear calculator.	**ON/c**	0	
2. Store first value.	50 **STO**	50.00	50
3. Add second value to first.	14.8 **SUM**	14.80	64.8
4. Enter third value and exchange with result.	84.42 **EXC**	64.80	84.42
5. Recall third value.	**RCL**	84.42	84.42

Section II
STATISTICS

Descriptive Statistics

Introduction

Statistics is the study of how to use information to make intelligent decisions in uncertain situations. Statistics and statistical methods attempt to explain and offer some control over the uncertainties involved in decision-making.

This chapter discusses what is meant by "information," what are "intelligent decisions," what uncertainties are involved, and how to quantify data for analysis.

Many of the aspects of statistics are illustrated in Figure 3-1, which is adapted from *Comparative Statistical Inference* by Vic Barnett, J. Wiley and Sons, 1973.

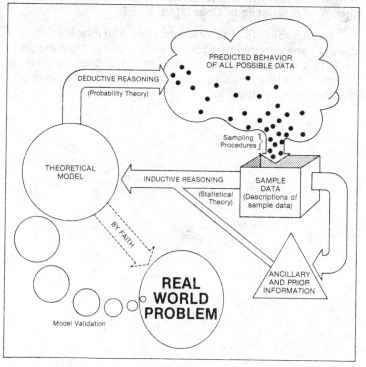

Figure 3-1

(Introduction–Continued)

To use the information in a sample, you must first summarize and describe it. This branch of statistics is called *descriptive statistics*, discussed in this chapter. Probability theory, a major component of intelligent decision-making, is presented and discussed in Chapter 4. In Chapter 5, sampling distributions which model the behavior of potential data are considered.

The practical purpose of statistics is to make generalizations about the whole, or "population," based on the data from a "sample." This branch of statistics is called *inferential statistics*. Inferential statistics, along with statistical theory, is discussed in Chapters 6 and 7.

The components of prior information and model validation are not considered in this book. However, all of the aspects of statistics illustrated in Figure 3-1 should be used to aid in intelligent decision-making. For more information, see the sources listed in the Bibliography.

The Population and the Sample

You normally want information about an entire population. Unfortunately, it is often difficult, if not impossible, to survey each individual. Instead, you can take a sample, learn the information it contains, and then make predictions about the entire population. Your ultimate objective is to describe the entire population, but you must first understand the information in the sample.

A *sample* is drawn or selected from a larger collection of items called the *population*. For example, suppose a marketing research firm is interested in testing a new product. The group of individuals who test this product and give their opinions constitutes a sample from the larger population of potential consumers. The marketing research firm draws conclusions about the population based on the sample. The firm tries to choose its sample such that they are likely to be representative of the larger population.

Population—the entire group you want information about. It may also refer to the set of the group's corresponding measurements.

Sample—a collection of selected items from a population. It may also refer to the measurements on those particular units.

Descriptive statistics, discussed in this chapter, is used to summarize the information contained in the sample. You can then use inferential methods, discussed in Chapters 6 and 7, to predict the characteristics of the population as a whole.

While dealing with statistical problems, you work with data from a sample. The underlying population may be described as a conceptual or idealized population, a real population, or a poorly-defined population.

A *conceptual or idealized population* is one that does not physically exist except in the mind of the experimenter. For example, if you flip a coin three times and observe the number of heads, the three tosses of the coin can be conceived as a sample of size three from a population consisting of all possible tosses of the coin.

(The Population and the Sample–Continued)

In contrast, sometimes a population consists of distinct, real entities, which could be assembled for observation. Such a population is said to be a *real or existing population*. For instance, the Constitution of the United States mandates that a general census be taken every 10 years. This population consists of all citizens of the United States.

Finally, a population, real or conceptual, may be *poorly-defined*. For example, suppose a sociologist questions 100 individuals leaving a college library on a Saturday morning. A sample is taken, but it is not clear what constitutes the population.

A sample may be classified as a simple random sample, a representative sample, a systematic sample, or a census. A *simple random sample* is one which is chosen so that every possible sample of equal size has an equal chance of being selected. A *representative sample* is one that claims to be a miniature "snap-shot" of the entire population. However, what constitues a representative sample is highly subjective. Note that a random sample need not be representative. A *systematic sample* is one in which the selected items are chosen using a random starting point and then a systematic choice of each succeeding item. For example, an investigator who selects the third person of column two on page seven from the New York City telephone directory and then chooses the individuals in the same position on pages 17, 27, 37, and so forth, has constructed a systematic sample. A *census* is a complete enumeration of every unit in the population. There are other types of samples, but these are the ones most frequently used.

(The Population and the Sample–Continued)

Statisticians use random samples. To obtain a random sample, the units or elements of a population are uniquely numbered and devices that simulate a random selection from among the associated population of numbers are used. The simplest device to use is a container of numbered chips which are stirred before the sampling takes place. Another useful device is a *table of random numbers*, which is provided in most statistical texts. Many computers and some calculators can generate *pseudo-random numbers*. Note that all these devices only simulate some idealized random selection procedure.

The following sections discuss the methods of summarizing and describing the information contained in a sample.

Summarizing Data

Concepts

Before inferences about a population can be made, you must describe the set of measurements to extract all relevant information. The measurements are first summarized by determining their frequency distribution. Then they may be described by using numerical techniques to produce tables or by using graphical techniques to produce histograms.

When describing and summarizing large data sets, categorize the data and tally the number of data units belonging to each category or class to determine the *class frequency*.

A *frequency distribution* is a tabular categorization of data into classes or categories along with the corresponding class frequencies.

The *relative frequency* is the ratio of the number of units in a particular class to the total number of data units collected. If f_i represents the number of units in the ith category and N data units are collected, then the relative frequency, r_i, of the ith class or category is given by:

$$r_i = \frac{f_i}{N} \qquad \qquad \textit{Equation (3-1)}$$

The *cumulative relative frequency* is the total relative frequency of all values less than the upper class boundary of the ith class interval. The class frequency, relative frequency, and cumulative frequency are shown in the frequency distribution in Table 3-2.

(Summarizing Data–Continued)

Example

The data in Table 3-1 represents a sample of the cost per pound paid by a nationwide chain of restaurants for choice T-bone steaks. Summarize this data in a frequency distribution and give the relative frequencies and cumulative frequency distribution.

2.85	2.13	2.66	2.66	2.31
2.32	2.88	2.63	2.65	2.38
2.58	2.55	2.46	2.71	2.41
2.58	2.56	2.49	2.37	2.47
3.05	2.61	2.64	2.67	2.52
2.41	2.69	2.39	2.34	2.53
2.75	1.96	2.12	2.39	2.39
2.79	2.15	2.90	2.20	2.48
2.27	2.43	2.87	2.15	2.41
2.52	2.43	2.54	2.26	2.41

Table 3-1
Cost Per Pound of Steaks in Dollars

Table Solution

Assume that the experimenter decides upon 12 classes of 10 cents each, the first one beginning with $1.90. The frequency distribution and cumulative frequency distribution for the above data are shown in Table 3-2.

(Summarizing Data–Continued)

Class	Class Boundaries	Tally	Class Frequency(f_i)	Relative Frequency(r_i)	Cumulative Relative Frequency(C_i)
1	1.90–1.99	I	1	1/50 = .02	.02
2	2.00–2.09	–	0	0/50 = .00	.02
3	2.10–2.19	IIII	4	4/50 = .08	.10
4	2.20–2.29	III	3	3/50 = .06	.16
5	2.30–2.39	IIIIIIII	8	8/50 = .16	.32
6	2.40–2.49	IIIIIIIIII	10	10/50 = .20	.52
7	2.50–2.59	IIIIIIII	8	8/50 = .16	.68
8	2.60–2.69	IIIIIIII	8	8/50 = .16	.84
9	2.70–2.79	III	3	3/50 = .06	.90
10	2.80–2.89	III	3	3/50 = .06	.96
11	2.90–2.99	I	1	1/50 = .02	.98
12	3.00–3.09	I	1	1/50 = .02	1.00
TOTAL			50	1.00	

Table 3-2

Frequency Distribution for the Data in Table 3-1

Note that the cumulative relative frequency of the last class equals one and, since you are accumulating relative frequencies, these numbers are nondecreasing.

Guidelines for Forming Frequency Distributions

When forming frequency distributions, use the following guidelines.

Number of Classes
It is usually best to have from four to 20 classes. Fewer than four classes tend to condense the data too much, while an excessive number of intervals may not condense the data enough.

(Summarizing Data–Continued)

Class Width
>Calculate the *range* (the largest data value minus the smallest data value) and divide by the number of classes you have chosen. The value is often not a convenient width, so adjust the value to a more convenient width. All classes should be of equal width.

Class Boundaries
>Class boundaries are determined by the location of the first class, so that class should be chosen so that it contains the smallest data value. Then append the remaining classes.

Graphical Representations: Histograms

Concepts

The results presented in Table 3-2 can be presented in graphical forms called *histograms*. Histograms have several limitations, the most serious being that they are difficult to use for making statistical inferences. Nevertheless, histograms are useful for visually conveying a general picture of the distribution of data.

Frequency Histogram—graph plotting the class boundaries versus the class frequencies. Rectangular regions are constructed over each class interval having heights proportional to the frequency of the class.

Relative Frequency Histogram—plotting the relative class frequencies instead of the class frequencies.

Descriptive Statistics

(Summarizing Data–Continued)

Example

Construct frequency and relative frequency histograms for the data in the first example in this chapter.

Graphical Solution

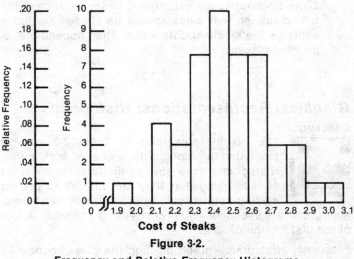

Figure 3-2.
Frequency and Relative Frequency Histograms
for the Data in Table 3-2

The histogram displayed in Figure 3-2 is both the frequency and relative frequency histogram. Their graphical forms are identical and the horizontal axis remains the same. The distinguishing features between these two are the vertical legends. Statisticians rarely make a distinction between these histograms and simply refer to both as histograms.

Cumulative frequency histograms—a graph plotting the class boundaries versus the cumulative relative frequencies. A horizontal line is drawn above each class interval at a height equal to the cumulative relative frequency of that class.

(Summarizing Data–Continued)

Example

Construct the cumulative frequency histogram for the data summarized in Table 3-2.

Graphical Solution

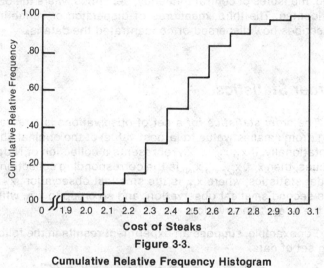

Figure 3-3.
Cumulative Relative Frequency Histogram
Associated with the Data Summarized in Table 3-2.

If the number of class intervals increases and their corresponding widths approach zero, at some point each data value itself becomes a class. Then the cumulative relative frequency distribution and histogram are called the *empirical distribution function*.

Descriptive Measures

Numerical descriptive measures are used when you want more than the general idea given by tables and histograms. The sample data is used to calculate a set of numbers which contain much of the information in the sample.

There are three common descriptive measures. The first, order descriptions, describes the order of the data. The second, measures of central tendency, describes where the data is located. The third, measures of dispersion or variability, describes how dispersed or concentrated the data is.

Order Statistics

The *order statistics* for a set of observations is a reordering (from smallest value to largest value) of the original data. Notationally, if x_1, x_2, ..., x_N represents a collection of N data values, then $x_{(1)}$, $x_{(2)}$, ..., $x_{(N)}$ is the corresponding collection of order statistics, where $x_{(1)}$ is the smallest observation, $x_{(2)}$ is the second smallest observation, and so on up to $x_{(N)}$, which is the largest observation.

For example, suppose an experiment results in the following set of data.

$x_1 = 21.2$	$x_4 = 24.3$	$x_7 = 22.3$
$x_2 = 23.7$	$x_5 = 22.7$	$x_8 = 25.2$
$x_3 = 24.8$	$x_6 = 21.8$	

The order statistics for this set of data are as follows.

$x_{(1)} = 21.2$	$x_{(4)} = 22.7$	$x_{(7)} = 24.8$
$x_{(2)} = 21.8$	$x_{(5)} = 23.7$	$x_{(8)} = 25.2$
$x_{(3)} = 22.3$	$x_{(6)} = 24.3$	

Note that the number of order statistics is always the same as the number of data points. However, x_i may or may not equal $x_{(i)}$. In the above example $x_{(1)}$ and x_1 both equal 21.2, but $x_{(5)}$ equals 23.7, while x_5 equals 22.7.

(Descriptive Measures–Continued)

Measures of Central Tendency

Measures of central tendency are used to measure the center or location of the data. Some rules for providing such estimates are presented in this section.

Arithmetic or Sample Mean

One of the most commonly-used measures of central tendency is the arithmetic average of a data set.

Sample Mean—the arithmetic average of the data values. Given the set of N measurements x_1, x_2, ..., x_N, the mean, denoted by $\bar{x}$, is given by:

$$\bar{x} = \frac{x_1 + x_2 + \ldots + x_{N-1} + x_N}{N} = \frac{\sum_{i=1}^{N} x_i}{N}$$

Equation (3-2)

The Greek letter $\sum$ (capital sigma) means "the sum of." The number below the $\sum$ indicates the starting point for the summation and the number above indicates the point at which to end the summation. Using $\sum$ allows you to write equations more simply than in the expanded form, as shown in equation (3-2).

Descriptive Statistics

(Descriptive Measures–Continued)

Example

Find the mean for the data given in the first example in this chapter. Use equation (3-2) with N = 50. Summing down the columns from left to right gives:

$$\bar{x} = \frac{2.85 + 2.32 + 2.58 + \ldots + 2.48 + 2.41 + 2.41}{50}$$

Calculator Solution

If the "DEC 2" indicator appears in the display, press 2nd Decimal before keying in the problem.

Procedure	Press	Display
1. Clear calculator and select statistics mode.	ON/c 2nd STAT	**0** STAT
2. Enter data from Table 3-1 using Σ+ key.	2.85 Σ+	**1** STAT
	2.32 Σ+	**2** STAT
	2.58 Σ+	**3** STAT
	.	.
	.	.
	.	.
	2.48 Σ+	**48** STAT
	2.41 Σ+	**49** STAT
	2.41 Σ+	**50** STAT
3. Calculate sample mean, x̄.	x̄	**2.4984** STAT

(Descriptive Measures–Continued)

Review

Press [2nd] [STAT] each time a new problem is started to clear the statistical registers.

Equation Value	Meaning	Keystroke
x_i	Enter data set.	x_i [Σ+]
Solution:	Calculate sample mean.	[x̄]

Sample Median

Another frequently used measure of location is the *sample median*, which is the half-way point or middle of the ordered sample. It is designated x_{MED}. The population median is the half-way point of an entire population.

Median—the midpoint of the data. Given the data x_1, x_2, ..., x_N, if the the number of observations, N, is odd, the median is the middle-order statistic. If N is even, the median is the average of the two middle-order statistics.

If N is *odd*:   If N is *even*:

$$x_{MED} = x_{\left(\frac{N+1}{2}\right)} \qquad x_{MED} = \frac{x_{\left(\frac{N}{2}\right)} + x_{\left(\frac{N}{2}+1\right)}}{2}$$

Equation (3-3)

Descriptive Statistics

(Descriptive Measures–Continued)

For example, the results of an hour exam for 14 students in Business Statistics 101 are:

$x_1 = 75$	$x_6 = 82$	$x_{11} = 65$
$x_2 = 13$	$x_7 = 68$	$x_{12} = 72$
$x_3 = 80$	$x_8 = 78$	$x_{13} = 72$
$x_4 = 41$	$x_9 = 64$	$x_{14} = 95$
$x_5 = 78$	$x_{10} = 66$	

First arrange the data points in order of increasing magnitude.

$x_{(1)} = 13$	$x_{(6)} = 68$	$x_{(11)} = 78$
$x_{(2)} = 41$	$x_{(7)} = 72$	$x_{(12)} = 80$
$x_{(3)} = 64$	$x_{(8)} = 72$	$x_{(13)} = 82$
$x_{(4)} = 65$	$x_{(9)} = 75$	$x_{(14)} = 95$
$x_{(5)} = 66$	$x_{(10)} = 78$	

Since there is an even number of observations (N = 14), the median is given by

$$x_{MED} = \frac{x_{(7)} + x_{(8)}}{2} = 72.$$

Sample Mode

Another measure of central tendency that is occasionally used is the value which appears most frequently. The *sample mode* is the value which appears most often in a list of data points. If no one value appears more often than all other values, there is no mode. When grouped into classes, the class having the greatest number of members is the modal class.

In a perfectly symmetrical distribution of data, the mean, median, and mode are essentially the same and are appropriate measures of central tendency. However, as the data becomes skewed, the median is usually the preferred predictor of the center of the underlying distribution. Personal preferences and experience with the data are usually good practical guidelines.

(Descriptive Measures–Continued)

Measures of Dispersion

Once the measures of central tendency are calculated for a particular distribution, you are interested in the spread of the data about the central tendency. For example, consider the four distributions represented by Figure 3-4.

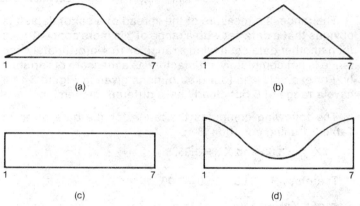

Figure 3-4
Variability or Dispersion of Data

Each of the distributions (a) through (d) ranges from 1 through 7 and has a central value of 4. Furthermore, each is symmetric about 4. Hence the measures of central tendency discussed in the previous section yield values approximately equal to four. But these are four distinct distributions, and the distinguishing feature is that each has a different variability about its center. Hence variation is a very important characteristic of the distribution of data.

Descriptive Statistics

(Descriptive Measures–Continued)

Sample Range

The *sample range* is the difference between the largest and smallest data values. If the data values are given by X_1, X_2, ..., X_N and the corresponding order statistics by $X_{(1)}$, $X_{(2)}$, ..., $X_{(N)}$, the range, R, is computed by the formula:

$$R = X_{(N)} - X_{(1)} \qquad \text{Equation (3-4)}$$

The range is a measure of the spread of a set of data. It is obvious that a data set with a range of 3 is more concentrated than another data set having a range of 15. Unfortunately, the range is not completely satisfactory as a measure of variability. For example, the four distributions given in Figure 3-4 all have a range of 6 but clearly have different dispersions.

The following computes the range for the data given in Table 3-1 using equation (3-4).

$X_{(50)} = 3.05$ and $X_{(1)} = 1.96$.

Therefore $R = 3.05 - 1.96 = 1.09$.

Sample Variance

Although the range is a measure of variability, its drawbacks prompted statisticians to search for another measure of variability more sensitive to variations in data. One method considers the deviations of each observation from the mean, defined by $d_i = x_i - \bar{x}$. Since it is easiest to work with one number to represent the total variation in a data set, these deviations d_i can be summed as shown below.

$$\sum_{i=1}^{N} d_i = \sum_{i=1}^{N} (x_i - \bar{x}) = \left(\sum_{i=1}^{N} x_i \right) - N\bar{x} = N\bar{x} - N\bar{x} = 0$$

(Descriptive Measures–Continued)

The sum of deviations about the mean equals zero and no additional information about the true variability in a data set is provided when using this measure. This occurs because the data values to the right of the mean form positive deviations, and observations to the left of the mean form negative deviations. Thus, the total is zero. To remedy this problem, either the absolute value of these differences or their squares can be used. In both cases, all of the measures of the deviation are positive. These two measures are represented by:

$$\sum_{i=1}^{N} |x_i - \overline{x}| \quad \text{and} \quad \sum_{i=1}^{N} (x_i - \overline{x})^2$$

Both provide positive numbers as measures of variability. The sum of the absolute deviations is usually difficult to use, so the sum of the squared deviations is used. It usually provides a more sensitive measure of variation than does the range.

The *sample variance* is the sum of the squares of the differences between the data points and the mean divided by $N - 1$. If N data values are given by $x_1, x_2, ..., x_N$, the sample variance, s^2, is defined by the following.

$$s^2 = \frac{\sum_{i=1}^{N} (x_i - \overline{x})^2}{N - 1} \quad \text{where} \quad \overline{x} = \frac{\sum_{i=1}^{N} x_i}{N}$$

Equation (3-5)

Here, $\overline{x}$ represents the sample mean of the N observations.

Sample Standard Deviation—the positive square root of the sample variance. It is denoted by s and is defined by:

$$s = |\sqrt{s^2}|$$ *Equation (3-6)*

Descriptive Statistics

(Descriptive Measures–Continued)

The sample variance as an estimate of the population variance is found by using the ⌐On-1⌐ key and squaring the result. The population variance is found by using the ⌐On⌐ key and squaring the result, if the population is finite. For large samples (over 30 elements) the sample standard deviation (s_x) is approximately equal to the population standard deviation, σ (lower-case sigma).

Example

Calculate the sample standard deviation and sample variance for the cost-per-pound of steak data given in the first example in this chapter.

Use equations (3-5) and (3-6) for finding the sample variance and sample standard deviation.

$$s^2 = \frac{(2.85 - 2.4984)^2 + \ldots (2.41 - 2.4984)^2}{50 - 1}$$

and $s = |\sqrt{s^2}|$ for s^2 calculated above.

(Descriptive Measures–Continued)

Calculator Solution

If the "DEC 2" indicator appears in the display, press [2nd] [Decimal] before keying in the problem.

Procedure	Press	Display
1. Clear calculator and select statistics mode.	[ON/c] [2nd] STAT	**0** _{STAT}
2. Enter data with [Σ+] key.	2.85 [Σ+]	**1** _{STAT}
	2.32 [Σ+]	**2** _{STAT}
	2.58 [Σ+]	**3** _{STAT}
	.	.
	.	.
	.	.
	2.48 [Σ+]	**48** _{STAT}
	2.41 [Σ+]	**49** _{STAT}
	2.41 [Σ+]	**50** _{STAT}
3. Calculate standard deviation.	[σn-1]	**0.2255004** _{STAT}
4. Calculate sample variance.	[2nd] x^2	**0.0508504** _{STAT}

Therefore, the sample standard deviation, s, is .2255004 and the sample variance, s^2, is .0508504.

Descriptive Statistics

(Descriptive Measures–Continued)

Review

Equation Value	Meaning	Keystroke
x_i	Enter data set.	x_i $\boxed{\Sigma+}$
Solution:	Calculate standard deviation.	$\boxed{\sigma\text{n-1}}$
	Calculate sample variance.	$\boxed{2\text{nd}}$ $\boxed{x^2}$

Chapter 4
PROBABILITY DISTRIBUTIONS

Probability Distributions

Introduction

In the previous chapter, the mean and variance were computed for the data available from a sample and other means for describing the sample were explored. This process, called descriptive statistics, allows you to summarize the sample data with a few numbers.

The objective of describing a sample is to use that description to draw inferences about the complete population. This process is discussed in Chapters 6 and 7. First, however, you need some information about probability theory and about what forms the population might take.

The theory of probability can be used to minimize the risk of making a wrong decision. This theory is concerned with the measurement of uncertainty. It allows information in descriptive statistics to be used to make more accurate inferences about the population from which the sample was taken. Probability theory is used to bridge the gap between descriptive statistics and statistical inferences made about the entire population.

For example, suppose you want to know the probability of selecting at least two red balls when choosing three balls at random from a box containing ten red and twenty blue balls. This is a problem in probability theory. On the other hand, suppose you want to estimate from a sample the proportion of red or blue balls in a box containing unknown numbers of balls of both colors. This is a problem in statistical inference.

A good understanding of statistical inferences and probability applications is important to help you choose the best options when making decisions such as buying new product lines, investing in the stock market, or purchasing bonds.

This chapter presents the basic concepts of statistical inference and various discrete and continuous probability distributions, beginning with a discussion of the theory of probability.

Fundamental Probability Concepts

This section discusses the basic methods of computing the probabilities of known events.

Events

An *experiment* is the process by which observations are obtained. Experiments can be numerical, as in the previous example of the red and blue balls. They can also be non-numerical, such as an interview with someone concerning their preferences on a particular subject.

An experiment may result in one of many possible outcomes. Any collection of these outcomes is called an *event*. Typical examples of random experiments are

- Tossing a coin.
- Rolling either a single die or a pair of dice.
- Selecting one or more balls from a box.
- Randomly dealing from a deck of cards.

For example, toss two coins and observe the outcome of heads or tails. In the ordered pair (x,y), x denotes the outcome of coin 1 and y represents the outcome of coin 2. The events are called event A, event B, event C, etc. Using this notation, all possible events can be identified as follows.

Event A = {Heads,Heads}   Event C = {Tails,Heads}

Event B = {Heads,Tails}   Event D = {Tails,Tails}

Notice that events B and C each have one head and one tail. They are different events because different coins show heads and tails.

An event can be composed of one or more simple events. An event that cannot be divided is called a *simple event* and is denoted by the symbol E_j.

(Fundamental Probability Concepts–Continued)

For example, suppose you roll a die and an even number appears on the upper face. Let E_2 mean a 2 appears, E_4 mean a 4 appears, and E_6 mean a 6 appears. Event A, an even number appearing, is composed of the three simple events E_2, E_4, and E_6.

Sometimes terms from set theory are used to define the events. A *set* is defined as a collection of definite and distinct objects. These objects are called *elements* of the set. A simple event is a set that contains only one element.

The collection of all possible outcomes of a random experiment is called the *sample space*. In terms of set theory, the sample space is the set of all possible elements.

In the example of tossing two coins, the sample space is as follows.

Sample Space = {(H,H),(H,T),(T,H),(T,T)}

where H = Heads and T = Tails. The simple events are (H,H), (H,T), (T,H), and (T,T), which can also be referred to as E_1, E_2, E_3, and E_4, respectively.

A *Venn diagram* is useful for portraying events and a sample space. A Venn diagram for a sample space consists of all simple events possible from a random experiment. These simple events are shown as points enclosed by a boundary.

(Fundamental Probability Concepts–Continued)

A Venn diagram for the example of tossing two coins is drawn as follows.

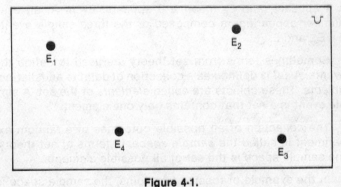

Figure 4-1.
Venn Diagram for Simple Events
for Two Coin Tossing

Listed below are the 12 other possible events that are made up of the simple events E_1, E_2, E_3, and E_4.

Event	Description	Notation
Event A	Coin 1 is Heads.	E_1, E_2
Event B	Coin 2 is Heads.	E_1, E_3
Event C	Coin 2 is Tails.	E_2, E_4
Event D	Coin 1 is Tails.	E_3, E_4
Event E	Coin faces are alike.	E_1, E_4
Event F	Coin faces are unalike.	E_2, E_3
Event G	At least one coin is Heads.	E_1, E_2, E_3
Event H	At least one coin is Tails.	E_2, E_3, E_4
Event I	Coin faces are not (T,H) respectively.	E_1, E_2, E_4
Event J	Coin faces are not (H,T) respectively.	E_1, E_3, E_4
Event K	Complete sample space (all outcomes).	E_1, E_2, E_3, E_4
Event L	Impossible event.	Null

(Fundamental Probability Concepts–Continued)

A Venn diagram for events E, F and I is drawn as follows.

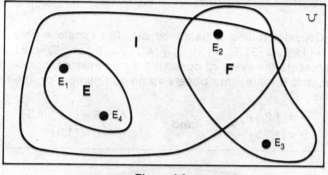

Figure 4-2.
Venn Diagram for Selected Events
for Tossing Two Coins

A set containing no elements, like Event L in the last example, is called the *null set* and is designated by the symbol ϕ (phi). The set of all elements possible, like Event K in the last example, is referred to as the *universal set* and is designated by the symbol $\cup$.

Events and Their Relationship (Compound Events)

Often events can be expressed in terms of one or more simple events and their relationship to each other. The composition of two or more events is called a *compound event*. This process of forming compound events takes place by the construction of *unions*, *intersections*, and *complements* of events.

The *complement* of A consists of all sample points not in set A and is denoted as $\bar{A}$ (A bar).

The *union* of event A with event B, denoted A ∪ B, is the event which contains the sample points in A, in B, or in both A and B.

(Fundamental Probability Concepts–Continued)

The *intersection* of event A and event B, denoted by A ∩ B, is the event which contains the sample points in both A and B.

Consider rolling a balanced die. The simple events are $E_1 = \{1\}$, $E_2 = \{2\}$, $E_3 = \{3\}$, $E_4 = \{4\}$, $E_5 = \{5\}$, and $E_6 = \{6\}$. If A represents the event of observing a maximum of four on the roll, and B represents observing an odd number on the roll, then

$$A = \{1,2,3,4\}$$
$$B = \{1,3,5\}$$
and
$$A \cup B = \{1,2,3,4,5\}$$
$$A \cap B = \{1,3\}$$

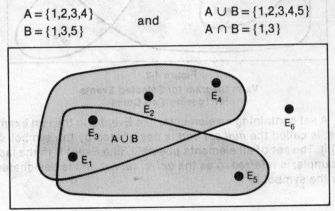

Figure 4-3.
Union A ∪ B

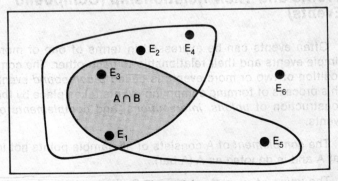

Figure 4-4.
Intersection A ∩ B

(Fundamental Probability Concepts–Continued)

Mutually Exclusive Events

Two events, A and B, are *mutually exclusive* if they cannot occur simultaneously. The property of mutually exclusive events is $A \cap B = \phi$ (null set).

In rolling a die, you may get a number less than or equal to four, an odd number, or an even number. These compound events are represented as shown below.

$A = \{1,2,3,4\}$ Number less than or equal to four
$B = \{1,3,5\}$ Odd number
$C = \{2,4,6\}$ Even number

Since $B \cap C = \{1,3,5\} \cap \{2,4,6\} = \phi$, events B and C are mutually exclusive. It is not possible to get both an odd number and an even number on one roll of a die.

Since $A \cap B = \{1,2,3,4\} \cap \{1,3,5\} = \{1,3\}$, which is not the null set, events A and B are not mutually exclusive. It is possible for a die on one roll to show an odd number that is less than or equal to four.

The Probability of an Event

The probability associated with an event should reflect the frequency of occurrence of this event if the experiment is repeated a large number of times. This interpretation of the meaning of probability is called the *relative frequency concept*.

For example, toss an unbiased coin. (Making sure the coin is unbiased is an important consideration.) If a large number of coin tosses is made, heads will turn up approximately half the time and tails the other half. For events $E_1 = \{Heads\}$ and $E_2 = \{Tails\}$, the probability is 1/2. This is expressed as $P(E_1) = P(E_2) = 1/2$, where the probability of A is denoted as $P(A)$.

(Fundamental Probability Concepts–Continued)

It is generally most useful to assign a probability to an event according to the frequency with which it is observed. However, any probability may be assigned as long as it meets the following properties.

- The probability of an event E, P(E), has a value from 0 through 1. This is expressed as

  $0 \leqslant P(E) \leqslant 1$

- If all possible simple events are E_1, E_2, ..., E_n, the sum of their probabilities is 1. This is expressed as

  $P(E_1) + P(E_2) + ... + P(E_n) = 1$.

- If events A and B are mutually exclusive, the probability of occurrence of either *A or B* is equal to the sum of their probabilities. This is expressed as

  $P(A \cup B) = P(A) + P(B)$

For example, roll a balanced die once. The simple events are $E_1 = \{1\}$, $E_2 = \{2\}$, $E_3 = \{3\}$, $E_4 = \{4\}$, $E_5 = \{5\}$, and $E_6 = \{6\}$. Since the die is balanced,

$P(E_1) = P(E_2) = ... = P(E_6) = 1/6$

Events E_1, E_2, E_3, E_4, E_5, and E_6 are mutually exclusive because each can occur only by itself.

If we define an event A as equal to $\{1,2,3,4\}$, then

$$P(A) = P(E_1) + P(E_2) + P(E_3) + P(E_4)$$
$$= 1/6 + 1/6 + 1/6 + 1/6$$
$$= 4/6$$
$$= 2/3$$

(Fundamental Probability Concepts–Continued)

Probability Relationships of Events

Probability of the Complement of an Event—the probability that an event will not occur.

For example, the probability of the complement of the event A is computed by

$$P(\overline{A}) = 1 - P(A) \qquad \text{Equation (4-1)}$$

Conditional Probability—the probability that one event will occur given that another event has occurred.

The conditional probability of event A, given event B has occurred, written P(A|B), is computed by

$$P(A|B) = \frac{P(A \cap B)}{P(B)} \qquad \text{Equation (4-2)}$$

provided P(B) is not equal to 0.

Similarly, the conditional probability of event B, given event A has occurred, is computed by

$$P(B|A) = \frac{P(B \cap A)}{P(A)} \qquad \text{Equation (4-3)}$$

provided P(A) is not equal to 0.

Probability Distributions

(Fundamental Probability Concepts–Continued)

For example, consider the roll of a balanced die. Let event A represent the observation of four or less, and let B represent an odd number. Thus

$$A = \{1,2,3,4\} \text{ and } B = \{1,3,5\}$$

Calculate $P(A|B)$ and $P(B|A)$.

$$P(A) = P(E_1) + P(E_2) + P(E_3) + P(E_4)$$
$$= 1/6 + 1/6 + 1/6 + 1/6$$
$$= 2/3$$

$$P(B) = P(E_1) + P(E_3) + P(E_5)$$
$$= 1/6 + 1/6 + 1/6$$
$$= 1/2$$

$$A \cap B = \{1,2,3,4\} \cap \{1,3,5\}$$
$$= \{1,3\}$$

$$P(A \cap B) = P(E_1) + P(E_3)$$
$$= 1/6 + 1/6$$
$$= 1/3$$

Therefore, $P(A|B) = \dfrac{P(A \cap B)}{P(B)} = \dfrac{1/3}{1/2} = 2/3$

$$P(B|A) = \dfrac{P(B \cap A)}{P(A)} = \dfrac{1/3}{2/3} = 1/2$$

When events are related, as in this example, the conditional probability of event A, given that event B has occurred, is the same as the unconditional probability of event A. The probability of A occurring is not affected by the occurrence or non-occurrence of B and vice versa.

Independence/Dependence

If the occurrence or non-occurrence of an event does not have any effect on the probability of another event, then the events are *independent* of each other. Mathematically, events A and B are independent if and only if

$$P(A|B) = P(A) \qquad \text{Equation (4-4)}$$

(Fundamental Probability Concepts–Continued)

Otherwise, events A and B are said to be *dependent*. If equation (4-4) is satisfied, then it is also true that $P(B|A) = P(B)$.

For example, consider the die-tossing experiment.

Let $A = \{1,2,3,4\}$

    $B = \{1,3,5\}$

    $C = \{2,4,6\}$

Are events A and C independent?

The intersection $A \cap C = \{1,2,3,4\} \cap \{2,4,6\} = \{2,4\}$ and $P(A \cap C) = 2/6$. The conditional probability

$$P(A|C) = \frac{P(A \cap C)}{P(C)} = \frac{2/6}{3/6} = 2/3$$

and since $P(A)$ is also equal to 2/3, events A and C are *independent*.

Rules of Probabilities

There are two rules of probability that determine the probability of $A \cup B$ and $A \cap B$ if A and B are two events. They are the addition rule of probability and the multiplication rule of probability.

The Addition Rule of Probability—the probability of $A \cup B$ is equal to the probability of A plus the probability of B minus the probability of $A \cap B$.

$$P(A \cup B) = P(A) + P(B) - P(A \cap B) \quad \textit{Equation (4-5)}$$

$P(A \cup B)$ does not necessarily equal $P(A) + P(B)$ because any intersection between A and B is counted twice. This is the reason for subtracting $P(A \cap B)$. However, if A and B are mutually exclusive, then $P(A \cap B) = 0$, and equation (4-5) reduces to the third property of a probability function, $P(A \cup B) = P(A) + P(B)$.

Probability Distributions

(Fundamental Probability Concepts–Continued)

As an illustration of the addition rule of probability, suppose you randomly draw one card from a standard 52-card deck. Let A be the event "red face card" and let B be the event "heart." Find $P(A \cup B)$.

Since a 52-card deck has 8 red face cards,

$P(A) = 8/52$

Since there are 13 cards in the hearts suit of a 52-card deck,

$P(B) = 13/52 = 1/4$

$A \cap B = \{red\ face\ card\} \cap \{heart\}$

$\qquad = \{face\ cards\ in\ the\ heart\ suit\}$

$P(A \cap B) = 4/52$

Therefore,

$P(A \cup B) = P(A) + P(B) - P(A \cap B)$

$\qquad = 8/52 + 13/52 - 4/52$

$\qquad = (8 + 13 - 4)/52$

$\qquad = 17/52$

The probability of getting either a red face card or a heart is 17/52.

The Multiplication Rule of Probability—the probability of $A \cap B$ is equal to either the conditional probability of B given A times the probability of A or the conditional probability of A given B times the probability of B, provided that the conditional probabilities exist.

$$P(A \cap B) = P(A) \times P(B|A) \qquad \text{Equation (4-6)}$$
$$= P(B) \times P(A|B)$$

If A and B are independent, then

$$P(A \cap B) = P(B) \times P(A) \qquad \text{Equation (4-7)}$$

(Fundamental Probability Concepts–Continued)

To illustrate the multiplication rule of probability, consider the following example. A box contains nine balls. Four of the balls are red and five are blue. Two balls are to be randomly drawn from the box, and you want to know the probability that these two balls will be red. Let A be the event that the first ball drawn is a red ball, and let B be the event that the second ball drawn is a red ball. What is the probability of the event that both the first and second balls are red. In other words, calculate $P(A \cap B)$.

Equations (4-6) and (4-7) are both available to calculate $P(A \cap B)$. To decide which of these two formulas to use, determine whether events A and B are independent. If A and B are not independent, use equation (4-6). If the events are independent, use equation (4-7). If the sampling takes place without replacement, events A and B are dependent. Use equation (4-6).

$P(A \cap B) = P(A) \times P(B|A)$

$P(A)$ = 4/9, since 4 balls are red out of a total of 9.

$P(B|A)$ = 3/8, since only 3 balls are red out of the 8 left after picking the first red ball.

Thus $P(A \cap B) = P(A) \times P(B|A) = 4/9 \times 3/8 = 1/6$.

If the sampling is done *with replacement*, then events A and B are *independent*. Use equation (4-7).

$P(A \cap B) = P(B) \times P(A)$

$P(A)$ = 4/9, since 4 balls are red out of a total of 9.

$P(B)$ = 4/9, since due to replacement there are again 4 red balls out of a total of 9.

Thus $P(A \cap B) = P(A) \times P(B) = 4/9 \times 4/9 = 16/81$.

(Fundamental Probability Concepts–Continued)

Counting Samples—Permutations and Combinations
Concepts

Permutations and combinations involve different groupings of a finite number of objects. In determining the number of possible groupings, you may assume that each event has an equal likelihood of occurring. Then, if n(A) is the number of sample points in event A, the probability of event A is equal to the ratio of the number of sample points in A to the total number of sample points in the sample space. This is expressed mathematically as P(A) = n(A)/n. Therefore finding the probability of event A involves counting the number of sample points in the event and the sample space.

In the previous example of the red and blue balls, it is a simple matter to list all of the points in the sample space and count those sample points that belong to event A ({red ball}). However, it becomes more difficult when the number of sample points becomes so large that enumeration is impractical. In such cases, you can use *combinatorial analysis*, which consists of combinations and permutations, among other concepts.

Permutation—an ordered arrangement of objects. The key word in this definition is "ordered." The number of permutations of n things taken r at a time is denoted by $_nP_r$.

$$_nP_r = \frac{n!}{(n-r)!}$$ Equation (4-8)

where $n! = n \times (n-1) \times (n-2) \times ... \times 1$

(Fundamental Probability Concepts–Continued)

For example, consider four objects labeled A, B, C, and D. There are 12 arrangements of those four things taken two at a time. They are

AB	CA
AC	CB
AD	CD
BA	DA
BC	DB
BD	DC

Since the order of arrangement is important, AB is not the same as BA.

The number of permutations can be counted in this case or figured by using equation (4-8).

$$_4P_2 = \frac{4!}{(4-2)!}$$

$$= \frac{4 \times 3 \times 2 \times 1}{2 \times 1}$$

$$= 12$$

(Fundamental Probability Concepts–Continued)

Example

How many ways can eight horses finish in win, place, and show with no ties?

Calculator Solution

Because the order of finish is important, use the permutation formula, equation (4-8), where $n = 8$ and $r = 3$. If the "DEC 2" indicator appears in the display, press [2nd] [Decimal] before keying in the solution.

Procedure	Press	Display
1. Clear calculator.	[ON/C]	**0** _{STAT}
2. Calculate 8! and store.	8 [2nd] [x!] [STO]	**40320** _{STAT}
3. Find $(8 - 3)!$.	8 [−] 3	
	[=] [2nd] [x!]	**120** _{STAT}
4. Divide 8! by $(8 - 3)!$.	[EXC] [÷] [RCL] [=]	**336** _{STAT}

There are 336 different ways in which eight horses can finish in win, place, and show.

(Fundamental Probability Concepts–Continued)

Review

Equation Value	Meaning	Keystroke
Inputs:		
n!	Find n! and store.	n [2nd] [x!] [STO]
(n − r)	Subtract r from n.	n [−] r [=]
(n − r)!	Find (n − r)!.	[2nd] [x!]
Solution:	Permutation.	[EXC] [÷] [RCL] [=]

Concepts

Combination—an arrangement of objects without regard to order. The number of combinations of n things taken r at a time is written as

$$\binom{n}{r} = \frac{n!}{r!(n-r)!} = \frac{{}_nP_r}{r!} \qquad \text{Equation (4-9)}$$

The symbol C_r^n is sometimes used to symbolize the combination of n things taken r at a time.

For example, consider four objects A, B, C, and D. The permutations of four things taken two at a time is

AB	CA
AC	CB
AD	CD
BA	DA
BC	DB
BD	DC

(Fundamental Probability Concepts–Continued)

Since the order of arrangement is not important for combinations, the following arrangements are identical.

AB = BA
AC = CA
AD = DA
BC = CB
BD = DB
CD = DC

Therefore there are six combinations, which are

AB   BC
AC   BD
AD   CD

The number of combinations can be figured by using equation (4-9).

$$\binom{4}{2} = \frac{4!}{2! \times (4-2)!}$$
$$= \frac{4 \times 3 \times 2 \times 1}{2 \times 1 \times 2 \times 1}$$
$$= 6$$

Example

How many five-card hands can be dealt from a standard 52-card deck so that all five cards are spades?

Since the ordering of the five spades in the hand is *not* important, this is a combination problem. Use equation (4-9) with n = 13 and r = 5. Note that the five cards must be selected from the spade suit and not the entire deck.

(Fundamental Probability Concepts–Continued)

Calculator Solution

If the "DEC 2" indicator appears in the display, press
[2nd] [Decimal] before keying in the solution.

Procedure	Press	Display
1. Clear calculator.	[ON/C]	0 STAT
2. Compute 13!.	13 [2nd] [x!]	6.227 09 STAT
3. Divide by 5! and store.	[÷] 5 [2nd] [x!] [=] [STO]	51891840 STAT
3. Find (13 − 5)!.	13 [−] 5 [=] [2nd] [x!]	40320 STAT
4. Divide amount stored by result.	[EXC] [÷] [RCL] [=]	1287 STAT

Thus $\binom{13}{5} = 1287$ is the number of spade hands.

Review

Equation Value	Meaning	Keystroke
Inputs:		
n!	Find n!.	n [2nd] [x!]
n!/r!	Divide by r! and store.	[÷] r [2nd] [x!] [=] [STO]
(n − r)!	Find (n − r)!.	n [−] r [=] [2nd] [x!]
Solution:	Divide stored amount by displayed amount.	[EXC] [÷] [RCL] [=]

(Fundamental Probability Concepts–Continued)

Differences Between Permutations and Combinations

The essential difference between combinations and permutations is the ordering of the components within a sample point. If the ordering of the components is important and any rearrangement of these components produces a different sample point, then you should use the permutation formula. The number of ways that horses can finish a race or the number of ways that political candidates can finish in an election are examples where ordering is important and permutations should be used.

If the ordering of the components is not important and a rearrangement of the components does not produce a different simple event, then you should use the combination formula. The arrangement of cards in a poker hand or a bridge hand is a combination because the order of the cards is unimportant.

The Mean and Variance of Probability Distributions

The first part of this chapter presented the basic tools of probability theory, the rules for assigning probabilities, and methods for computing probabilities. This section builds on these ideas by introducing the concepts of a *random variable* and the *probability distribution function*. These two concepts let you calculate the probabilities of events more easily.

In most sample spaces, each simple event can be assigned a number. These numbers may be the height of a person, the number that appeared on the top face of a die, and so forth. Since the simple events themselves are random, the associated numbers are also random. A variable, such as X, is used to designate all of the possible numbers. This variable is called a *random variable*. The collection of all possible values of a random variable is called the *range* of the random variable.

Suppose a coin is tossed three times. The sample space $\cup$ is given by

$$\cup = \{(H,H,H),(H,H,T),(H,T,H),(T,H,H),(T,T,H),(T,H,T),\\ (H,T,T), (T,T,T)\}$$

Let the random variable X = "number of heads observed in the three tosses." The possible values that the random variable X can assume are 0, 1, 2, and 3. The collection {0,1,2,3} is called the range of the random variable X. Note that if the sample space, $\cup$, is finite or countably infinite, then the range of X is also finite or countably infinite. Such a random variable is called a *discrete random variable*.

Discrete Probability Distributions

Since every simple event in a sample space has a probability assigned to it, the probabilities are "carried-over" to the random variable, X. Suppose X = 1. Then the probability that X equals the value 1 is the sum of all of the probabilities associated with the simple events that yield the value X = 1.

Probability Distributions

(The Mean and Variance of Probability Distributions–Continued)

Discrete Probability Distribution—a probability function, p(x), that systematically lists all the values in the range of the random variable along with the respective probabilities.

Since a probability distribution is constructed from a probability sample space, all discrete probability distributions have the following properties.

- p(x) is greater than or equal to 0 for every value of X.
- $\sum_x p(x) = 1$, where "$\sum_x$" means to sum all the values in the range of X.

Referring to the last example, suppose that each simple event is assumed to be equally likely. Then each has a probability of 1/8. These concepts are summarized in Table 4-1.

Outcomes in the Simple Space	Probabilities Associated with Each Outcome	Value of the Random Variable X	Probabilities Associated with the Range of X
(H,H,H)	1/8	3	P[X = 3] = 1/8
(H,H,T)	1/8	2	
(H,T,H)	1/8	2	P[X = 2] = 3/8
(T,H,H)	1/8	2	
(H,T,T)	1/8	1	
(T,H,T)	1/8	1	P[X = 1] = 3/8
(T,T,H)	1/8	1	
(T,T,T)	1/8	0	P[X = 0] = 1/8

Table 4-1.
Relationship of the Sample Space to a Discrete Random Variable

(The Mean and Variance of Probability Distributions–Continued)

The discrete probability distribution of the random variable X for this random experiment is summarized in the following compact form.

X	0	1	2	3
p(x)	1/8	3/8	3/8	1/8

where p(x) is the probability that the random variable x takes on the value x. So $p(x) = P[X = x]$. Also note that the sum of the probabilities is one.

$$\sum_x p(x) = p(0) + p(1) + p(2) + p(3)$$
$$= 1/8 + 3/8 + 3/8 + 1/8$$
$$= 1$$

Graphic Representation

Discrete probability distributions can be illustrated by *bar graphs*. The values of a random variable, X, are plotted along the horizontal axis and the values of p(X) are plotted on the vertical axis. The probability at each value of X is shown by the relative height of a bar. Figure 4-5 is a bar graph of the information in Table 4-1.

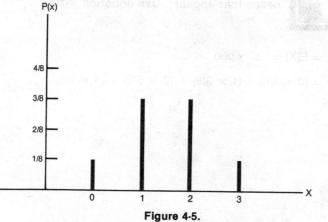

Figure 4-5.
Graph of a Discrete Probability Function

(The Mean and Variance of Probability Distributions—Continued)

The Mean or Expected Value of a Discrete Random Variable

Concepts

Probability distribution functions have many important properties, and several attempts have been made to categorize these distributions according to those properties. Two of these properties are the mean and the variance of the distribution function.

Mean of a Discrete Distribution—the weighted average of the values assumed by a discrete random variable. If X is a random variable with the corresponding probability distribution function p(X), then the *mean* (or *expected* value) of the random variable X is given by the following formula.

$$\mu = E[X] = \sum_{x} x\, p(x) \qquad \text{Equation (4-10)}$$

where "E[X]" means the "expected value of X" and the small Greek letter "μ" (mu) represents the mean.

Example

Toss a coin three times. Find the mean (expected value) of the random variable X = {number of heads that appear}. Use equation (4-10).

$$\mu = E[X] = \sum_{x=0}^{3} x\, p(x)$$
$$= (0 \times 1/8) + (1 \times 3/8) + (2 \times 3/8) + (3 \times 1/8)$$

*(The Mean and Variance of Probability
Distributions-Continued)*

Calculator Solution

If the "DEC 2" indicator appears in the display, press
[2nd] [Decimal] before keying in the solution.

Procedure	Press	Display
1. Clear calculator.	[ON/C]	0 _{STAT}
2. Compute 0 times 1/8 and store.	0 [X] 1 [÷] 8 [=] [STO]	0 _{STAT}
3. Add 1 times 3/8 and sum.	1 [X] 3 [÷] 8 [=] [SUM]	0.375 _{STAT}
4. Add 2 times 3/8 and sum.	2 [X] 3 [÷] 8 [=] [SUM]	0.75 _{STAT}
5. Add 3 times 1/8 and sum.	3 [X] 1 [÷] 8 [=] [SUM]	0.375 _{STAT}
6. Recall mean.	[RCL]	1.5 _{STAT}

In this case, the value of the mean, or expected value of
the random variable X, is 1.5. This is a theoretical mean and
can be interpreted as the average value of X. It may also
represent the average number of heads observed if the coin is
repeatedly tossed three times. Note that the mean of the
distribution does not have to be a value in the range of the
random variable. $\mu = 1.5$ is not in the set {0,1,2,3}.

Probability Distributions

(The Mean and Variance of Probability Distributions–Continued)

Variance and Standard Deviation

Concepts

An important characteristic of a probability distribution is its dispersion or variability about its mean. One such measure is called the *variance*.

Variance—with probability distribution function p(x), the expected value of the squared deviation of the random variable from its mean.

$$\sigma^2 = E[(X - \mu)^2] = \sum_x (x - \mu)^2 p(x) = Var[X]$$

Equation (4-11)

where μ is the mean of the distribution and σ^2 (sigma squared) denotes the variance.

Standard Deviation—the positive square root of a random variable's variance, usually denoted by

$$\sigma = \sqrt{\sigma^2}$$

Equation (4-12)

Alternate Formula for Computing Variances

To calculate the variance of a distribution, the following shortcut formula is available. Equation (4-11) is equivalently given by

$$\sigma^2 = E[X^2] - \mu^2 = \sum_x x^2 p(x) - \mu^2$$

Equation (4-13)

(The Mean and Variance of Probability Distributions–Continued)

Example

The results of a population census of individuals in Texas produced the following demographic data. The variable x is the number of children per married couple after 15 years of marriage.

X	0	1	2	3	4	5	6
p(x)	.20	.26	.21	.15	.12	.04	.02

Show that the function is a probability distribution and find the mean, variance, and standard deviation.

To demonstrate that a function is a valid probability distribution function, show that p(x) is greater than or equal to 0 for all X and that $\sum_x p(x) = 1$.

For the given distribution, all probabilities involved are non-negative. Furthermore,

$$\sum_x p(x) = p(0) + p(1) + p(2) + p(3) + p(4) + p(5) + p(6)$$
$$= .20 + .26 + .21 + .15 + .12 + .04 + .02$$

Calculator Solution

Sum the probabilities to find if the result is one, indicating that the function is a valid probability distribution. If the "DEC 2" indicator appears in the display, press ⟨2nd⟩ ⟨Decimal⟩ before keying in the solution.

Procedure	Press	Display
1. Clear calculator.	⟨ON/c⟩	**0** _{STAT}
2. Sum the probabilities.	.20 ⟨+⟩ .26 ⟨+⟩	**0.46** _{STAT}
	.21 ⟨+⟩ .15 ⟨+⟩	**0.82** _{STAT}
	.12 ⟨+⟩ .04 ⟨+⟩	**0.98** _{STAT}
	.02 ⟨=⟩	**1** _{STAT}

Since the sum is one, the function is a valid probability distribution.

Probability Distributions

(The Mean and Variance of Probability Distributions–Continued)

To find the mean, use equation (4-10).

$$\mu = \sum_{x=0}^{6} x\, p(x) = (0 \times .20) + (1 \times .26) + (2 \times .21) + (3 \times .15) +$$
$$(3 \times .15) + (4 \times .12) + (5 \times .04) + (6 \times .02)$$

Procedure	Press	Display
1. Clear calculator.	[ON/C]	0 STAT
2. Compute sum of products given above.	0 [X] .20 [=] [STO]	0 STAT
	1 [X] .26 [=] [SUM]	0.26 STAT
	2 [X] .21 [=] [SUM]	0.42 STAT
	3 [X] .15 [=] [SUM]	0.45 STAT
	4 [X] .12 [=] [SUM]	0.48 STAT
	5 [X] .04 [=] [SUM]	0.2 STAT
	6 [X] .02 [=] [SUM]	0.12 STAT
3. Recall mean.	[RCL]	1.93 STAT

The mean of the distribution is $\mu = 1.93$, so the expected value of X, the number of children the couples have on the average, is given by $E[X] = 1.93$.

(The Mean and Variance of Probability Distributions–Continued)

Use equations (4-12) and (4-13) to find the variance and standard deviation of this distribution.

$$\sigma^2 = \sum_{x=0}^{6} x^2 p(x) - \mu^2$$

$$= (0^2 \times .20) + (1^2 \times .26) + (2^2 \times .21) + (3^2 \times .15) + (4^2 \times .12)$$
$$+ (5^2 \times .04) + (6^2 \times .02) - 1.93^2$$

$$\sigma = \sqrt{\sigma^2}$$

Procedure	Press	Display
1. Clear calculator.	$\boxed{\text{ON/c}}$	0
2. Compute sum of products.	0 $\boxed{\text{2nd}}$ $\boxed{x^2}$ $\boxed{\times}$	
	.20 $\boxed{=}$ $\boxed{\text{STO}}$	0
	1 $\boxed{\text{2nd}}$ $\boxed{x^2}$ $\boxed{\times}$	
	.26 $\boxed{=}$ $\boxed{\text{SUM}}$	0.26
	2 $\boxed{\text{2nd}}$ $\boxed{x^2}$ $\boxed{\times}$	
	.21 $\boxed{=}$ $\boxed{\text{SUM}}$	0.84
	3 $\boxed{\text{2nd}}$ $\boxed{x^2}$ $\boxed{\times}$	
	.15 $\boxed{=}$ $\boxed{\text{SUM}}$	1.35
	4 $\boxed{\text{2nd}}$ $\boxed{x^2}$ $\boxed{\times}$	
	.12 $\boxed{=}$ $\boxed{\text{SUM}}$	1.92
	5 $\boxed{\text{2nd}}$ $\boxed{x^2}$ $\boxed{\times}$	
	.04 $\boxed{=}$ $\boxed{\text{SUM}}$	1
	6 $\boxed{\text{2nd}}$ $\boxed{x^2}$ $\boxed{\times}$	
	.02 $\boxed{=}$ $\boxed{\text{SUM}}$	0.72
3. Recall sum.	$\boxed{\text{RCL}}$	6.09
4. Subtract mean squared.	$\boxed{-}$ 1.93	
	$\boxed{\text{2nd}}$ $\boxed{x^2}$ $\boxed{=}$	2.3651
5. Calculate standard deviation.	$\boxed{\sqrt{x}}$	1.5378882

So the variance is 2.3651, and the standard deviation is 1.5378882.

(The Mean and Variance of Probability Distributions–Continued)

For valid discrete probability distributions, you can get the same result by using the $\boxed{\Sigma+}$, $\boxed{FRQ}$, and $\boxed{\sigma n}$ keys. First multiply the values of p(x) times 100 so that the results are integers with values from 0 through 99. The problem is then solved as follows.

Procedure	Press	Display
1. Clear calculator and select statistics mode.	$\boxed{ON/c}$ $\boxed{2nd}$ $\boxed{STAT}$	0 <small>STAT</small>
2. Enter probabilities.	0 $\boxed{FRQ}$ 20 $\boxed{\Sigma+}$	20 <small>STAT</small>
	1 $\boxed{FRQ}$ 26 $\boxed{\Sigma+}$	46 <small>STAT</small>
	2 $\boxed{FRQ}$ 21 $\boxed{\Sigma+}$	67 <small>STAT</small>
	3 $\boxed{FRQ}$ 15 $\boxed{\Sigma+}$	82 <small>STAT</small>
	4 $\boxed{FRQ}$ 12 $\boxed{\Sigma+}$	94 <small>STAT</small>
	5 $\boxed{FRQ}$ 4 $\boxed{\Sigma+}$	98 <small>STAT</small>
	6 $\boxed{FRQ}$ 2 $\boxed{\Sigma+}$	100 <small>STAT</small>
3. Calculate standard deviation.	$\boxed{\sigma n}$	1.5378882 <small>STAT</small>
4. Calculate variance.	$\boxed{2nd}$ $\boxed{x^2}$	2.3651 <small>STAT</small>

*(The Mean and Variance of Probability
Distributions–Continued)*

Review

Equation Value	Meaning	Keystroke
Input:		
x p(x)	Enter data set.	x [FRQ] p(x) × 100 [Σ+]
Solution:	Calculate standard deviation.	[σn]
	Calculate variance.	[2nd] x^2

(The Mean and Variance of Probability Distributions–Continued)

Continuous Random Variable

If a random variable can conceivably take on any value between two numbers, say a and b, it is called a *continuous random variable*. Such variables arise when measuring items such as weight, height, length, and temperature. Probabilities associated with continuous random variables are computed differently from those of discrete distributions. Probability distributions of such random variables are generally represented by smooth curves. In these cases, it is important to note that, unlike the case of a discrete probability function, the height of the function does not indicate the probability. In continuous cases, probabilities are computed by finding areas under the curve, above the horizontal axis, and between two desired limits.

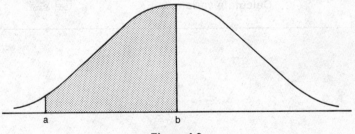

Figure 4-6.
P[a ⩽ X ⩽ b] for the
Continuous Random Variable X.

In order to find such areas, use the methods of integral calculus. Refer to the books listed in the Bibliography for a discussion of calculus. The only continuous random variable described in this book is the Normal Distribution.

The Binomial Distribution

Concepts

The Binomial Distribution is one of the most widely-used models in statistics and applied probability. A fundamental component of this distribution is the concept of a *Bernoulli trial*, developed by James Bernoulli (1654-1705).

Bernoulli trial—a single experiment which can result in one of two mutually exclusive outcomes, labeled "success" and "failure."

For example, suppose you toss a fair coin 10 times. Let the *random variable* X equal the number of heads observed in the ten tosses. Each individual toss of the coin is a Bernoulli trial. Heads is arbitrarily designated as a success. Note that P("success") = P(Heads) = p = 1/2 on each of the Bernoulli trials. The trials are mutually independent and the probability of a success does not change from trial to trial.

If n Bernoulli trials are conducted, find the probability of the number of successes observed. The discrete probability distribution of the number of successes observed in these repeated Bernoulli trials is called the *Binomial Distribution*. There are two essential assumptions that must be met in this distribution.

- n independent, identical Bernoulli trials must exist.
- The probability of success on any given trial, denoted by p, must remain constant from trial to trial.

Binomial Distribution—the probability of observing exactly X successes in n trials of a Bernoulli process satisfying the above requirements is

$$P(X = x) = \binom{n}{x} p^x(1 - p)^{n-x} \text{ for } x = 0, 1, 2, ..., n$$
$$= 0 \text{ elsewhere}$$

Equation (4-14)

where the random variable X is the number of successes observed, p is the constant probability of success on any given trial, and $\binom{n}{x}$ is the number of combinations of n things taken x at a time.

(The Binomial Distribution–Continued)

Example

A multiple choice exam consists of four questions, each possessing three possible choices. If a student guesses at each question, what is the probability that he guesses exactly two correct answers?

A particular Bernoulli trial is the answer to one specific question. Each answer is independent of the others, and the probability of successfully answering a question is 1/3. If X represents the total number of correct answers given by the student, X follows the Binomial Distribution.

To determine the chance of guessing exactly two answers correctly, use equation (4-14) with $n = 4$, $p = 1/3$ and $X = 2$.

$$P[X = 2] = \binom{4}{2} (1/3)^2 (1 - 1/3)^{4-2}$$

$$= \frac{4!}{2!\,(4-2)!} (1/3)^2 (2/3)^2$$

Calculator Solution

If the "DEC 2" indicator appears in the display, press 2nd Decimal before keying in the solution.

Procedure	Press	Display
1. Clear calculator.	`ON/C`	0 STAT
2. Calculate $\binom{4}{2}$ and	4 `2nd` `x!` `÷` 2	
	`2nd` `x!`	2 STAT
store value.	`÷` 2	
	`2nd` `x!` `=` `STO`	6 STAT
3. Compute $(1/3)^2$ times	1 `÷` 3 `=` `yˣ`	
	2 `=`	0.1111111 STAT
$\binom{4}{2}$ and store value.	`×` `RCL` `=` `STO`	0.6666667 STAT
4. Compute $(2/3)^2$ times	2 `÷` 3 `=` `yˣ`	
	2 `=`	0.4444444 STAT
the stored value.	`×` `RCL` `=`	0.2962963 STAT

(The Binomial Distribution–Continued)

Therefore, $P[X = 2] = .2962963$. This represents the probability of the student randomly guessing two correct answers in four attempts.

Review

Note: When you are not using the statistical keys, you may enter the financial mode and use (%i), (PMT), (PV), and (FV) as memories. ((N) can be used as a memory if you only need four significant digits.) You enter the number by pressing the key when the value you wish to store is in the display, and recall it with (2nd)(RCL) and the key you used when entering the value.

You must enter the financial mode by pressing (2nd)(FIN) in order to use the following key sequence. The "FIN" indicator appears in the display. If you store a value with the (PMT) key, the "ANN" indicator appears. These indicators are not relevant to the use of these keys as memories, and attempting to find financial results will not give helpful results.

(The Binomial Distribution–Continued)

Equation Value	Meaning	Keystroke
Inputs:		
$\binom{n}{x}$	Calculate $\binom{n}{x}$.	n [2nd] [x!] [÷] x [2nd] [x!] [=] [STO] n [−] x [=] [2nd] [x!] [EXC] [÷] [RCL] [=] [STO]
p^x	Multiply by p^x and store.	p [y^x] x [=] [×] [RCL] [=] [STO]
$n - x$	Compute $n - x$ and store in [%i].	n [−] x [=] [%i]
$(1 - p)^{n - x}$	Compute $(1 - p)^{n - x}$.	1 [−] p [=] [y^x] [2nd] [RCL] [%i] [=]
Solution:	Multiply displayed value by stored value.	[×] [RCL] [=]

(The Binomial Distribution–Continued)

Combinatorial Coefficient $\binom{n}{x}$ in Equation (4-14)

Suppose that the student in the example above answers the first two questions correctly (C) and the remaining two questions incorrectly (I). This particular sequence of outcomes is represented by {C,C,I,I}. The probability of this specific outcome is $(1/3)(1/3)(2/3)(2/3) = (1/3)^2(2/3)^2$. This is the probability of obtaining the specific sequence of outcomes in the order shown and is an application of the multiplication rule of probability to a sequence of independent events.

However, in the example any combination which resulted in exactly two correct answers is acceptable. The specific sequence is not important. There are six such sequences that have exactly two correct answers, and each occurs with probability $(1/3)^2(2/3)^2$. These are summarized in Table 4-2.

Sequence Number	Sequence
1	C, C, I, I
2	C, I, C, I
3	C, I, I, C
4	I, C, C, I
5	I, C, I, C
6	I, I, C, C

Table 4-2.
All possible sequences of two correct and two incorrect answers

In the above example, a sequence of answers consists of four guesses. Two of the guesses are designated as correct answers. This is the number of combinations of four guesses, taken two at a time and is equal to $\binom{4}{2} = 6$.

The problem is to count the number of sequences that result in exactly x successes in n Bernoulli trials. This is accomplished by using the combinatorial formula, $\binom{n}{x}$.

(The Binomial Distribution–Continued)

This is the first factor in the equation. Then multiply by the proababilities of correct answers, $(1/3)^2$, and the probability of incorrect answers, $(2/3)^2$. The result is

$$6 \times (1/3)^2 \times (2/3)^2$$
$$= 6 \times .1111111 \times .4444444$$
$$= .2962963$$

This is the same answer as obtained in the calculator solution.

Tables of Binomial Probabilities

Concepts

When finding binomial probabilities, you generally consult tables of the distribution. Various tables use different formats for presenting the Binomial Distribution. These tables are generally provided since the calculation of binomial probabilities using equation (4-14) can be tedious if the arithmetic is done by hand. However, with the aid of your calculator such probabilities are computed easily. Therefore, no tables are provided in this book.

Example

An insurance company has evidence that 37.5% of its claims for fire damage are the result of arson. If 15 such claims are brought to the company, what is the probability that *at least* three of the cases are due to arson?

Assuming that all the conditions for the Binomial Distribution are satisfied, let X = the number of fires involving arson in n claims. Then the desired probability is

$$P(X \geqslant 3) = P(X = 3) + P(X = 4) + ... + P(X = 15)$$
$$= 1 - (P(X = 0) + P(X = 1) + P(X = 2))$$

(The Binomial Distribution–Continued)

The complement of the desired events is $X < 3$. Using the relationship given in equation (4-1) between the probability of an event and its complement simplifies the arithmetic involved. Use equation (4-14) with $n = 15$, $p = .375$ and $X = 0, 1$, and 2 respectively.

Calculator Solution

In the following sequence, the financial keys $\boxed{\text{PV}}$, $\boxed{\text{%i}}$, and $\boxed{\text{PMT}}$ are used as memories. Enter the financial mode by pressing $\boxed{\text{2nd}}\boxed{\text{FIN}}$. If the "DEC 2" indicator appears in the display, press $\boxed{\text{2nd}}\boxed{\text{Decimal}}$ before keying in the solution.

Procedure	Press	Display
1. Clear calculator and enter financial mode.	$\boxed{\text{ON/c}}$ $\boxed{\text{2nd}}$ $\boxed{\text{FIN}}$	0 _{FIN}
2. Compute $P(X = 0)$ and store answer in $\boxed{\text{PV}}$.		
a. Calculate $\binom{15}{0}$ and store.	15 $\boxed{\text{2nd}}$ $\boxed{x!}$	1.3077 12 _{FIN}
	$\boxed{\div}$ 0 $\boxed{\text{2nd}}$ $\boxed{x!}$	1 _{FIN}
	$\boxed{\div}$ 15 $\boxed{\text{2nd}}$ $\boxed{x!}$	
	$\boxed{=}$ $\boxed{\text{STO}}$	1 _{FIN}
b. Calculate $(.375)^0$ times $\binom{15}{0}$.	.375 $\boxed{y^x}$ 0 $\boxed{=}$	1 _{FIN}
	$\boxed{\times}$ $\boxed{\text{RCL}}$	
	$\boxed{=}$ $\boxed{\text{STO}}$	1 _{FIN}
c. Calculate $(.625)^{15}$ times stored value.	.625 $\boxed{y^x}$ 15 $\boxed{=}$	0.0008674 _{FIN}
	$\boxed{\times}$ $\boxed{\text{RCL}}$ $\boxed{=}$	0.0008674 _{FIN}
d. Store result in $\boxed{\text{PV}}$	$\boxed{\text{PV}}$	0.0008674 _{FIN}
3. Compute $P(X = 1)$ and store answer in $\boxed{\text{%i}}$.		
a. Calculate $\binom{15}{1}$ and store.	15 $\boxed{\text{2nd}}$ $\boxed{x!}$	1.3077 12 _{FIN}
	$\boxed{\div}$ 1 $\boxed{\text{2nd}}$ $\boxed{x!}$	1 _{FIN}
	$\boxed{\div}$ 14	
	$\boxed{\text{2nd}}$ $\boxed{x!}$ $\boxed{=}$ $\boxed{\text{STO}}$	15 _{FIN}

(continued)

(The Binomial Distribution–Continued)

(continued)

Procedure	Press	Display
b. Calculate $(.375)^1$	.375 y^x 1 $=$	0.375 _{FIN}
times $\binom{15}{1}$.	$\times$ RCL $=$ STO	5.625 _{FIN}
c. Calculate $(.625)^{14}$	.625 y^x 14 $=$	0.0013878 _{FIN}
times stored value.	$\times$ RCL $=$	0.0078063 _{FIN}
d. Store result in %i.	%i	0.0078063 _{FIN}
4. Compute $P(X = 2)$ and store answer in PMT.		
a. Calculate $\binom{15}{2}$ and	15 2nd $x!$	1.3077 12 _{FIN}
store.	$\div$ 2 2nd $x!$	2 _{FIN}
	$\div$ 13	
	2nd $x!$ $=$ STO	105 _{FIN}
b. Calculate $(.375)^2$	.375 y^x 2 $=$	0.140625 _{FIN}
times $\binom{15}{2}$.	$\times$ RCL $=$ STO	14.765625 _{FIN}
c. Calculate $(.625)^{13}$	.625 y^x 13 $=$	0.0022204 _{FIN}
times stored value.	$\times$ RCL $=$	0.0327863 _{FIN}
d. Store result in PMT.	PMT	0.0327863 _{ANN FIN}
5. Add $P(X = 0) + P(X = 1) +$	2nd RCL PV $+$	0.0008674 _{ANN FIN}
$P(X = 2)$.	2nd RCL %i $+$	0.0086736 _{ANN FIN}
	2nd RCL PMT $=$	0.0414599 _{ANN FIN}
6. Determine $P(X \geqslant 3)$ by subtracting this sum from 1.	$+/-$ $+$ 1 $=$	0.9585401 _{ANN FIN}

So $P(X \geqslant 3) = 0.9585401$, and it is highly probable that at least three of the 15 claims involve arson.

(The Binomial Distribution–Continued)

The Mean and Variance of the Binomial Distribution

The mean and variance of the Binomial Distribution are computed using the following equations, where n is number of trials and p is the probability of success.

$$\mu = np$$ *Equation (4-15)*

$$\sigma^2 = np\,(1 - p)$$ *Equation (4-16)*

You can use some algebraic manipulations to derive the mean and variance. The mean of the Binomial Distribution is interpreted as the expected number of successes in n Bernoulli trials. The variance is a measure of the dispersion of the distribution.

The Hypergeometric Distribution

Concepts

 One of the assumptions necessary for a random variable to have the Binomial Distribution is that the probability of success on each trial must be constant. In sampling situations where items are randomly chosen from a larger population, this requirement is met in one of two ways.

- If the population is infinite and the proportion of that population labeled "success" is equal to p, then the probability that a chosen member of the population will be a "success" is constant and equal to p.
- If the population is finite, then sampling with replacement ensures that the proportion of members of the population labeled "success" remains constant and equal to p for every member selected.

When sampling is from a finite population and done without replacement, then the binomial model is not valid and you must use a different probability distribution.

For example, suppose a shipment of 10 transistors is received. Assume that there are four defective items among these 10 transistors, and a random sample of size 2 is to be taken and destructively tested for possible defects. The probability that the first transistor chosen is defective is equal to $4/10 = 2/5$.

The probability that the second transistor chosen is defective is equal to either $4/9$ or $3/9 = 1/3$, depending upon whether the first transistor selected was nondefective or defective. So the probability of choosing a defective item is not constant on each trial. Sampling with replacement is not appropriate in this experiment since destructive testing is used. There is no alternative but to consider some distribution other than the Binomial Distribution.

(The Hypergeometric Distribution–Continued)

Fortunately, such a distribution does exist and is known as the *Hypergeometric Probability Distribution*. For the Hypergeometric Distribution to be a valid model, the following conditions must exist.

- Sampling must be done without replacement from a population with N members, where N is a finite number. N is usually small to moderate in size.
- The population of N elements is divided into two mutually exclusive subsets consisting of N_1 elements of one type (successes) and N_2 elements of another type (failures). The total number of elements, N, is equal to the sum of the successes, N_1, and the failures, N_2.
- A sample of size n is drawn from the population, and the random variable X denotes the number of successes observed in the sample.
- The sample space for this experiment is the set of all possible subsets of size n chosen from the N elements. Each point in the sample space is assumed to be equally likely.

If simple events are equally likely, then the probability of event A is given by $P(A) = \dfrac{n(A)}{n(\cup)}$, where n(A) represents the number of elements in event A and $n(\cup)$ denotes the number of elements in the sample space $\cup$. The event A is "x successes and $n - x$ failures in the sample of size n." The x successes are chosen from the N_1 elements, and the remaining $n - x$ failures are selected from the N_2 elements. So

$$n(A) = \binom{N_1}{x} \times \binom{N_2}{n-x}$$

Also, the number of simple events in the sample space $\cup$ is equal to the number of subsets of size n chosen from N elements and is given by

$$n(\cup) = \binom{N}{n}$$

Probability Distributions

(The Hypergeometric Distribution–Continued)

Therefore, the Hypergeometric Probability Distribution is defined as

$$P(X = x) = \frac{\binom{N_1}{x} \binom{N_2}{n-x}}{\binom{N}{n}}$$

Equation (4-17)

where x is greater than or equal to the maximum of 0 and $n - N_2$, less than or equal to the minimum of n and N_1, and zero elsewhere. The above conditions must be satisfied.

Example

What is the probability that an auditor finds three erroneous accounting transactions if he randomly selects six transactions from among 20, of which eight contain errors?

Use equation (4-17) with $n = 6$, $N = 20$, $N_1 = 8$, $N_2 = 12$, and $x = 3$.

$$P(X = 3) = \frac{\binom{8}{3} \binom{12}{6-3}}{\binom{20}{6}}$$

$$= \frac{\frac{8!}{3!\,5!} \times \frac{12!}{3!\,9!}}{\frac{20!}{6!\,14!}}$$

(The Hypergeometric Distribution–Continued)

Calculator Solution

If the "DEC 2" indicator appears in the display, press
[2nd] [Decimal] before keying in the solution.

Procedure	Press	Display
1. Clear calculator.	[ON/C]	0 STAT
2. Calculate $\binom{8}{3}$ and store.	8 [2nd] [x!]	40320 STAT
	[÷] 3 [2nd] [x!]	6 STAT
	[÷] 5	
	[2nd] [x!] [=] [STO]	56 STAT
3. Calculate $\binom{12}{3}$, multiply	12 [2nd] [x!]	4.79 08 STAT
	[÷] 3 [2nd] [x!]	6 STAT
by $\binom{8}{3}$, and store.	[÷] 9	
	[2nd] [x!] [=]	220 STAT
	[X] [RCL] [=] [STO]	12320 STAT
4. Calculate $\binom{20}{6}$.	20 [2nd] [x!]	2.4329 18 STAT
	[÷] 6 [2nd] [x!]	720 STAT
	[÷] 14	
	[2nd] [x!] [=]	38760 STAT
5. Compute $1/\binom{20}{6}$ and	[1/x] [X] [RCL] [=]	0.3178535 STAT

multiply by stored value.

Thus $P(X = 3) = 0.3178535$, and the chances of finding three
errors are about one in three.

(The Hypergeometric Distribution–Continued)

Mean and Variance of the Hypergeometric Distribution

The mean and variance of the Hypergeometric Probability Distribution are calculated as follows, with n equal to the number of items selected, N_1 equal to the number of possible successes, N_2 equal to the number of possible failures, and N equal to the number of sample points in the population.

$$\mu = E[X] = \frac{nN_1}{N} \qquad \textit{Equation (4-18)}$$

$$\sigma^2 = n\left(\frac{N_1}{N}\right)\left(\frac{N_2}{N}\right)\left(\frac{N-n}{N-1}\right) \qquad \textit{Equation (4-19)}$$

The Poisson Distribution

Concepts

Suppose in using the Binomial Distribution as a model in an experiment, the number of trials, n, becomes very large and the probability of success, p, becomes very small. Then the binomial probabilities are difficult to calculate. The *Poisson Distribution* is helpful in calculating these probabilities.

For example, suppose a traffic safety engineer monitors the occurrence of accidents during rush hour at a dangerous intersection for many months. Each hour of observation constitutes a *Bernoulli trial* where "success" indicates that at least one accident was observed during the hour and "failure" indicates that no accidents were observed. Furthermore, the probability of success in this situation on any given day is small, so the Binomial Distribution is a fitting model for this experiment. However, since the number of hours is very large and the probability of success is very small, the calculations involved are quite difficult. Often, in such cases, you do not know p (the probability of success), but do know the average number of successes that occurred in a given time period. In this case you do not know n and p separately, but do know the mean (μ).

Typical examples of other situations where this type of modeling is appropriate include

- The demand for a given commodity during a given week.
- The number of typographical errors on a given page in a book.
- The number of radioactive particles detected per cubic centimeter per second near a nuclear reactor.

(The Poisson Distribution–Continued)

The random occurrence of events in these examples possess several common characteristics.

- The events occur independently. Whether or not an event occurs during a specified amount of time does not affect the probability that other events occur during certain times.
- Theoretically, an infinite number of events can occur in the same interval.
- For any given interval of time or space, the probability of an event occurring once in the interval is proportional to the length (or area or volume) of that interval.
- The probability that any two events occur in a small portion of the interval is negligible.

When these characteristics are satisfied, the random occurrences of these events form a Poisson Process, and the random variable associated with the process is said to follow a *Poisson Distribution*.

Poisson Distribution—a random variable (X) that equals the number of times an event occurs in a specified interval of time for a Poisson process. The probability function is

$$P(X = x) = \frac{\lambda^x e^{-\lambda}}{x!} \qquad x = 0, 1, 2, 3, \ldots$$
$$= 0 \text{ elsewhere}$$

Equation (4-20)

The Greek letter λ (lambda) is called the parameter of the distribution and is the mean rate of occurrence of an event in an interval of time. The symbol e is a constant and is approximately equal to 2.71828....

(The Poisson Distribution–Continued)

Example

A local electric company is experiencing occasional power outages. A new industry is considering locating a plant in the town but is concerned with the possibility of a power shortage. The number of power shortages per year seems to be a Poisson random variable with mean equal to 5 ($\lambda = 5$). What is the probability that no more than two power failures occur per year?

Use equation (4-20) with $\lambda = 5$ and compute $P(X \leqslant 2)$. Your calculator has a key that provides values for e^x.

$$P(X \leqslant 2) = P(X = 0) + P(X = 1) + P(X = 2)$$
$$= \frac{5^0 \times e^{-5}}{0!} + \frac{5^1 \times e^{-5}}{1!} + \frac{5^2 \times e^{-5}}{2!}$$

Probability Distributions

(The Poisson Distribution–Continued)

Calculator Solution

If the "DEC 2" indicator appears in the display, press [2nd] [Decimal] before keying in the solution.

Procedure	Press	Display
1. Clear calculator.	[ON/C]	0 STAT
2. Calculate $\frac{5^0 e^{-5}}{0!}$ and store.	5 [yˣ] 0 [=]	1 STAT
	[X] 5	
	[+/−] [2nd] [eˣ]	0.0067379 STAT
	[÷] 0	
	[2nd] [x!] [=] [STO]	0.0067379 STAT
3. Calculate $\frac{5^1 e^{-5}}{1!}$, and sum.	5 [yˣ] 1 [=]	5 STAT
	[X] 5	
	[+/−] [2nd] [eˣ]	0.0067379 STAT
	[÷] 1	
	[2nd] [x!] [=] [SUM]	0.0336897 STAT
4. Calculate $\frac{5^2 e^{-5}}{2!}$ and add to stored value.	5 [yˣ] 2 [=]	25 STAT
	[X] 5	
	[+/−] [2nd] [eˣ]	0.0067379 STAT
	[÷] 2	
	[2nd] [x!] [=]	0.0842243 STAT
	[SUM] [RCL]	0.124652 STAT

Thus, $P(X \leqslant 2) = .124652$, and there is about a one-in-eight probability that fewer than three power outages occur in a year.

(The Poisson Distribution–Continued)

Mean and Variance of the Poisson Distribution

The mean and variance of the Poisson Distribution are

$$\mu = E[X] = \lambda \qquad \textit{Equation (4-21)}$$

and

$$\sigma^2 = \text{Var}[X] = \lambda \qquad \textit{Equation (4-22)}$$

In the Poisson Distribution, the mean and variance are equal.

Approximating the Binomial Distribution with the Poisson Distribution

Concepts

Under appropriate conditions, the Binomial Distribution can be approximated by the Poisson Distribution. The conditions are

• n (the number of Bernoulli trials) is large.
• p (the probability of success for each Bernoulli trial) is small.

The Poisson Distribution is a *limiting distribution* of the Binomial Distribution as n becomes large and p becomes small.

In conclusion, the following relationship exists between equation (4-14) and equation (4-20).

$$\binom{n}{x} p^x (1-p)^{n-x} \approx \frac{(np)^x e^{-np}}{x!}$$

where "$\approx$" means approximately equal.

Probability Distributions

(The Poisson Distribution–Continued)

Example

The probability that a certain type of seed will not germinate is .04. If 20 such seeds are planted, what is the probability that exactly one of these seeds does not germinate?

Calculator Solution—Binomial Distribution

To use the Binomial Distribution, use equation (4-14) with $n = 20$ and $p = .04$. Find the probability.

$$P(X = 1) = \binom{20}{1} (.04)^1 (1 - .04)^{19}$$

$$= \frac{20!}{1! \ 19!} \ (.04)(.96)^{19}$$

If the "DEC 2" indicator appears in the display, press [2nd] [Decimal] before keying in the solution.

Procedure	Press	Display
1. Clear calculator.	[ON/C]	0 _{STAT}
2. Calculate $\binom{20}{1}$.	20 [2nd] [x!]	2.4329 18 _{STAT}
	[÷] 1 [2nd] [x!]	1 _{STAT}
	[÷] 19	
	[2nd] [x!] [=]	20 _{STAT}
3. Multiply by (.04) and store.	[×] .04 [=] [STO]	0.8 _{STAT}
4. Multiply (.96)¹⁹ times stored value.	.96 [yˣ] 19	
	[×] [RCL] [=]	0.3683354 _{STAT}

So, $P(X = 1) = .3683354$, calculated by the Binomial Distribution formula.

(The Poisson Distribution–Continued)

Calculator Solution—Poisson Distribution

To do the same problem using the Poisson Distribution, use equation (4-20) with $\lambda = np = (20)\ (.04) = 0.80$, and find

$$P(X = 1) = \frac{(.80)^1 e^{-(.80)}}{1!}$$

If the "DEC 2" indicator appears in the display, press [2nd] [Decimal] before keying in the solution.

Procedure	Press	Display
1. Clear calculator.	[ON/c]	0 STAT
2. Calculate $e^{-(.80)}$.	.8 [+/−] [2nd] [eˣ]	0.449329 STAT
3. Multiply by (.80).	[×] .8	0.8 STAT
4. Divide by 1!.	[÷] 1	
	[2nd] [x!] [=]	0.3594632 STAT

So $P(X = 1) = 0.3594632$, computed with the Poisson Distribution formula. The approximation is fairly accurate and improves as n becomes larger.

The Normal Distribution

The previous three sections present important discrete probability distributions. This section discusses a continuous probability distribution, commonly called the *Normal Distribution*, that is widely used in applications.

The family of Normal Distributions is a collection of bell-shaped curves which approximate histograms of many different types of data. The equation defining the curves in the family of Normal Distributions is

$$f(x) = \frac{1}{\sqrt{2\pi\sigma^2}} \, e^{-\frac{1}{2}\left(\frac{x-\mu}{\sigma}\right)^2}$$

Equation (4-23)

where a unique member of the family is specified by values for μ and σ^2. The value of π is 3.14159... and the value of e is 2.71828.... In the Normal Distribution, the following must also be true.

- $-\infty < x < \infty$
- $0 \le \sigma^2$
- $-\infty < \mu < \infty$

The properties of the Normal Distribution include the following.

- The mean (expected value) of the Normal Distribution is

$$E[X] = \mu \qquad \text{Equation (4-24)}$$

- The variance of the Normal Distribution is

$$\text{Var}[X] = \sigma^2 \qquad \text{Equation (4-25)}$$

- The bell-shaped curve is symmetric about its mean, μ.
- The mean, median, and mode are all equal.
- The total area under the curve is 1, since this is a valid continuous probability distribution.

(The Normal Distribution–Continued)

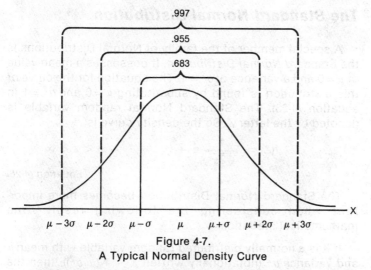

Figure 4-7.
A Typical Normal Density Curve

- 68.3% of the area under the curve lies between $\mu - \sigma$ and $\mu + \sigma$ (within one standard deviation of the mean).
- 95.5% of the area under the curve lies between $\mu - 2\sigma$ and $\mu + 2\sigma$ (within two standard deviations of the mean).
- 99.7% of the area under the curve lies between $\mu - 3\sigma$ and $\mu + 3\sigma$ (within three standard deviations of the mean).
- As with all continuous probability distributions, probabilities such as $P(a \leqslant X \leqslant b)$ are found by determining the area bounded by the bell-shaped curve, the horizontal axis, and the limits a and b.

Abraham DeMoivre (1667-1754) was the first to discover that the Normal Distribution could be used as a formula for finding Binomial probabilities. But the distribution was named by Karl Pearson in 1893 during one of his lectures at Gresham College, London, England. He later indicated that he regretted calling it the "Normal" Distribution since the name implied that all other distributions were "abnormal." The Normal Distribution is sometimes referred to as the Gaussian Distribution.

(The Normal Distribution–Continued)

The Standard Normal Distribution

A special member of the family of Normal Distributions is the *Standard Normal Distribution*. It possesses a mean value of $\mu = 0$ and a variance of $\sigma^2 = 1$. The equation for the curve of this distribution is found by substituting $\mu = 0$ and $\sigma^2 = 1$ in equation (4-23). The Standard Normal random variable is denoted by the letter Z. So the density curve is

$$f(Z) = \frac{1}{\sqrt{2\pi}}\, e^{-Z^2/2} \qquad -\infty < z < \infty$$

Equation (4-26)

The Standard Normal Distribution becomes more important when considering the following result from mathematical statistics.

If X is a normally distributed random variable with mean μ and variance σ^2 (notationally written X $\sim$ N(μ, σ^2)), then the random variable

$$Z = \frac{X - \mu}{\sigma}$$

is distributed as the Standard Normal Distribution (notationally written Z $\sim$ N(0, 1)), where $\sigma = \sqrt{\sigma^2}$.

The process of subtracting the mean from a random variable and then dividing by the standard deviation is called "standardizing the variable." Since any Normally Distributed random variable can be standardized, the only tables of probabilities needed are those for the Standard Normal Distribution.

(The Normal Distribution–Continued)

The Standard Normal Table

The probability that $a \leqslant Z \leqslant b$ is equal to the area bounded by the curve, the horizontal axis, and the limits a and b with a less than b. Areas under continuous curves are found using the techniques of integral calculus.

$$P(a \leqslant Z \leqslant b) = \int_a^b \frac{1}{\sqrt{2\pi}}\, e^{-t^2/2}\, dt$$

However, no known closed form for this integral exists, so it is necessary to calculate these probabilities using the techniques of numerical analysis. Results of these numerical calculations are presented in tabular form. One such table of Standard Normal probabilities is given in Table B-1 of Appendix B.

Since the Standard Normal Distribution is symmetric about zero, the table lists the areas that are under the curve between zero and a specified value larger than zero. So the table entries for $Z = z_0$ are $P(0 < Z < z_0)$. The shaded area in Figure 4-8 represents the probabilities listed in Table B-1.

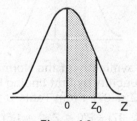

Figure 4-8
$P(0 \leqslant Z \leqslant z_0)$ for
the Standard Normal Distribution

(The Normal Distribution–Continued)

Using Table B-1, you can find any area under the curve. It may help you to draw sketches. The following examples illustrate the use of Table B-1.

For example, let Z have the Standard Normal Distribution, written $Z \sim N(0, 1)$. Find $P(0 \leqslant Z \leqslant 2.37)$.

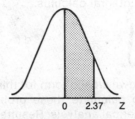

Locate $z = 2.37$ from Table B-1, and identify the corresponding entry in the table. The desired probability is .49111. So $P(0 > Z > 2.37) = .49111$

For example, let $Z \sim N(0, 1)$, find $P(-1.5 \leqslant Z \leqslant .97)$.

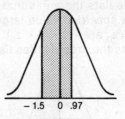

Because of the symmetry of the Normal Distribution, you can figure this probability by first finding $P(0 \leqslant Z \leqslant +1.5)$ and adding it to $P(0 \leqslant Z \leqslant .97)$. From Table B-1

$$P(-1.5 \leqslant Z \leqslant .97) = P(0 \leqslant Z \leqslant +1.5) + P(0 \leqslant Z \leqslant .97)$$
$$= .43319 + .33398$$
$$= .76717$$

(The Normal Distribution–Continued)

For example, given $Z \sim N(0, 1)$, find $P(-1.96 < Z < \infty)$.

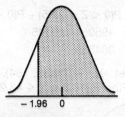

Again using the symmetry,

    $P(0 < Z < 1.96) = P(-1.96 < Z < 0)$.

Thus

$$P(-1.96 < Z < \infty) = P(-1.96 < Z \leqslant 0) + P(0 \leqslant Z < \infty)$$
$$= P(0 \leqslant Z < 1.96) + P(0 < Z)$$
$$= .47500 + .50000$$
$$= .97500$$

For example, let $Z \sim N(0, 1)$. Find $P(-2.65 < Z < -.5)$.

    Note that $P(-2.65 < Z < -.5) = P(.5 < Z < 2.65)$

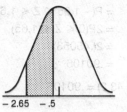

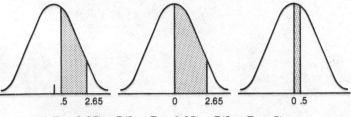

$P(.5 < Z < 2.65) = P(0 < Z < 2.65) - P(0 < Z < .5)$

(The Normal Distribution–Continued)

Then

$$P(.5 < Z < 2.65) = P(0 < Z < 2.65) - P(0 < Z < .5)$$
$$= .49598 - .19146$$
$$= .30452$$

For example, let $X \sim N(30, 64)$. Then $\mu = 30$ and $\sigma = \sqrt{\sigma^2} = \sqrt{64} = 8$. Find P $(16.8 \leqslant X \leqslant 43.2)$.

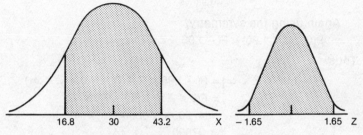

To compute $P(16.8 \leqslant X \leqslant 43.2)$

$$P(16.8 \leqslant X \leqslant 43.2) = P\left(\frac{16.8 - 30}{8} \leqslant \frac{X - 30}{8} \leqslant \frac{43.2 - 30}{8} \right)$$
$$= P(-1.65 \leqslant Z \leqslant 1.65)$$
$$= 2P(0 \leqslant Z \leqslant 1.65)$$
$$= 2(.45053)$$
$$= .90106$$

Thus, $P(16.8 \leqslant X \leqslant 43.2) = .90106$

(The Normal Distribution–Continued)

An Application of the Normal Distribution

   The Normal Distribution is an important distribution in applied statistics. However, it is a theoretical distribution, and no set of data exactly adheres to it. But you may still use the distribution in attempts to answer practical questions regarding your data, assuming the set of measurements is approximately Normal.

   For example, suppose a bank official observes that the length of waiting time for service at the drive-in windows is normally distributed with mean $\mu = 13$ minutes and $\sigma = 2$ minutes ($\sigma^2 = 4$). Let W represent the waiting time, and assume that $W \sim N(13, 4)$.

   a. What proportion of the customers wait longer than 10 minutes but less than 15 minutes for service?
   b. What proportion of customers wait 8 minutes or less for service?
   c. What is the probability that a customer has to wait longer than 16 minutes for service.

$$\begin{aligned}
\textit{Part (a):}\ P(10 < W < 15) &= P\left(\frac{10-13}{2} < \frac{W-13}{2} < \frac{15-13}{2}\right)\\
&= P(-1.5 < Z < 1)\\
&= P(0 < Z < 1.5) + P(0 < Z < 1)\\
&= .43319 + .34134\\
&= .77453
\end{aligned}$$

   Thus $P(10 < W < 15) = .77453$. Roughly 77.5% of the bank's customers wait between 10 and 15 minutes for service.

(The Normal Distribution–Continued)

$$\text{Part (b): } P(W \leqslant 8) = P\left(\frac{W-13}{2} \leqslant \frac{8-13}{2}\right)$$

$$= P(Z \leqslant -2.5)$$
$$= P(2.5 \leqslant Z)$$
$$= .5 - P(0 \leqslant Z \leqslant 2.5)$$
$$= .5 - .49379$$
$$= .00621$$

Therefore, only about .62% of the customers are served in eight minutes or less.

$$\text{Part (c): } P(16 < W) = P\left(\frac{16-13}{2} < \frac{W-13}{2}\right)$$

$$= P(1.5 < Z)$$
$$= P(0 < Z) - P(0 < Z < 1.5)$$
$$= .50000 - .43319$$
$$= .06681$$

Roughly 6.68% of the customers wait longer than 16 minutes before receiving service.

Chapter 5

SAMPLING DISTRIBUTIONS

Introduction

The material in this chapter, together with the probability theory in Chapter 4, bridges the gap between the descriptive statistics in Chapter 3 and statistical inferences presented in Chapters 6 and 7.

Chapter 3 considers the basic concepts and procedures for summarizing and organizing data. It discusses the mean, variance, and standard deviation, which are the basic measures that can be computed from the data and then be used to describe a larger set of observations. When these measures are computed from the data of a sample, they are called statistics; when they are computed for the entire population, they are called the population parameters. The two most important sample measures, the sample and mean variance, are denoted by $\bar{x}$ and s^2, respectively. The population counterparts to these are the population mean and population variance, denoted by μ and σ^2.

In Chapter 4, the basic concepts of probability theory and probability distributions are introduced. These results are used to predict the potential behavior of the computed statistics, given the assumed model.

This chapter includes the distributions which can be mathematically derived for several important statistics. As a general example, consider a population which has a certain mean. A sample taken from the population may or may not have the same mean, depending on the sample. It is useful to know the possible values of the sample mean, as well as the distribution of those values. The distribution of the sample mean is useful for predicting the population mean even when you know only one sample mean.

(Introduction–Continued)

In a more advanced treatment of statistics, the mathematics to derive these *sampling distributions* and their implications would be given, using probability and distribution theory. However, these results are simply stated and illustrated here.

Sampling distribution—the distribution of all possible values that can be assumed by the statistic t_n when $x_1, x_2, ..., x_n$ are a sample of size n from some population and t_n is a statistic computed from this sample data.

For example, t_n might be the different values of the sample median that can be obtained for samples taken from a given population. Likewise, the sampling distribution of the mean, sample variance, and the range can be considered. The results that can be obtained for one of these statistics apply only to it.

When a random sample is drawn from a discrete, finite population, the sampling distributions of statistics such as the mean can be empirically derived. The steps to construct such a sampling distribution are given and illustrated in a later section of this chapter. However, when sampling from continuous populations, exact sampling distributions cannot be constructed by empirical arguments and can be approximated only by taking extremely large samples, which is impractical. All sampling distributions can be derived mathematically, but the analysis involves complex mathematics. For more information, see the books listed in the Bibliography.

(Introduction–Continued)

In the remainder of this chapter, the sampling distributions of several statistics in different situations are stated. Each sampling distribution possesses three characteristics that are of paramount interest to the statistician. They are:

- its mean
- its variance
- its functional form

Each of these is a description of the sampling distribution. The mean and variance are as defined in Chapter 4. The functional form is the shape that the sampling distribution takes when it is graphed. Like any function, it can take on a wide variety of shapes, including a Binomial Distribution, Hypergeometric Distribution, Normal Distribution, and so forth. In some cases, it is not possible to tell what the functional form of a distribution is. In those cases, only the mean and variance are provided.

In Chapter 3, the concept of a sample is discussed, including descriptions of a simple random sample, a representative sample, a systematic sample, and a census. The following section discusses these concepts in more detail.

Sampling

One way of dividing sampling procedures is according to the number of elements, N, which a population contains. When N is finite and small, then sampling is usually omitted and the entire population is examined.

If the population is too large to perform a census, sampling can be performed with or without replacement. When sampling with replacement, every item of the population is available each time a selection is made because each item is restored to the population before the next item is selected. Sampling with replacement is similar to sampling from an infinite population.

In sampling without replacement, once an item is chosen for the sample, it is not returned to the population. Thus, each item can appear only once in the sample. Some of the aspects and consequences of sampling with and without replacement are discussed in Chapter 4. More on these procedures and their effect on the mean and variance of the sample mean is presented in the section Sampling Without Replacement.

Whether the population is finite or infinite, and whether sampling is done with or without replacement, a special type of sample is the simple random sample, introduced in Chapter 3. A simple random sample is a finite sample chosen so that every sample of size n has an equal probability of being chosen.

When selecting a simple random sample, at least some sense of randomness should be maintained by using a *table of random digits* or a computer's random number generator. Table B-2 in Appendix B is a table of random digits arranged so that each digit in the table is at least approximately statistically independent. The use of this table is demonstrated in the following example.

(Sampling–Continued)

Suppose you are an I.R.S. auditor and are given 113 income tax returns selected by a computer as likely to have violations. Because of time and expense limitations, you are told to examine only 12 of these returns. In this case the population size, N, is 113, the sample size, n, is 12, and sampling is done without replacement.

The following is a process for randomly choosing 12 of the returns. First, uniquely identify each return with the consecutive integers one through 113. Next, consult the table of random digits in Appendix B and choose a starting point. For illustration, suppose you choose the fourth group of digits on row 25. The number there is 41532. Since you only need a number up to 113, use 415. The chosen number, 415, is larger than 113; so modular arithmetic is performed by subtracting an appropriate multiple of 113 from 415 to obtain a number in the range one through 113.

Move in any direction to choose the next group of numbers. Assume you choose to move down. The next random numbers are therefore 490, followed by 937, and so forth. The results of this sampling are summarized below.

Sequence Number	Table Entry	–	Multiple of 113	=	Number Chosen
1	415	–	339	=	76
2	490	–	452	=	38
3	937	–	904	=	33
4	891	–	791	=	100
5	009	–	0	=	9
6	283	–	226	=	57
7	839	–	791	=	48
8	114	–	113	=	1
9	274	–	226	=	48 (duplicate)
10	931	–	904	=	27
11	941	–	904	=	37
12	424	–	339	=	85
13	136	–	113	=	23

(Sampling–Continued)

Note that the ninth choice produces 48, which had already been selected. Since sampling is without replacement, it must be discarded. Therefore, a 13th selection is made. If there had been more duplicates, additional random digits would be chosen until 12 distinct numbers that range from one through 113 are selected.

Thus, the sample chosen by the auditor is as follows.

$$x_1 = 76 \qquad x_7 = 48$$
$$x_2 = 38 \qquad x_8 = 1$$
$$x_3 = 33 \qquad x_9 = 27$$
$$x_4 = 100 \qquad x_{10} = 37$$
$$x_5 = 9 \qquad x_{11} = 85$$
$$x_6 = 57 \qquad x_{12} = 23$$

These numbers uniquely identify the 12 income tax returns to be examined.

When the term simple random sample is used in the remainder of this chapter, it means that the sample is drawn in this or an equivalently random fashion.

If the population size is infinite, this method cannot be used because it is impossible to list each member of the population with a unique identifying number. Instead, the "Monte Carlo technique" can be used. This method is not discussed further in this text. For a detailed discussion, see the books listed in the Bibliography.

Construction of a Sampling Distribution when Sampling a Finite Distribution

Concepts

The sampling distributions of statistics can be derived empirically as demonstrated in this section. The steps used in this construction are as follows.

1. For a discrete, finite population of size N, list all possible samples of size n.
2. Compute the value of the statistic for each of the samples.
3. List the distinct values of the statistic with their corresponding frequencies of occurrence. This listing is the sampling distribution of the statistic.

Example

Consider the discrete, finite population consisting of the five equally likely scores 4, 5, 6, 7, and 8. Find the mean and variance of this population. (In the next two examples, the same population is considered and the sampling distribution of x̄, its mean, and its variance are found.)

Sampling Distributions

(Construction of Sampling Distribution when Sampling a Finite Distribution–Continued)

Calculator Solution

Since the probabilities associated with each value of X are equally likely, the keys ⌨x̄ and ⌨σn may be used rather than the methods presented in Chapter 4. If the "DEC 2" indicator appears in the display, press [2nd] [Decimal] before keying in the solution.

Procedure	Press	Display
1. Clear calculator and statistical registers.	[ON/c] [2nd] [STAT]	0 STAT
2. Enter data with [Σ+] key.	4 [Σ+]	1 STAT
	5 [Σ+]	2 STAT
	6 [Σ+]	3 STAT
	7 [Σ+]	4 STAT
	8 [Σ+]	5 STAT
3. Find the population mean, μ.	[x̄]	6 STAT
4. Find the population standard deviation.	[σn]	1.4142136 STAT
5. Find the population variance.	[2nd] [x^2]	2 STAT

Note that the [σn] key is used rather than the [σn-1] key because you are finding the population variance rather than the sample variance. The [x̄] and [σn] keys can be used to calculate the population mean and variance using the [FRQ] key as previously described.

(Construction of Sampling Distribution when Sampling a Finite Distribution–Continued)

Example

Using the same population as in the previous example, construct the sampling distribution of samples of size two and find the distribution's mean and variance.

Table Solution

Use the three step procedure to construct the sampling distribution.

1. List all the possible samples of two test scores that can be drawn out of the population of five.

2. Calculate the sample mean, $\bar{X}$, for each of the possible samples.

3. List the distinct values of the sample mean along with their corresponding probabilities. Since each element in the population is equally likely and sampling is done with replacement, each of the 25 possible samples occurs with a probability of 1/25.

(Construction of Sampling Distribution when Sampling a Finite Distribution–Continued)

The following table lists all possible ways of picking a sample of two elements and the mean of each sample.

All Possible Samples of 2 Elements	Value of the Mean for Each Sample	Label for Mean Value
4,4	4.0	$\bar{x}_1$
4,5	4.5	$\bar{x}_2$
4,6	5.0	$\bar{x}_3$
4,7	5.5	$\bar{x}_4$
4,8	6.0	$\bar{x}_5$
5,4	4.5	$\bar{x}_6$
5,5	5.0	$\bar{x}_7$
5,6	5.5	$\bar{x}_8$
5,7	6.0	$\bar{x}_9$
5,8	6.5	$\bar{x}_{10}$
6,4	5.0	$\bar{x}_{11}$
6,5	5.5	$\bar{x}_{12}$
6,6	6.0	$\bar{x}_{13}$
6,7	6.5	$\bar{x}_{14}$
6,8	7.0	$\bar{x}_{15}$
7,4	5.5	$\bar{x}_{16}$
7,5	6.0	$\bar{x}_{17}$
7,6	6.5	$\bar{x}_{18}$
7,7	7.0	$\bar{x}_{19}$
7,8	7.5	$\bar{x}_{20}$
8,4	6.0	$\bar{x}_{21}$
8,5	6.5	$\bar{x}_{22}$
8,6	7.0	$\bar{x}_{23}$
8,7	7.5	$\bar{x}_{24}$
8,8	8.0	$\bar{x}_{25}$

*(Construction of Sampling Distribution when Sampling a
Finite Distribution–Continued)*

The following table displays the sampling distribution of $\bar{X}$
for this problem.

$\bar{X}$	4.0	4.5	5.0	5.5	6.0	6.5	7.0	7.5	8.0
$P(\bar{X} = \bar{x})$	1/25	2/25	3/25	4/25	5/25	4/25	3/25	2/25	1/25

Constructing the frequency histogram for the above
sampling distribution helps show how the sample means (the
$\bar{x}$'s) vary.

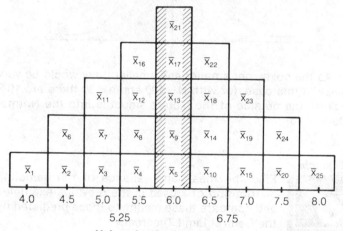

Values for the Sample Means

In this picture there is a mean label inside each box and
the boxes are stacked according to the value of their means.
This picture represents the chances of finding a sample pick-
ed at random with a sample mean equal to the population
mean value of 6. Five of the sample means ($\bar{x}_{21}$, $\bar{x}_{17}$, $\bar{x}_{13}$, $\bar{x}_9$ and
$\bar{x}_5$) have mean values of 6. In fact, the most probable choice is
a value of 6. In many situations, the most probable value of $\bar{x}$
is the population mean or is very close to the population
mean. The sampling distribution of $\bar{X}$ is a discrete, symmetric, and fairly "bell-shaped" function.

Sampling Distributions

(Construction of Sampling Distribution when Sampling a Finite Distribution–Continued)

Consider what happens if the number of elements in the population increases from five to 100, and the sample size increases from two to 30. Arranging all the sample means pictorially shows something like the behavior below.

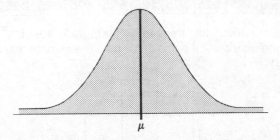

μ

As the boxes get smaller and smaller (they would be very small in this case, for with N = 100 and n = 30 there are 10^{60} boxes), the outside of the picture smooths into the Normal Curve.

Example

Find the mean and variance of the sampling distribution of $\bar{x}$ used in the previous examples and compare these results to those predicted by the Central Limit Theorem.

The Central Limit Theorem, discussed later in this chapter, says that the mean of the sampling distribution of $\bar{x}$ is the population mean, $\mu = 6$, and that the variance of $\bar{x}$ is $\dfrac{\sigma^2}{n} = \dfrac{2}{2} = 1$.

(Construction of Sampling Distribution when Sampling a Finite Distribution–Continued)

Calculator Solution

For valid probability distributions, you can obtain the result by using the $\Sigma+$, FRQ, and σn keys. First multiply the values of $p(x_i)$ times 25 so that the results are integers with values from 0 through 99. The problem is solved as follows.

If the "DEC 2" indicator appears in the display, press 2nd Decimal before keying in the solution.

Procedure	Press	Display
1. Clear calculator and select statistics mode.	ON/c 2nd STAT	0 STAT
2. Enter probabilities.	4 $\Sigma+$	1 STAT
	4.5 FRQ 2 $\Sigma+$	3 STAT
	5 FRQ 3 $\Sigma+$	6 STAT
	5.5 FRQ 4 $\Sigma+$	10 STAT
	6 FRQ 5 $\Sigma+$	15 STAT
	6.5 FRQ 4 $\Sigma+$	19 STAT
	7 FRQ 3 $\Sigma+$	22 STAT
	7.5 FRQ 2 $\Sigma+$	24 STAT
	8 $\Sigma+$	25 STAT
3. Calculate mean.	$\bar{x}$	6 STAT
4. Calculate standard deviation.	σn	1 STAT
5. Calculate variance.	2nd x^2	1 STAT

Thus, the mean of this sampling distribution is $\mu_{\bar{x}} = 6.0$, the same as the population mean and $\sigma_{\bar{x}}^2 = 1$, which is the variance predicted by the Central Limit Theorem, discussed later in this chapter.

Sampling Distributions when Sampling A Normal Distribution

As mentioned in the introduction to this chapter, there are three characteristics of sampling distributions—the mean, variance, and functional form of the sampling distribution—that are of special interest to statisticians. In this section, these properties are given for a sampling distribution when sampling from a normally distributed population.

Distribution of $\bar{X}$ when Sampling a Normal Distribution

Suppose X_1, X_2, X_3, ..., X_n are a random sample of size n selected from a normal distribution. You need to determine information about the sample mean, $\bar{x}$. The sample mean of the possible random samples of size n is a random variable in its own right and has a probability distribution.

When sampling from a normal distribution, the sampling distribution of $\bar{x}$ is *normal* with mean $\mu_{\bar{x}}$ and variance $\sigma_{\bar{x}}^2$ given by:

$$\mu_{\bar{x}} = \mu_x = \mu$$

$$\sigma_{\bar{x}}^2 = \frac{\sigma_x^2}{n} = \frac{\sigma^2}{n}$$

Note that in the above statement, the three characteristics of sampling distributions—the mean, variance, and functional form—are clearly stated.

For example, suppose the daily revenue of a small business is normally distributed with a mean of $200 and a standard deviation of $40. Find the probability that the average daily revenue for the next 25 days will be between $190 and $210.

(Sampling Distributions when Sampling A Normal Distribution–Continued)

First, the solution is stated in terms of a probability statement about $\bar{x}$, the sample mean. Then the inequalities are standardized as shown in Chapter 4. Finally, the probability is found using Table B-1 in Appendix B.

Population parameters:

$\mu = 200$

$\sigma^2 = 1600 \ (\sigma = 40)$

Sample Size: $n = 25$

Find $P(190 \leq \bar{x} \leq 210)$. Standardize the inequalities by subtracting $\mu_{\bar{x}} = 200$ and dividing by the standard deviation, $\sigma_{\bar{x}} = \sqrt{1600/25} = 40/5 = 8$. The letter Z denotes the Standard Normal random variable.

$$P\left(\frac{190 - 200}{8} \leq \frac{\bar{x} - \mu_{\bar{x}}}{\sigma_{\bar{x}}} \leq \frac{210 - 200}{8}\right)$$

$$= P\left(\frac{-10}{8} \leq Z \leq \frac{10}{8}\right)$$

$$= P(-1.25 \leq Z \leq 1.25)$$

$$= 2 \times P \ (0 \leq Z \leq 1.25)$$

$$= 2 \times (.39435)$$

$$= 0.7887$$

The probability that the average daily revenue for the next 25 days will be between \$190 and \$210 is approximately .79.

The Central Limit Theorem

In many actual situations, the populations being sampled are *not* normally distributed. In such situations, the sampling distribution of $\bar{x}$ can be derived from a very important theorem called the *Central Limit Theorem*.

Central Limit Theorem—If X_1, X_2, ..., X_n is a random sample from a population of any functional form with mean μ and variance σ^2 (both finite), then the sample mean, $\bar{x}$, is approximately normally distributed with mean μ and variance σ^2/n for large values of n. The Central Limit Theorem is illustrated in the following figure, which is adapted from *Business Statistics Basic Concepts and Methodology*, Second Edition, by W.W. Daniel and J.C. Terrell, Houghton Mifflin Company, 1979.

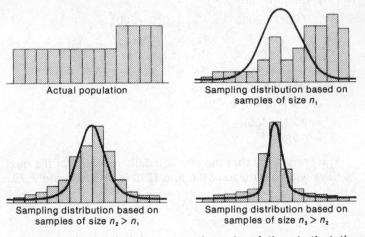

Actual population

Sampling distribution based on samples of size n_1

Sampling distribution based on samples of size $n_2 > n_1$

Sampling distribution based on samples of size $n_3 > n_2$

In general, statisticians use the rule of thumb that the value of n must be 30 or larger for this theorem to be valid. However, this approximation is a function of so many different aspects of the problem, that giving an absolute number is impossible.

(The Central Limit Theorem–Continued)

Note that the only requirement on the distribution of X is that it has a finite mean and variance. Nothing is required of the functional form of the distribution of X. The distribution function may be symmetric or asymmetric, discrete or continuous, unimodal or multimodal, and so forth. $\bar{X}$ is still approximately normally distributed as long as μ and σ^2 exist and n is sufficiently large.

It can be mathematically shown in some situations, that as the sample size gets larger, the function very quickly becomes almost exactly normally distributed. For distributions that are symmetric and unimodal (including the uniform), the approximation is quite good for sample sizes as small as 10. For n as large as 30, excellent results are obtained. (Sometimes, for distributions that are asymmetric and/or multimodal, slightly larger sample sizes are required to achieve a good approximation.)

(The Central Limit Theorem–Continued)

For example, suppose the average life of a certain brand of 60-watt light bulbs is $\mu = 1{,}000$ hours, with a variance $\sigma^2 = 2{,}500$ hours squared. What is the probability that the average life of 25 such light bulbs is greater than 1,015 hours?

First, note that life expectancies of electronic devices generally are *not* normally distributed. So the sample is not from a normally distributed population. However, by the Central Limit Theorem, the sample mean is approximately normally distributed. Second, $n = 25$ is assumed to be "large enough."

Population parameters:
$$\mu = 1000$$
$$\sigma^2 = 2500$$

Sample Size: $n = 25$

You must find $P(1015 < \bar{X} < \infty)$.

$$= P\left(\frac{1015 - 1000}{\sqrt{100}} < \frac{\bar{X} - \mu_{\bar{X}}}{\sigma_{\bar{X}}} < \frac{\infty - 1000}{\sqrt{100}}\right)$$

$$= P\left(\frac{15}{10} < Z < \infty\right)$$

$$= P(1.5 < Z < \infty)$$

$$= 0.5 - P(0 \leqslant Z \leqslant 1.5)$$

$$= 0.5 - .43319$$

$$= 0.06681$$

Thus it is very unlikely that the average life of any set of 25 bulbs is greater than 1,015 hours.

Sampling Distribution of the Sample Proportion, $\hat{p}$

Many situations exist in which the data consists of counts, such as opinion surveys. An important statistic in this case is the sample proportion, labeled $\hat{p}$. You must be able to calculate the probabilites of certain events concerning this estimated proportion. To do this, the properties of the sampling distribution of $\hat{p}$ must be known.

This problem is related to the binomial distribution. If the random variable $X = n \times \hat{p}$, where n is the sample size, then X follows a binomial distribution with parameters n and p (the proportion of the elements in the sampled population with the characteristic of interest). Therefore, the sampling distribution of $\hat{p}$ can be derived from the binomial distribution with parameters n and $p = \hat{p}$. However, this can be tedious, especially if n is quite large. Therefore, approximations of this sampling distribution are needed. Since $\hat{p}$ is actually a mean value of all the responses, the Central Limit Theorem provides an answer.

Let $\hat{p}$ be the sample proportion of the number of successes in n independent, repeated Bernoulli trials. The Central Limit Theorem implies that the sampling distribution of $\hat{p}$ is approximately a normal distribution with mean $\mu_{\hat{p}}$ equal to the true population proportion p, and variance $\sigma_{\hat{p}}^2 = \left[\dfrac{p(1-p)}{n} \right]$.

Note that the sampling distribution of $\hat{p}$ is only approximately normally distributed. How closely it approximates the normal distribution depends on the size of n. A general rule of thumb states that if np and $n(1-p)$ are both greater than 5, the approximation is adequate.

*(Sampling Distribution of the
Sample Proportion, p̂–Continued)*

For example, suppose a manufacturer of screws learns from experience that 4% of the screws produced are defective. If a random sample of size n = 200 screws is examined, what is the probability that the proportion of defective ones is between 0.03 and 0.045?

Note that $np = (200)(.04) = 8$ and $n(1 - p) = (200)(.96) = 192$ are both greater than five. Thus, the normal approximation can be used.

Use the result above and the methods of Chapter 4.

$$\mu_{\hat{p}} = p = .04$$

$$\sigma_{\hat{p}}^2 = \frac{p(1-p)}{n} = \frac{(.04)(.96)}{200}$$

Thus, p̂ is approximately distributed

$$N\left(0.04, \frac{(.04)(.96)}{200}\right)$$

and you must find:

$$P(.03 \leqslant \hat{p} \leqslant .045)$$

$$= P\left(\frac{0.03 - 0.04}{\sqrt{\frac{(0.04)(0.96)}{200}}} \leqslant \frac{p - \mu_p}{\sigma_p} \leqslant \frac{0.045 - 0.04}{\sqrt{\frac{(0.04)(0.96)}{200}}}\right)$$

$$= P\left(\frac{-.01}{.0139} \leqslant Z \leqslant \frac{.005}{.0139}\right)$$

$$= P(-.72 \leqslant Z \leqslant .36)$$

$$= P(0 \leqslant Z \leqslant .72) + P(0 \leqslant Z \leqslant .36)$$

$$= 0.26424 + 0.14058$$

$$= 0.40482$$

There is about a 40% probability that the proportion of defective screws is between 0.03 and 0.45.

Sampling Finite Distributions when Sampling With and Without Replacement

The results given in the normal and central limit section assume that the sample sizes are large and are from an infinite population or from a finite population with replacement. However, sampling with replacement is not practical in many situations. Therefore, the sampling distribution properties of $\bar{x}$ must be obtained when sampling is without replacement from a finite population, and when sampling is from nonnormal, infinite populations, and the sample size is small. In both cases, complete answers are not available.

In general, the mean and variance of a sampling distribution can be computed directly from the statistic and the original population distribution. However, finding the functional form of a sampling distribution in many situations simply cannot be done. The results that follow concern the sampling distribution of $\bar{x}$ from a finite population, with and without replacement, and taking a small sample from a nonnormal infinite population.

Sampling Distribution of $\bar{X}$ when Sampling Without Replacement from a Finite Population

Concepts

Suppose that the variable being sampled consists of N distinct values and that sampling is done without replacement. The sampling distribution of $\bar{X}$ is partially described in the following statement.

(Sampling Finite Distributions when Sampling With and Without Replacement–Continued)

Let X_1, X_2 ..., X_n be a random sample of size n selected without replacement from the set of N distinct values for a variable X. Also let the population mean and variance for the random variable X be denoted by μ and σ^2, respectively. Then the sampling distribution of $\overline{X}$ has mean $\mu_{\overline{x}}$ and variance $\sigma_{\overline{x}}^2$ given by:

$$\mu_{\overline{x}} = \mu \qquad \textit{Equation (5-1)}$$

$$\sigma_{\overline{x}}^2 = \frac{\sigma^2}{n}\left(\frac{N-n}{N-1}\right) \qquad \textit{Equation (5-2)}$$

The functional form of the sampling distribution of X is not specified by the above result. Three alternatives are available to calculate the functional form:

- Empirically derive the sampling distribution as shown in following examples.
- Analytically derive the sampling distribution using modern mathematical analysis. This type of approach is illustrated by the Hypergeometric Distribution in Chapter 4.
- Provided n is large, use the Central Limit Theorem to obtain the approximate distributional result:

$$\overline{X} \text{ is approximately distributed } N\left(\mu, \frac{\sigma^2}{n}\left(\frac{N-n}{N-1}\right)\right)$$

The factor $\left(\frac{N-n}{N-1}\right)$ is called the *finite population correction factor*. Its purpose is to reduce the size of σ^2/n because of the dependence in the sample caused by sampling without replacement. If N is much larger than n, this factor is approximately equal to 1 and may be ignored. For example, suppose a sample of size 30 is drawn without replacement from N = 10,000 elements. Then:

$$\frac{N-n}{N-1} = \frac{10,000-30}{9999} = \frac{9970}{9999}$$

$$= 0.9970997, \text{ which is almost one.}$$

Sampling Distributions

(Sampling Finite Distributions when Sampling With and Without Replacement–Continued)

The results given in equations (5-1) and (5-2) apply to *all* situations where sampling is without replacement from a finite population, regardless of the functional form of the original population distribution.

Example

Suppose 4 chips numbered 1, 2, 3, and 4 are placed in a bowl. Without replacement, randomly select two chips. Find the mean and variance of the population assuming that each of these 4 chips is assigned equally likely probabilities.

Calculator Solution

The probabilities associated with each value are equally likely, so the keys $\boxed{\bar{x}}$ and $\boxed{\sigma_n}$ may be used. If the "DEC 2" indicator appears in the display, press $\boxed{2nd}$ $\boxed{Decimal}$ before keying in the solution.

Procedure	Press	Display
1. Clear calculator and statistical registers.	$\boxed{ON/c}$ $\boxed{2nd}$ $\boxed{STAT}$	**0** <small>STAT</small>
2. Enter data with $\boxed{\Sigma+}$ key	1 $\boxed{\Sigma+}$	**1** <small>STAT</small>
	2 $\boxed{\Sigma+}$	**2** <small>STAT</small>
	3 $\boxed{\Sigma+}$	**3** <small>STAT</small>
	4 $\boxed{\Sigma+}$	**4** <small>STAT</small>
3. Find population mean, μ.	$\boxed{\bar{x}}$	**2.5** <small>STAT</small>
4. Find population standard deviation, σ.	$\boxed{\sigma_n}$	**1.118034** <small>STAT</small>
5. Find population variance, σ^2.	$\boxed{2nd}$ $\boxed{x^2}$	**1.25** <small>STAT</small>

Thus, the population mean and variance for this distribution are $\mu = 2.5$ and $\sigma^2 = 1.25$.

Sampling Distributions

Example

Using the same information as in the previous example, construct the sampling distribution of $\bar{x}$ based on the samples of size $n = 2$ selected without replacement.

Table Solution

All possible samples of two observations are listed in the following table, along with their means and associated probabilities.

Population of 4 Numbers: 1, 2, 3, 4

All Possible Samples of two elements	Value of the mean for each sample	Probability associated with outcome
1,2	1.5	1/6
1,3	2.0	1/6
1,4	2.5	1/6
2,3	2.5	1/6
2,4	3.0	1/6
3,4	3.5	1/6

Now list the distinct values of the sample mean along with their corresponding probabilities. The following table displays the sampling distribution of $\bar{x}$.

$\bar{X}$	1.5	2.0	2.5	3.0	3.5
$P(\bar{X} = \bar{x})$	1/6	1/6	2/6	1/6	1/6

(Sampling Finite Distributions when Sampling With and Without Replacement–Continued)

Example

Find the mean and variance of the sampling distribution of $\overline{X}$ given in the solution to the previous example. Furthermore, compare these to the results predicted by equations (5-1) and (5-2).

Equations (5-1) and (5-2) predict the following results.

$$\mu_{\overline{X}} = \mu = 2.5$$

$$\sigma^2_{\overline{X}} = \frac{\sigma^2}{n} \times \frac{N-n}{N-1} = \frac{1.25}{2} \times \frac{4-2}{4-1}$$

$$= \frac{(1.25)(2)}{(2)(3)} = 0.4166667$$

Use equations (4-10) and (4-13) to find the mean and variance.

$$\mu_{\overline{x}} = E[\ \overline{X}\ ] = \sum_{i=1}^{4} \overline{x}_i\ p(\overline{x}_i)$$

$$= (1.5)\ (1/6) + (2.0)\ (1/6) + (2.5)\ (2/6) + (3.0)\ (1/6)$$
$$+ (3.5)\ (1/6)$$

$$= 1/6\ [1.5 + 2.0 + 2.5 + 3.0\ + 3.5]$$

$$E[\ \overline{X}^2] = \sum_{i=1}^{4} \overline{x}_i^2\ p(\overline{x}_i)$$

$$= (1.5)^2\ (1/6) + (2.0)^2\ (1/6)\ + (2.5)^2\ (2/6) + (3.0)^2\ (1/6)$$
$$+ (3.5)^2\ (1/6)$$

$$= 1/6\ [(1.5)^2 + (2.0)^2 + (2.5)^2\ (2) + (3.0)^2 + (3.5)^2]$$

$$\sigma^2_{\overline{x}} = E[\ \overline{X}^2] - (\mu_{\overline{x}})^2$$

(Sampling Finite Distributions when Sampling With and Without Replacement–Continued)

Calculator Solution

For valid probability distributions, you can obtain the result by using the $\boxed{\Sigma+}$, $\boxed{\text{FRQ}}$, and $\boxed{\sigma n}$ keys. First multiply the values of $p(x_i)$ times 6 so that the results are integers with values from 0 through 99. The problem is solved as follows.

If the "DEC 2" indicator appears in the display, press $\boxed{\text{2nd}}\boxed{\text{Decimal}}$ before keying in the solution.

Procedure	Press	Display
1. Clear calculator and select statistics mode.	$\boxed{\text{ON/c}}\,\boxed{\text{2nd}}\,\boxed{\text{STAT}}$	**0**
2. Enter probabilities.	1.5 $\boxed{\Sigma+}$	**1**
	2 $\boxed{\Sigma+}$	**2**
	2.5 $\boxed{\text{FRQ}}$ 2 $\boxed{\Sigma+}$	**4**
	3 $\boxed{\Sigma+}$	**5**
	3.5 $\boxed{\Sigma+}$	**6**
3. Calculate mean.	$\boxed{\bar{x}}$	**2.5**
4. Calculate standard deviation.	$\boxed{\sigma n}$	**0.6454972**
5. Calculate variance.	$\boxed{\text{2nd}}\,\boxed{x^2}$	**0.4166667**

Thus, $\mu_{\bar{x}} = 2.5$, the same as the population mean, which agrees with equation (5-1), and $\sigma^2_{\bar{x}} = 0.4166667$, the value predicted by equation (5-2). The previous examples might indicate that it is necessary to find the sampling distribution of $\bar{x}$ to find $\mu_{\bar{x}} = E[\bar{X}]$ and $\sigma^2_{\bar{x}} = \text{Var}[\bar{X}]$. This is not the case. To find $\mu_{\bar{x}}$ and $\sigma^2_{\bar{x}}$, simply apply equations (5-1) and (5-2), as long as sampling is without replacement from a finite population. Note that the *only* information you need are the values of μ, σ^2, N, and n. You do *not* need to know the original population, nor do you need to know the functional form of the sampling distribution.

(Sampling Finite Distributions when Sampling With and Without Replacement–Continued)

Sampling Distribution of $\overline{X}$ when Sampling With Replacement from a General Population

When sampling is accomplished with replacement, it does not matter whether the population is finite or infinite. The effect of sampling with replacement from a finite population is to make it "appear" as if it were infinite; hence, the same results apply to both situations. The purpose of this discussion is to present the properties of the sampling distribution of $\overline{x}$ when sampling with replacement from an arbitrary, general, yet unknown population.

Let X_1, X_2, ..., X_n be a random sample of size n selected with replacement from an arbitrary population with random variable denoted by X, and with the population mean and variance of X denoted by μ and σ^2, respectively. Then the sampling distribution of $\overline{x}$ has mean and variance given by:

$$\mu_{\overline{x}} = \mu \qquad \text{Equation (5-3)}$$

$$\sigma^2_{\overline{x}} = \frac{\sigma^2}{n} \qquad \text{Equation (5-4)}$$

The functional form of the sampling distribution of $\overline{x}$ is not specified by the above result. Alternatives exist and are as follows.

- Empirically derive the sampling distribution, provided the original population is finite. This is illustrated in the previous examples.
- Analytically derive the sampling distribution using mathematical analysis. This approach is illustrated by the presentation of the Binomial Distribution in Chapter 4.
- When n is large, use the Central Limit Theorem to obtain the approximate result that $\overline{X}$ is approximately distributed N $(\mu, \frac{\sigma^2}{n})$.

The results of equations (5-3) and (5-4) apply to all distributions. They are true for discrete and continuous random variables, regardless of the functional form of the original distributions.

(Sampling Finite Distributions when Sampling With and Without Replacement–Continued)

The only difference between equations (5-4) and (5-2) is the finite population correction factor, $(N - n)/(N - 1)$. In sampling with replacement, N is effectively ∞. Thus, $\lim\limits_{N \to \infty} \left(\dfrac{N - n}{N - 1} \right) = 1$, and the "correction factor" is 1 in equation (5-4).

Sampling Distribution of $\overline{X}$ when Sampling Nonnormal, Infinite Populations: n Small.

Specifying the sampling distribution of $\bar{x}$ when sampling from infinite populations with a large sample size has already been discussed via the Central Limit Theorem. Therefore, discussion here is restricted to the case where n is small.

If the experimenter is satisfied with knowing only the mean and variance of the sampling distribution of $\bar{x}$, then the results of equations (5-3) and (5-4) suffice. However, if more information about the sampling distribution of $\bar{x}$ is desired, you may do one of the following.

- Assume that the original population is approximately normally distributed and then use the results presented in the "Sampling from a Normal Distribution" section. However, in many situations this is obviously not appropriate.
- Empirically simulate the distribution via the use of computers and simulation software. However, this only provides an "estimate" of the sampling distribution.
- Analytically derive the sampling distribution of $\bar{x}$ by using the techniques of integral calculus and transformation theory.

Solutions do not come easily in any of these cases, and in some situations have defied the best efforts of many statisticians. The best solution, where possible, is to obtain a larger sample.

Chapter 6
STATISTICAL ESTIMATION

Statistical Estimation

Introduction

The theory presented in the preceding chapters provides the background for statistical estimation theory. The techniques used in this chapter are based on the results of the statistical computations and the statistics computed in the previous chapter and what they can tell us about a larger population through statistical inference.

The two basic types of statistical inference are estimation and hypothesis testing. This chapter presents estimation theory. Tests of statistical hypotheses are discussed in Chapter 7.

The two general types of statistical estimation are point and interval. Interval estimation usually is more useful, but it usually is easier to construct an interval estimate by starting with a point estimate.

This chapter uses the foundations of descriptive statistics, probability theory, and sampling distributions presented in the previous chapters to construct meaningful point and interval estimates. In addition, it explains statistical inference and its relationship to point estimation theory.

Interval estimation of population means is discussed for large samples both when the variance is known and unknown. The final section deals with estimation tasks for small samples. The Student's t-distribution is used to help solve estimation problems in these situations.

Point Estimation

In making a model of natural processes, you often introduce unknown parameters into statistical inference by assuming that the population has a certain probability distribution. The objective of point estimation techniques is to use the sample values to provide the one best possible value for each unknown parameter.

Point estimate—a specific, single numerical value computed from the data of a sample. This point estimate is then used as the best conjecture for the corresponding population value.

An estimator is the mathematical formula that describes how an estimate is computed. The estimate of an unknown parameter is the specific, numerical value obtained when the data is put into the estimator. After an estimate is obtained, it requires no further study. However, estimators not only can, but must be studied to determine which estimator is the best one to use.

To determine how good an estimator is, examine its unbiasedness, efficiency (or minimum variance), consistency, and sufficiency. For more information on these concepts, see the books listed in the Bibliography.

(Point Estimation–Continued)

Point Estimation for the Normal Distribution

When considering the normal distribution as a model for the probability structure of a population, μ and σ^2 (the mean and variance of the normal distribution, which are assumed to be the same as the population mean and variance) must be estimated. The best point estimators of these parameters are:

$$\bar{X} = \frac{\sum\limits_{i=1}^{n} X_i}{n}$$

$$S_x^2 = \frac{1}{n-1} \sum\limits_{i=1}^{n} (X_i - \bar{X})^2$$

Symbolically, this is written $\hat{\mu} = \bar{X}$ and $\hat{\sigma}^2 = S_x^2$, where the "^" (read "hat") indicates that an estimator of the parameter is being considered.

These estimators can be evaluated by using the $\boxed{\Sigma+}$, $\boxed{\bar{x}}$, and $\boxed{\sigma_{n\text{-}1}}$ keys on your calculator.

Point Estimation for the Binomial Distribution

In the binomial probability model, the one unknown parameter is p, the probability of a success on each Bernoulli trial. The proportion of the population exhibiting the success characteristic is represented by p. The best point estimator of p is given by:

$$\hat{p} = \frac{x}{n},$$

where x is the number of successes in n independent, repeated Bernoulli trials. The sample proportion of successes is used to provide a best estimate of the population proportion.

Statistical Estimation

Interval Estimates of the Mean Using a Large Sample

The amount of information in a sample is fixed, but it can be expressed in different ways. For instance, a mechanic who has repaired many automobile transmissions (his sample of all possibilities), has a good idea of how long it will take to repair your car. He might tell you that, in his experience, most such repairs take four to five hours. If you say that you need to be 99% sure of the time involved, he might say it should take three to nine hours. His experience does not change, but he knows that it is possible to take much more or much less time in extreme circumstances.

The following sections show several different situations in which you can use interval estimates with a large sample.

Interval Estimates for the Mean

Concepts

An *interval estimate* consists of an interval of real numbers with end points that are usually functions of the data. There is some degree of confidence that the interval contains a parameter being estimated. If the sample size, n, is large, then the sample variance, $S_x{}^2$, is considered to be essentially equal to the population variance, σ^2. Since $\overline{X}$ is a good point estimate of μ, by considering the sample distribution of $\overline{X}$ and the result of the Central Limit Theorem,

$$P\left[Z_{(\alpha/2)} \leqslant \frac{\overline{X} - \mu}{\sigma/\sqrt{n}} \leqslant Z_{(1-\alpha/2)}\right] \approx 1 - \alpha$$

Equation (6-1)

for any $0 < \alpha < 1$. $Z_{(p)}$ represents the pth population quantile of the standard normal distribution. Equation (6-1) can be rewritten as:

$$P\left[\overline{X} + Z_{(\alpha/2)}\frac{\sigma}{\sqrt{n}} \leqslant \mu \leqslant \overline{X} + Z_{(1-\alpha/2)}\frac{\sigma}{\sqrt{n}}\right] \approx 1 - \alpha$$

Equation (6-2)

(Interval Estimates of the Mean Using a Large Sample–Continued)

When the sample size, n, is large enough, σ can be replaced by the sample standard deviation S_x and an approximate $100(1-\alpha)\%$ confidence interval for μ is still obtained. These confidence intervals are given by the following equations.

If σ is known:

$$\left[\overline{X} + Z_{(\alpha/2)}\frac{\sigma}{\sqrt{n}}, \ \overline{X} + Z_{(1-\alpha/2)}\frac{\sigma}{\sqrt{n}} \right]$$

Equation (6-3)

If σ is unknown:

$$\left[\overline{X} + Z_{(\alpha/2)}\frac{S_x}{\sqrt{n}}, \ \overline{X} + Z_{(1-\alpha/2)}\frac{S_x}{\sqrt{n}} \right]$$

Equation (6-4)

The notation [a,b] means that the interval is from a through b.

The meaning attached to such an interval should be carefully considered. The probability expression on the left side of equation (6-2) is approximately equal to $1-\alpha$ when $\overline{X}$ is considered as a random variable. Before any data is collected, the probability that the random intervals include the actual, yet unknown, fixed parameter μ is approximately $1-\alpha$. Further, if enough independent samples of size n are drawn from the population, and for each sample the intervals given in equations (6-3) or (6-4) are constructed, then approximately $100(1-\alpha)\%$ of the intervals will contain the parameter μ. However, once data is collected and an interval estimate for μ is constructed, either μ lies in this interval or it does not. The belief that a particular interval contains μ is based on the observation that a large number of intervals constructed similarly would contain μ the expected percentage of the time.

(Interval Estimates of the Mean Using a Large Sample–Continued)

In Figure 6-1, the sampling distribution has been drawn for the sample means of a population with mean μ. If a sample that has mean $\bar{x}$ is taken from the population, then the lower and upper limits, μ_L and μ_U, of the confidence interval can be determined using equation (6-3) or (6-4). Choosing $\alpha = .10$ means that on the average nine out of 10 of the confidence intervals generated from different sample $\bar{x}$'s will contain the population mean μ.

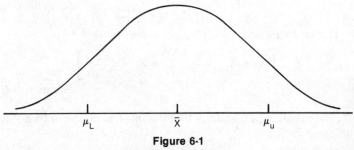

Figure 6-1
Sampling Distribution

When σ is Known

The following example shows how to compute an interval estimate when σ is known.

Example

The Good Tire Company advertizes that one of its top lines lasts 30,000 miles. A random sample of 60 tires is selected from the production line and test results yield $\bar{X} = 29{,}500$ miles. If the population standard deviation for this line is known to be $\sigma = 2500$ miles, calculate a 95% confidence interval for μ, the true average lifetime of this line of tires.

(Interval Estimates of the Mean Using a Large Sample–Continued)

Calculator Solution

Use equation (6-3) since $\sigma = 2500$ is known.

Since $\alpha = .05$, $\alpha/2 = .05/2 = .025$, and $1 - \alpha/2 = .975$, the quantiles from the standard normal distribution are:

$$Z_{.025} = -1.96 \text{ and } Z_{.975} = 1.96$$

Therefore, the 95% confidence interval for μ is given by:

$$\left[\overline{X} + Z_{.025} \frac{\sigma}{\sqrt{60}} , \; \overline{X} + Z_{.975} \frac{\sigma}{\sqrt{60}} \right]$$

Substituting the known values gives:

$$\left[29{,}500 + (-1.96) \frac{2500}{\sqrt{60}} , \; 29{,}500 + (1.96) \frac{2500}{\sqrt{60}} \right]$$

If the "DEC 2" indicator appears in the display, press 2nd Decimal before keying in the example.

Procedure	Press	Display
1. Clear calculator.	ON/C	0 STAT
2. Compute $\sigma/\sqrt{60}$ and store.	2500 ÷ 60	
	√x = STO	322.74861 STAT
3. Compute lower limit of 95% confidence interval $\overline{X} + Z_{(.025)} \times \sigma/\sqrt{60}$.	× 1.96 +/−	−1.96 STAT
	+ 29500 =	28867.413 STAT
4. Compute upper limit of 95% confidence interval $\overline{X} + Z_{.975} \times \sigma/\sqrt{60}$.	RCL × 1.96	1.96 STAT
	+ 29500 =	30132.587 STAT

Therefore, the 95% confidence interval for μ is given by:

[28,867.413, 30,132.587]

Statistical Estimation

(Interval Estimates of the Mean Using a Large Sample–Continued)

The manufacturer's claim for μ is within this interval, so there is not sufficient statistical evidence to refute the advertisement with 95% confidence, as shown in Figure 6-2.

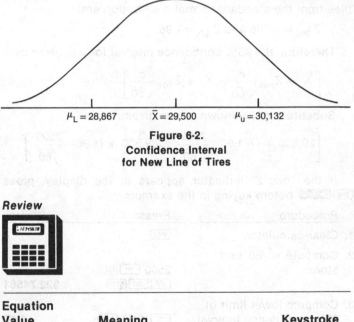

$\mu_L = 28,867$ $\bar{X} = 29,500$ $\mu_u = 30,132$

Figure 6-2.
Confidence Interval
for New Line of Tires

Review

Equation Value	Meaning	Keystroke
Inputs:		
$\sigma/\sqrt{n}$	Find $\sigma/\sqrt{n}$ and store.	σ ÷ n $\sqrt{x}$ = STO
$\bar{X} + Z_{(\alpha/2)}\ \sigma/\sqrt{n}$	Compute lower limit.	× $Z_{(\alpha/2)}$ +/− + X =
$\bar{X} + Z_{(1-\alpha/2)}\ \sigma/\sqrt{n}$	Compute upper limit.	RCL × $Z_{(1-\alpha/2)}$ + $\bar{X}$ =

(Interval Estimates of the Mean Using a Large Sample–Continued)

When σ is Not Known

In many situations σ^2 (or σ) may be unknown. In these cases, when the sample size n is large, you may construct a $100(1-\alpha)\%$ confidence interval for μ using equation (6-4).

Example

A random sample of 100 boxes of breakfast cereal is selected from a production line. The sample mean weight of the cereal in them is $\overline{X}=13.2$ ounces. Construct a 90% confidence interval for μ, the true average weight of the cereal produced by this production line, given that the sample variance $S_x^2 = 6.25$ for the random sample.

Use equation (6-4) with $n = 100$, $\overline{X} = 13.2$, and $S_x^2 = 6.25$, since the sample size is large.

Since $\alpha = .10, \alpha/2 = .10/2 = .05$, and $1 - \alpha/2 = 1 - .05 = .95$, the quantiles from the standard normal distribution are:

$$Z_{.05} = -1.645 \text{ and } Z_{.95} = 1.645$$

Therefore a 90% confidence interval for μ is given by:

$$\left[\overline{X} + Z_{.05}\,\frac{S_x}{\sqrt{100}} \;,\; \overline{X} + Z_{.95}\,\frac{S_x}{\sqrt{100}} \right]$$

Substituting the known values gives

$$\left[13.2 + (-1.645)\,\frac{2.5}{\sqrt{100}}\,,\; 13.2 + (1.645)\,\frac{2.5}{\sqrt{100}} \right]$$

since

$$S_x = \sqrt{S_x^2} = \sqrt{6.25} = 2.5$$

Statistical Estimation

(Interval Estimates of the Mean Using a Large Sample–Continued)

Calculator Solution

If the "DEC 2" indicator appears in the display, press [2nd] [Decimal] before keying in the example.

Procedure	Press	Display
1. Clear calculator.	[ON/c]	**0** _{STAT}
2. Compute $\dfrac{S_x}{\sqrt{100}}$ and store.	6.25 [÷] 100 [=] [√x] [STO]	**0.25** _{STAT}
3. Compute lower limit of 90% confidence interval, $\overline{X} + Z_{.05}\dfrac{S_x}{\sqrt{100}}$	[×] 1.645 [+/−] [+] 13.2 [=]	**12.78875** _{STAT}
4. Compute upper limit of 90% confidence interval, $\overline{X} + Z_{.95}\dfrac{S_x}{\sqrt{100}}$	[RCL] [×] 1.645 [+] 13.2 [=]	**13.61125** _{STAT}

The 90% confidence interval for μ is given by [12.78875, 13.61125], so there is a 90% confidence that the weight of the cereal is between those limits, as shown in Figure 6-3.

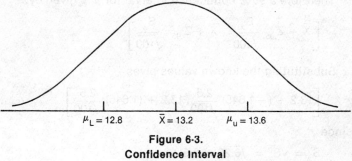

Figure 6-3.
Confidence Interval
for Cereal Weight

(Interval Estimates of the Mean Using a Large Sample–Continued)

When a Proportion is Needed

The final example of this section demonstrates the construction of a large sample confidence interval for the proportion of items in a population possessing an attribute of interest. The following example illustrates the method of constructing such an interval.

Example

A manufacturer of florescent light bulbs would like to determine the true proportion, p, of defective bulbs produced by the company's manufacturing process. Since testing light bulbs is a relatively simple task, a large sample can easily be tested. If 144 randomly selected bulbs yield nine defectives, compute an approximate 90% confidence interval for p.

Using the result of the Central Limit Theorem, it can be shown that an approximate 90% confidence interval for p is given by:

$$\left[\hat{p} + Z_{.05}\left(\frac{\hat{p}(1-\hat{p})}{n} \right)^{\frac{1}{2}}, \hat{p} + Z_{.95}\left(\frac{\hat{p}(1-\hat{p})}{n} \right)^{\frac{1}{2}} \right]$$

where $\hat{p}$ is the sample proportion of defectives. Thus, for this problem

$$\hat{p} = \frac{9}{144} = .0625$$

and the approximate 90% confidence interval is given by:

$$\left[.0625 + (-1.645)\left(\frac{(.0625)(1-.0625)}{144} \right)^{\frac{1}{2}}, .0625 + (1.645) \right.$$
$$\left. \left(\frac{(.0625)(1-.0625)}{144} \right)^{\frac{1}{2}} \right]$$

Statistical Estimation

(Interval Estimates of the Mean Using a Large Sample–Continued)

Calculator Solution

If the "DEC 2" indicator appears in the display, press ⟨2nd⟩ ⟨Decimal⟩ before keying in the example.

Procedure	Press	Display
1. Clear calculator.	⟨ON/C⟩	0 STAT
2. Compute $\sqrt{\dfrac{\hat{p}(1-\hat{p})}{n}}$	9 ⟨÷⟩ 144 ⟨=⟩ ⟨STO⟩ 1 ⟨−⟩	1 STAT
	⟨RCL⟩ ⟨×⟩ ⟨RCL⟩ ⟨÷⟩	0.0585938 STAT
	144 ⟨=⟩ ⟨√x̄⟩	0.0201718 STAT
3. Compute 1.645 times display and store.	⟨×⟩ 1.645 ⟨=⟩ ⟨STO⟩	0.0331826 STAT
4. Compute lower limit for p.	9 ⟨÷⟩ 144 ⟨−⟩ ⟨RCL⟩ ⟨=⟩	0.0293174 STAT
5. Compute upper limit for p.	9 ⟨÷⟩ 144 ⟨+⟩ ⟨RCL⟩ ⟨=⟩	0.0956826 STAT

An approximate 90% confidence interval for the true proportion of defective florescent bulbs manufactured from this production line is given by:

[0.0293174, 0.0956826]

as shown in Figure 6-4.

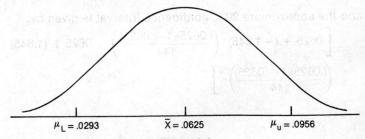

$\mu_L = .0293$ $\bar{X} = .0625$ $\mu_u = .0956$

Figure 6-4.
Confidence Interval
for Light Bulbs

Interval Estimates with Small Sample Sizes

To obtain useful interval estimates, knowledge of the sampling distributions of the estimators being considered must be used. For example, if you want an interval estimate of a population mean, the sampling distribution of $\bar{x}$ must be considered. By the Central Limit Theorem discussed in Chapter 5, the sampling distribution of $\bar{x}$ is approximately normally distributed with mean $\mu_{\bar{x}} = \mu$ and variance $\sigma_{\bar{x}}^2 = \sigma^2/n$. Knowing that $\bar{x}$ is normally distributed allows the construction of useful confidence intervals. In the previous section, the examples showed how to find the confidence intervals when σ^2 is known and when it is unknown for large samples. When σ^2 is known, the solution is found from equation (6-3). If σ^2 is unknown, use the following statistic.

$$t = \frac{\bar{x} - \mu}{\sigma_x/\sqrt{n}}$$

Equation (6-5)

This statistic is approximately normally distributed with zero mean and unit variance, provided the sample size n is large. Thus, the confidence interval is given by equation (6-4).

Student's t-Distribution

The next problem to consider is the situation in which σ^2 is unknown and n is not large enough to allow an appeal to the Central Limit Theorem. In such situations, where point and interval estimation and/or tests of hypotheses are conducted and the sample sizes are relatively small, these procedures are understandably referred to as "small-sample inferences". It is extremely important to know the exact sampling distributions of statistics in these situations; otherwise, considerable errors in judgement could be made. This is the case for the statistic "t" given in equation (6-5). In the following, the sampling distribution of t is discussed.

Statistical Estimation

(Interval Estimates with Small Sample Sizes–Continued)

The nature of the sampling distribution of t was first investigated by W.S. Gosset (1876-1937). It was later mathematically derived by Sir R. A. Fisher. Gosset published under the pseudonym "Student," so the distribution of t is frequently referred to as the *Student's t-distribution*.

The distribution of t is, in some respects, like the normal distribution, but it differs in that it contains a parameter, df, which is commonly called "degrees of freedom." For each value of the degrees of freedom a unique distribution is obtained. When the degrees of freedom equals ∞, the distribution is the same as the normal distribution. The value of df is generally related to the sample size. In the case of equation (6-5), $df = n - 1$. Other important properties of the t-distribution are as follows.

- The mean of the t-distribution is 0.
- The t-distribution is symmetrical about 0.
- The variable t can take on any value between $-\infty$ and $+\infty$.
- In general, the t-distribution has a lower density function than the standard normal near zero, but is higher away from the center of the distribution.
- The t-distribution approaches the standard normal distribution as df increases. Note that this is consistent with the Central Limit Theorem.

(Interval Estimates with Small Sample Sizes–Continued)

As with the standard normal distribution, the Student's t-distribution has had tables constructed. Quantiles of the Student's t-distribution are given in Table B-3 of Appendix B. The table entries are the upper cumulative quantiles and are denoted by:

$t_{(p,df)}$

In other words, $t_{(p,df)}$ is the quantity that satisfies

$P(T \leqslant t_{(p,df)}) = p$

where T is a random variable that follows a Student's t-distribution with df degrees of freedom. To use Table B-3 you need to know the value of the confidence coefficient, say $(1 - \alpha)$, and the degrees of freedom, df. For example, suppose $\alpha/2 = .05$ and df $= 7$. Then $p = (1 - \alpha/2) = (1 - .05) = .95$ and from Table B-3, $t_{(.95, 7)} = 1.895$.

The Student's t-distribution is symmetrical, so for small values of p,

$t_{(p,df)} = -t_{(1-p,df)}$ for $0 < p < 1$

For example, suppose you wish to find $t_{(.10, 13)}$, with $p = .10$ and df $= 13$ degrees of freedom. Since $(1 - p) = (1 - .10) = .90$, the table entry is $t_{(.10,13)} = -t_{(.90,13)} = -1.350$.

In the following section, two examples are presented that use the t-distribution to find confidence intervals.

(Interval Estimates with Small Sample Sizes–Continued)

Concepts

When the sample size is small, confidence intervals for the mean μ can still be constructed using critical values from the Student t-distribution. Specifically, if a random sample of size n, X_1, X_2, ..., X_n, is drawn from a population that is normally distributed and if

$$S_{\bar{x}}^2 = \frac{\dfrac{1}{n-1} \sum_{i=1}^{n} (X_i - \bar{X})^2}{n} = \frac{S^2}{n},$$

then the random variable

$$T_{(n-1)} = \frac{\bar{X} - \mu}{S_{\bar{x}}}, \text{ where } S_{\bar{x}} = \sqrt{\frac{S^2}{n}}$$

has Student's t-distribution based on $(n-1)$ degrees of freedom. Since the sampling distribution of $T_{(n-1)}$ is determined in this case for $0 < \alpha < 1$, the critical points $t_{(\alpha/2,\, n-1)}$ and $t_{(1-\alpha/2,\, n-1)}$ can be selected from a table of values of Student's t-distribution and

$$P[t_{(\alpha/2,\, n-1)} \leqslant T_{(n-1)} \leqslant t_{(1-\alpha/2,\, n-1)}] = 1 - \alpha$$

Equivalently,

$$P[\bar{X} + t_{(\alpha/2,\, n-1)}\, S_{\bar{x}} \leqslant \mu \leqslant \bar{X} + t_{(1-\alpha/2,\, n-1)}\, S_{\bar{x}}] = 1 - \alpha$$

Thus a 100 $(1 - \alpha)$% confidence interval for the mean, μ, with a small sample size for data that is normally distributed is

$$[\bar{X} + t_{(\alpha/2,\, n-1)}\, S_{\bar{x}},\ \bar{X} + t_{(1-\alpha/2,\, n-1)}\, S_{\bar{x}}]$$

Equation (6-6)

Statistical Estimation

(Interval Estimates with Small Sample Sizes–Continued)

Example

Assume that the starting hourly wages of electronics technicians at a manufacturing plant are normally distributed. A random sample of eight hourly wages yields $6.52, $6.59, $7.14, $6.89, $7.25, $7.12, $6.98, and $7.50. Find a 95% confidence interval for μ, the true average hourly starting wage of electronics technicians at this plant.

Use equation (6-6). Since the sample size, n, equals 8, the degrees of freedom is 7. Thus, since $\alpha = .05$, $\alpha/2 = .025$, and $1 - \alpha/2 = .975$,

$$t_{(.025,7)} = -t_{(.975,7)} = -2.365$$

by the symmetry of Student's t-distribution. The 95% confidence interval for μ is given by:

$$[\bar{X} + t_{(.025,\ 7)}\ S_{\bar{x}},\ \bar{X} + t_{(.975,\ 7)}\ S_{\bar{x}}]$$

where $\bar{x}$ and $S_{\bar{x}}$ are computed from the given data.

Statistical Estimation

(Interval Estimates with Small Sample Sizes–Continued)

Calculator Solution

If the "DEC 2" indicator appears in the display, press [2nd] [Decimal] before keying in the example.

Procedure	Press	Display
1. Clear calculator and statistical registers.	[ON/c] [2nd] [STAT]	0 _{STAT}
2. Enter data.	6.52 [Σ+]	1 _{STAT}
	6.59 [Σ+]	2 _{STAT}
	7.14 [Σ+]	3 _{STAT}
	6.89 [Σ+]	4 _{STAT}
	7.25 [Σ+]	5 _{STAT}
	7.12 [Σ+]	6 _{STAT}
	6.98 [Σ+]	7 _{STAT}
	7.5 [Σ+]	8 _{STAT}
3. Compute $S_{\bar{x}} \times t_{(.975, 7)}$ and store value.	[σn-1] [÷] 8 [√x̄]	2.8284271 _{STAT}
	[×] 2.365	
	[=] [STO]	0.2750584 _{STAT}
4. Compute upper and lower limits of the confidence interval.	[x̄] [−] [RCL] [=]	6.7236916 _{STAT}
	[x̄] [+] [RCL] [=]	7.2738084 _{STAT}

Thus the appropriate 95% confidence interval for the mean hourly wage of the technicians is [$6.72, $7.27]. You can state with 95% confidence that the average starting hourly wage is from $6.72 to $7.27.

(Interval Estimates with Small Sample Sizes–Continued)

Construction of a Confidence Interval for the Difference in Population Means

Concepts

The final example of this section deals with the construction of a confidence interval for the true difference in population means. Suppose populations P_1 and P_2 have population means μ_1 and μ_2 and common variance σ^2, and you are in-terested in setting a confidence interval on $\mu_1 - \mu_2$. This type of confidence interval also depends on Student's t-distribution when small sample sizes are involved. Assume that the probability distributions governing both populations are normal distributions.

Furthermore, if the two populations are independent of each other and random samples of sizes m and n are drawn from P_1 and P_2 respectively, then the random variable

$$T_{m+n-2} = \frac{(\bar{X} - \bar{Y}) - (\mu_1 - \mu_2)}{S_p \sqrt{\dfrac{1}{m} + \dfrac{1}{n}}}$$

has Student's T-distribution based on $m+n-2$ (the sum of both sample sizes less 2) degrees of freedom. Here $\bar{X}$ and $\bar{Y}$ are the sample mean estimators from populations P_1 and P_2 and $S_p = \sqrt{S_p{}^2}$, where $S_p{}^2$ is called the *pooled estimator* of the variance and is given by:

$$S_p^2 = \frac{(m-1)S_x^2 + (n-1)S_y^2}{m+n-2}$$

$$= \frac{\displaystyle\sum_{i=1}^{m}(x_i - \bar{x})^2 + \sum_{j=1}^{n}(y_j - \bar{y})^2}{m+n-2}$$

Statistical Estimation

(Interval Estimates with Small Sample Sizes–Continued)

Further, if α is selected between zero and one and $df = m + n - 2$ for notational convenience, then

$$P[t_{(\alpha/2,\,df)} \leqslant T_{df} \leqslant t_{(1-\alpha/2,\,df)}] = 1 - \alpha$$

where $t_{(\alpha/2,\,df)}$ represents the $\alpha/2$th quantile of Student's t-distribtution based on $df = m + n - 2$ degrees of freedom. Equivalently,

$$P\left[\left(\overline{X} - \overline{Y}\right) + t_{(\alpha/2,\,df)}\, S_p \sqrt{\frac{1}{m} + \frac{1}{n}} \leqslant \mu_1 - \mu_2 \leqslant \left(\overline{X} - \overline{Y}\right)\right.$$
$$\left. + t_{(1-\alpha/2,\,df)}\, S_p \sqrt{\frac{1}{m} + \frac{1}{n}}\,\right] = 1 - \alpha$$

and construct a $(1-\alpha)100\%$ confidence interval for $\mu_1 - \mu_2$ using the expression within the probability statement. Thus a $100(1-\alpha)\%$ confidence interval for $\mu_1 - \mu_2$ is given by:

$$\left[\left(\overline{X} - \overline{Y}\right) + t_{(\alpha/2,\,df)}\, S_p \sqrt{\frac{1}{m} + \frac{1}{n}},\right.$$
$$\left.\left(\overline{X} - \overline{Y}\right) + t_{(1-\alpha/2,\,df)}\, S_p \sqrt{\frac{1}{m} + \frac{1}{n}}\,\right] \qquad \textit{Equation (6-7)}$$

This type of confidence interval can be used to test or question claims of significant differences in population means, as the final example illustrates.

(Interval Estimates with Small Sample Sizes–Continued)

Example

A manufacturer of powdered sugar produces 5-pound bags from each of two production lines. If μ_1 and μ_2 represent the true average weights of the bags of sugar produced by production lines 1 and 2 respectively, and if it is assumed that these weights are normally distributed about their respective means having a common unknown variance σ^2, then compute a 90% confidence interval for $\mu_1 - \mu_2$ given the following data.

	Sample Mean	Sample Variance	Sample Size
Production Line 1	$\bar{y} = 4.75$ lbs	$S_y^2 = .16$	$n = 6$
Production Line 2	$\bar{x} = 5.10$ lbs	$S_x^2 = .64$	$m = 4$

Use the confidence interval from equation (6-7) constructed with $\alpha = .10$ and $df = m + n - 2 = 4 + 6 - 2 = 8$ degrees of freedom.

$$\bar{X} - \bar{Y} = 5.10 - 4.75 = .35$$

$$S_p^2 = \frac{(m-1)S_x^2 + (n-1)S_y^2}{m+n-2} = \frac{(3)(.64) + 5(.16)}{4+6-2}$$

$$t_{(.05,8)} = -t_{(.95,8)} = -1.860$$

and

$$\sqrt{\frac{1}{m} + \frac{1}{n}} = \sqrt{\frac{1}{4} + \frac{1}{6}}$$

Statistical Estimation

(Interval Estimates with Small Sample Sizes–Continued)

Calculator Solution

If the "DEC 2" indicator appears in the display, press [2nd] [Decimal] before keying in the example.

Procedure	Press	Display
1. Clear calculator.	[ON/c]	**0** _{STAT}
2. Compute $t_{(.95, 8)} S_p \sqrt{\dfrac{1}{4} + \dfrac{1}{6}}$.	3 [X] .64 [=] [STO]	**1.92** _{STAT}
	5 [X] .16 [=] [SUM]	**0.8** _{STAT}
	4 [+] 6 [−] 2 [=] [1/x] [X]	**0.125** _{STAT}
	[RCL] [=] [√x] [STO] 4 [1/x]	**0.25** _{STAT}
	[+] 6 [1/x] [=] [√x] [X]	**0.6454972** _{STAT}
	1.86 [=] [X] [RCL] [=] [STO]	**0.7000786** _{STAT}
3. Compute lower limit of confidence interval.	.35 [−] [RCL] [=]	**−0.3500786** _{STAT}
4. Compute upper limit of confidence interval.	.35 [+] [RCL] [=]	**1.0500786** _{STAT}

The 90% confidence interval for $\mu_1 - \mu_2$ is given by [−0.3500786, 1.0500786], and there is 90% confidence that the same average amount of sugar is packaged by each of the production lines.

Chapter 7
STATISTICAL HYPOTHESIS TESTING

Statistical Hypothesis Testing

Contents

Introduction

The topics concerning statistical hypothesis testing discussed in this chapter rely on some of the methods and techniques explored in Chapters 3 through 6. Chapter 3 discusses how to describe data from a sample. Chapter 4 provides some information about probability theory and the forms a population might take. Chapter 5 describes some of the forms that sampling distributions can take. Chapter 6 examines the use of interval estimates.

Many times in business, science, or everyday life, you must make decisions about accepting or buying large quantities of items. Time and expense usually allow examination and testing of only a few samples. When you make decisions concerning a large population based on only a small sample, a degree of uncertainty is present. The Statistical Theory of Hypothesis Testing is used in reaching a decision about a population by examining the data contained in a sample from the population.

Claims or conjectures about the characteristics of a population are called *hypotheses*. The claim to be tested is called the *null hypothesis*, labeled H_0. It is either *rejected* or *not rejected* based on sample data. The *alternative hypothesis*, labeled H_1, represents a belief concerning the population that is contrary to the null hypothesis. Using T to represent the test, it is sometimes written in the form

T: Reject H_0 in favor of H_1 if and only if ...

followed by the reasons for rejecting the null hypothesis.

Two types of errors may be encountered when testing hypotheses. The first kind of error, called a Type I error, occurs when you reject the null hypothesis when it is true. The second kind of error, called a Type II error, occurs when you accept the null hypothesis when it is false. Risks are associated with making either of these types of errors; thus, a wise decision is one in which the probabilities of making such errors are small, or at least tolerable.

(Introduction–Continued)

Ideally, the probability of these errors is zero. However, in most testing situations the probability is greater than zero. Moreover, statisticians have shown mathematically that in most practical situations a decrease in the probability of committing a Type I error usually is accompanied by an increase in the probability of making a Type II error.

Many times, this dilemma can be avoided by choosing a tolerable level for committing a Type I error, and then choosing a sample size large enough to provide a Type II error of acceptably small size. Unfortunately, in many practical situations the sample size is predetermined so that the size of the Type II error is determined when you choose an appropriately small size for the probability of committing a Type I error. The probabilities of Type II errors are not computed in the examples in this chapter.

Elements of Statistical Hypothesis Testing

The following terms and definitions have evolved with the theory of Statistical Hypothesis Testing. It is assumed that some fixed population is identified for study and a pair of null and alternative hypotheses are specified.

Test of a Statistical Hypothesis—a rule, method, or procedure used to decide whether to reject the null hypothesis.

Test Statistic—an observable function of the data which does not involve any unknown parameters. Test statistics are sometimes used as *estimators*. When data is collected and the function is calculated, an *estimate* is produced from that data.

The value produced by a test statistic is used, in conjunction with the test of statistical hypothesis, to decide whether to reject the null hypothesis.

These steps are used in statistical hypothesis testing.

- Create *null* and *alternative* hypotheses for a parameter associated with the underlying probability distribution of the sample data values.
- Formulate an appropriate *test statistic*.
- Choose a specified, tolerable probability of committing a Type I error for a given sample size, n.
- Select a *random sample* from the underlying population.
- Formulate the test of hypothesis, T.
- *Calculate* the value of the test statistic.
- *Decide* either to reject or not reject H_0 based on the calculated value of the test statistic.

Many questions can be raised about this process. Not all of them have easy answers. One question that can be answered is what it means to say that you accept or reject the null hypothesis. While a decision to reject a hypothesis is equivalent to the opinion that it is false, a decision to accept a null hypothesis means only that you did not reject it. The decision to accept a hypothesis is *not* equivalent to stating that it is true.

(Elements of Statistical Hypothesis Testing–Continued)

As an example of statistical hypothesis testing, suppose that it is suspected that a coin is biased so that heads appear more (or less) often than tails on any one flip of the coin. Then a simple statement of the null hypothesis is

H_0: The coin is fair.

and the corresponding alternative hypothesis is

H_1: The coin is biased.

You might expect that flipping the coin 10 times should give you five heads if the coin is fair and more (or fewer) than five heads if the coin is biased. However, it is too simple to say that H_1 is the correct hypothesis if six heads appear because six heads could appear if the coin is unbiased. It is not possible to predetermine exactly the number of heads and tails that appear.

To remedy this, you could flip the coin many times. If you flipped it 1,000,000 times, then you could more precisely determine if the coin is biased. However, this is not practical.

Instead, an appropriate test of the hypothesis, if a decision is to be based on 10 independent flips of this coin, is as follows:

Let Q equal the number of times a head appears in the 10 flips of the coin. Q is a random variable that may take on any one of the values $\{0,1,2,...,10\}$. If p represents the probability of observing heads on any one trial, then the null and alternative hypotheses can be restated as

H_0: p = .5
H_1: p ≠ .5

If H_0 is true, the random variable Q has a binomial distribution with parameters N = 10 and p = .5. Thus, if H_0 is true, on the average the number of heads appearing in repeated sequences of 10 flips is $E[Q] = Np = 10(.5) = 5$. Thus, if either "too many" or "too few" heads occur in the 10 flips, you would tend to believe that p ≠ .5 and H_1 is true.

(Elements of Statistical Hypothesis Testing–Continued)

Suppose you decide that the coin is biased if and only if fewer than two or more than eight heads are observed. Then you can write

T: Reject H_0 if and only if $Q < 2$ or $Q > 8$ in the random sample of size 10.

The probability of committing a Type I error (the probability of rejecting a true null hypothesis) using this testing rule can be computed as shown below.

P(Type I error)

$= $ P(Rejecting H_0 given $p = .5$)

$= $ P[Q < 2 or $Q > 8$ given $p = .5$]

$$= \sum_{k=0}^{1} \binom{10}{k}(.5)^k(1-.5)^{10-k} + \sum_{k=9}^{10} \binom{10}{k}(.5)^k(1-.5)^{10-k}$$

$$= \binom{10}{0}(.5)^0(1-.5)^{10-0} + \binom{10}{1}(.5)^1(1-.5)^{10-1}$$

$$+ \binom{10}{9}(.5)^9(1-.5)^{10-9} + \binom{10}{10}(.5)^{10}(1-.5)^{10-10}$$

$$= (.5)^{10} + 10(.5)^{10} + 10(.5)^{10} + (.5)^{10}$$

$$= 22 \times (.5)^{10}$$

$$= .0214844$$

(Elements of Statistical Hypothesis Testing–Continued)

Therefore, using this decision rule, the probability of rejecting the null hypothesis when it is actually true is less than .022. Thus, if repeated sequences of 10 flips of a fair coin are performed, the number of heads recorded, and a decision made to accept or reject H_0, 97.8% of such decisions will be correct. This does not guarantee that any *one* decision is correct, but it does justify the opinion that an individual decision is correct. Figure 7-1 illustrates this decision rule.

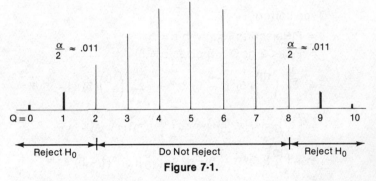

Figure 7-1.

The rest of this chapter examines specific situations in which the theory of statistical hypothesis testing can be used.

Large-sample Tests based upon Sample Means

This section deals with tests of hypotheses concerning population means in which the experimenter can afford to take many samples. The sample mean is a good point estimator of μ, so it seems natural to propose statistical tests which are based upon $\bar{x}$.

Acceptance Based on Upper and Lower Limits

Concepts

In the first example, a decision is made based on whether a container has more or less than a claimed amount. By the Central Limit Theorem (see Chapter 5) $\bar{x}$ has approximately the distribu-

tion $N\left(\mu, \dfrac{\sigma^2}{n}\right)$ and therefore for any value of μ,

$$Z = \frac{\bar{x} - \mu}{\sigma/\sqrt{n}}$$

has approximately the distribution N(0,1).

Thus, for any probability of Type I error (significance level), α, where $0 < \alpha < 1$,

$$P[Z_{(\alpha/2)} \leqslant Z \leqslant Z_{(1-\alpha/2)}] = 1 - \alpha$$

where Z_p is a real number such that $P[Z \leqslant Z_{(p)}] = p$ if Z is the Standard Normal random variable.

Note: The number Z_p, where $P[Z \leqslant Z_p] = p$, is called the pth quantile of the standard normal distribution for any $0 \leqslant p \leqslant 1$. Since you generally prefer the confidence to be high (i.e. 90%, 95%, 97-1/2%, 99%), the following table of quantiles can be used.

p	.90	.95	.975	.99
$Z_{(p)}$	1.282	1.645	1.96	2.326

Table 7.1

(Large-Sample Tests Based on Sample Means–Continued)

Example

A large shipment of aerosol insecticide cans arrives at your receiving dock. The manufacturer claims that the cans contain, on the average, 510 grams of insecticide. You would like to be sure of this claim. These particular cans do not work properly if they are too full and you are not getting what you paid for if they are less than full. The following describes how to formulate your decision to accept or reject the shipment based on a sample of 40 randomly selected cans.

Let μ represent the actual average number of grams of insecticide per can. Then the null and alternative hypotheses are

$$H_0: \mu = 510g$$
$$H_1: \mu \neq 510g$$

Since the sample size of 40 is considered large, the sample standard deviation (S_x) is an acceptable estimate of the population standard deviation (σ). Moreover, the sample mean $\bar{x}$ is a good point estimate of μ.

Therefore, you should reject the shipment if and only if

$$Z = \frac{\bar{x} - 510}{\sigma/\sqrt{n}} > Z_{(1-\alpha/2)}$$

or

$$Z = \frac{\bar{x} - 510}{\sigma/\sqrt{n}} < Z_{\alpha/2}$$

This should happen only (100 times α)% of the time if μ is 510g.

Suppose you want to be 95% certain that your decision is correct. After having a technician collect the data, suppose you compute the sample mean and sample standard deviation and find that

$$\bar{X} = 508.75$$
$$\sigma = S_x = 19.97$$

(Large-Sample Tests Based on Sample Means–Continued)

Since you want to be 95% sure, the probability of a Type I error, P(Type I error), must be .05. From the standard normal table

$P[Z \leqslant 1.96] = .975$, so $Z_{.975} = 1.96$

and

$P[Z \leqslant -1.96] = .025$, so $Z_{.025} = -1.96$

Furthermore

$$Z = \frac{\bar{x} - 510}{\sigma/\sqrt{n}} = \frac{508.75 - 510}{1997/\sqrt{40}}$$

You reject H_0 only if $Z < -1.96$ or $Z > 1.96$.

Calculator Solution

If the "DEC 2" indicator appears in the display, press [2nd] [Decimal] before keying in the example.

Procedure	Press	Display
1. Clear calculator.	[ON/c]	0 _{STAT}
2. Compute $(\bar{x} - \mu)$ and store.	508.75 [−] 510 [=] [STO]	−1.25 _{STAT}
3. Compute $\sigma/\sqrt{n}$.	19.97 [÷] 40 [√x̄] [=]	3.1575342 _{STAT}
4. Exchange with stored value and compute Z.	[EXC] [÷] [RCL] [=]	−0.3958785 _{STAT}

(Large-Sample Tests Based on Sample Means–Continued)

Thus, $Z = -0.396$ and since $-1.96 < -0.396 < 1.96$, you must accept the null hypothesis (H_0: $\mu = 510$g) based on the statistical evidence. This is shown in Figure 7-2. Thus you tentatively accept the manufacturer's claim that the true average amount of insecticide per can in the shipment is 510g. Moreover, if this test is repeated many times based on many samples of size 40, then roughly 95% of the decisions are correct. This high percentage gives us faith in *this* decision.

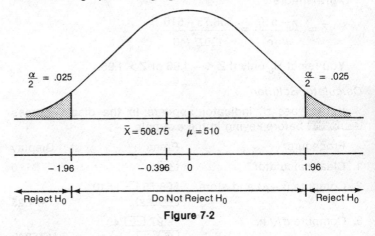

$\frac{\alpha}{2} = .025$ $\frac{\alpha}{2} = .025$

$\bar{X} = 508.75$ $\mu = 510$

-1.96 -0.396 0 1.96

Reject H_0 Do Not Reject H_0 Reject H_0

Figure 7-2

Acceptance Based on Lower Limit Only

Concepts

The relationship $Z_{(\alpha)} = -Z_{(1-\alpha)}$ exists between the quantiles of the standard normal distribution, so you really need to find only the "upper" quantiles in an applied problem. The following example demonstrates a situation in which only the lower limit is important.

(Large-Sample Tests Based on Sample Means–Continued)

Example

A soft-drink bottler manufactures a product which indicates on each bottle that it contains 16 ounces. The bottler is anxious not to ship bottles that contain less than this amount. The following establishes a test based on a sample of 100 randomly-selected bottles.

In this example, you are only concerned with the bottles being less than full. Therefore, if μ represents the true, but unknown, average amount of drink placed in the bottles, the null and alternative hypotheses are

$H_0: \mu = 16$

$H_1: \mu < 16$

$\bar{X}$ is a good point estimator of μ and $\bar{X}$ has approximately the normal distribution, whatever the true value of μ is.

Suppose you want to be 90% sure that your decision is correct (i.e. $\alpha = P[\text{Type I error}] = .10$). From the Central Limit Theorem,

$$P\left[\frac{\bar{x} - \mu}{\sigma/\sqrt{n}} < Z_{(.10)} \right] = .10$$

Therefore, the decision rule is as follows.

T: Reject $H_0: \mu = 16$ if and only if

$$Z = \frac{\bar{x} - 16}{\sigma/\sqrt{n}} < -1.282$$

Suppose that after the 100 observations are collected, the sample mean and sample standard deviaton are found to be

$\bar{X} = 15.1$ ounces

$S_x = 5.57$ ounces.

Therefore

$$Z = \frac{15.1 - 16}{5.57/\sqrt{100}}$$

You reject the null hypothesis if and only if Z is less than -1.282.

(Large-Sample Tests Based on Sample Means–Continued)

Calculator Solution

If the "DEC 2" indicator appears in the display, press ⟨2nd⟩ ⟨Decimal⟩ before keying in the example.

Procedure	Press	Display
1. Clear calculator.	⟨ON/C⟩	0 STAT
2. Compute $(\bar{x} - \mu)$ and store.	15.1 ⟨−⟩ 16 ⟨=⟩⟨STO⟩	−0.9 STAT
3. Compute $\sigma/\sqrt{n}$.	5.57 ⟨÷⟩ 100 ⟨√x̄⟩⟨=⟩	0.557 STAT
4. Exchange with stored value and compute Z.	⟨EXC⟩⟨÷⟩⟨RCL⟩⟨=⟩	−1.6157989 STAT

Figure 7-3 shows that, since $Z = -1.616$, which is less than -1.282, you reject the null hypothesis, $\mu = 16$, in favor of the alternative hypothesis, $H_1: \mu < 16$. You should notify the bottler so that the bottling process can be adjusted. The significance level of this test is $\alpha = .10$.

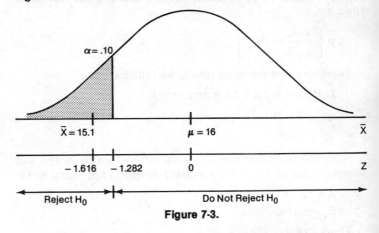

Figure 7-3.

(Large-Sample Tests Based on Sample Means–Continued)

Acceptance Based on Comparison of the Means

Concepts

In many experimental situations, you may wish to test hypotheses concerning the means of two different populations. Suppose $x_1, x_2, ..., x_m$ are observations from population A possessing population mean μ_x and population variance σ_x^2, and $y_1, y_2, ..., y_n$ are data values from population B having population mean μ_y and variance σ_y^2. Then you might wish to know if μ_x is equal to, greater than, or less than μ_y.

The sample means $\bar{X}$ and $\bar{Y}$ are good estimators of μ_x and μ_y, respectively, so it seems natural to base tests of hypotheses concerning μ_x and μ_y on their respective sample estimates. The next example illustrates a method for testing the equality of population means.

Example

The professor of a business statistics course prepares two different tests for two classes and is concerned that the true levels of difficulty for the tests be the same. It is reasonable to assume that the classes are random samples of business statistics students. Is there any reason to believe that either the 9:00 a.m. or 10:00 a.m. class received a significantly harder exam?

The data available are as shown below.

	Sample Mean Grade	Sample Standard Deviation	Sample Size
9:00 a.m. Class	$\bar{x} = 83$	$S_x = 11.00$	$m = 55$
10:00 a.m. Class	$\bar{y} = 79$	$S_y = 5.00$	$n = 60$

Statistical Hypothesis Testing

(Large-Sample Tests Based on Sample Means–Continued)

Let μ_x represent the average performance of the business statistics students who could take the test during the 9:00 a.m. class. Likewise, let μ_y represent the average performance of the business statistics students who could take the test during the 10:00 a.m. class. It is supposed that the populations taking the respective tests are independent. The instructor's concern can be expressed as

$$H_0: \mu_x = \mu_y$$
$$H_1: \mu_x \neq \mu_y$$

Since the sample sizes are large, S_x is approximately equal to σ_x, and S_y is approximately equal to σ_y. Moreover, $\bar{x} - \bar{y}$ is a good estimator of $\mu_x - \mu_y$ having variance $\sigma_x^2/m + \sigma_y^2/n$. With this observation you can rewrite the null and alternative hypotheses as

$$H_0: \mu_x - \mu_y = 0$$
$$H_1: \mu_x - \mu_y \neq 0$$

and base the test on the difference in sample means, $D = \bar{X} - \bar{Y}$.

When the null hypothesis is true, by the Central Limit Theorem, D is approximately distributed

$$N\left(0, \frac{\sigma_x^2}{m} + \frac{\sigma_y^2}{n}\right)$$

and thus

$$Z = \frac{D - 0}{\sqrt{\dfrac{\sigma_x^2}{m} + \dfrac{\sigma_y^2}{n}}} \text{ is approximately distributed } N(0,1).$$

Furthermore, for any α such that $0 < \alpha < 1$,

$$P[Z_{(\alpha/2)} \leqslant Z \leqslant Z_{(1-\alpha/2)}] = 1 - \alpha.$$

(Large-Sample Tests Based on Sample Means–Continued)

Therefore, reject the null hypothesis, $\mu_x = \mu_y (\mu_x - \mu_y = 0)$, in favor of the alternative hypothesis, $\mu_x \neq \mu_y (\mu_x - \mu_y \neq 0)$, if and only if

$$Z < Z_{(\alpha/2)}$$

or

$$Z > Z_{(1 - \alpha/2)}.$$

The significance level of this test is approximately α.

Suppose you choose a significance level $\alpha = .10 \left(\dfrac{\alpha}{2} = .05 \right)$ for your test of the hypothesis. Then from Table 7.1

$$Z_{\left(\frac{.10}{2}\right)} = Z_{(.05)} = -Z_{(.95)} = -1.645$$

and

$$Z_{(1 - .05)} = Z_{(.95)} = 1.645$$

Let

$$Z = \frac{D - 0}{\sqrt{\dfrac{\sigma_x^2}{m} + \dfrac{\sigma_y^2}{n}}}$$

You reject H_0 if and only if

$$Z < -1.645$$

or

$$Z > 1.645$$

For the given data,

$$\bar{x} = 83$$
$$\bar{y} = 79$$
$$S_x^2 = 121.00$$
$$S_y^2 = 25.00$$

Thus

$$Z = \frac{83 - 79}{\sqrt{\dfrac{121}{55} + \dfrac{25}{60}}}$$

(Large-Sample Tests Based on Sample Means–Continued)

Calculator Solution

If the "DEC 2" indicator appears in the display, press [2nd] [Decimal] before keying in the example.

Procedure	Press	Display
1. Clear calculator.	[ON/c]	0 STAT
2. Calculate $\dfrac{S_x^2}{m}$ and store.	121 [÷] 55 [=] [STO]	2.2 STAT
3. Calculate $\dfrac{S_y^2}{n}$, and add to stored value.	25 [÷] 60 [=] [SUM]	0.4166667 STAT
4. Compute $D = \bar{x} - \bar{y}$.	83 [−] 79 [=]	4 STAT
5. Divide by stored value, take square root, and compute Z.	[÷] [RCL] [√x̄] [=]	2.4727818 STAT

(Large-Sample Tests Based on Sample Means–Continued)

Thus, $Z = 2.473$. Since 2.473 is greater than 1.645, reject the null hypothesis in favor of the alternative hypothesis. There seems to be a significant difference between the levels of difficulty of the exams, as shown in Figure 7-4.

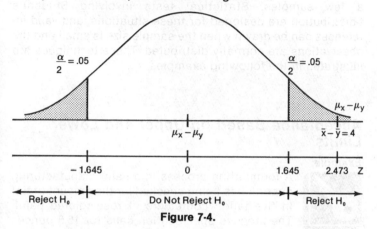

Figure 7-4.

This type of statistic is usually called a *two-tailed test* since the decision is to reject for values larger than 1.645 or smaller than -1.645. One-tailed tests are those which either reject for larger or smaller values of the test statistic, but not both. A more complete description of these types of tests can be found in statistical texts.

Small-Sample Tests Based on Sample Means

In many experimental situations, obtaining many samples may be time consuming or costly. The latter is true particularly in the case of destructive testing. In these cases the statistician may be forced to draw conclusions based on only a few samples. Statistical tests involving Student's t-distribution are designed for these situations, and valid inferences can be drawn when the sample size is small and the observations are normally distributed. These techniques are illustrated in the following examples.

Acceptance Based on Upper and Lower Limits

Example

A formulating process in a paint manufacturing operation is being checked for the amount of tint in five-gallon containers of rose-colored paint. The process specification calls for 15.5 ounces of red tint in each can. To perform the check, eight cans are randomly selected. Through analysis, the tint content of the cans is found to be:

15.2 oz	15.8 oz
15.0 oz	16.1 oz
15.7 oz	15.6 oz
15.9 oz	15.9 oz

The analysis is expensive, so a small sample quantity is all that can be analyzed. The manufacturer is concerned that neither too little nor too much red tint be added to the paint. The following describes how you can determine if the manufacturing process should be adjusted.

Let μ denote the actual amount of tint added to the cans. Null and alternative hypotheses expressing the manufacturer's concerns are:

H_0: $\mu = 15.5$ oz
H_1: $\mu \neq 15.5$ oz

(Small-Sample Tests Based on Sample Means–Continued)

Since the sample size is small, you cannot appeal to the Central Limit Theorem. Instead, since $\bar{x}$ is a good estimator of μ, use the random variable

$$T = \frac{\bar{x} - \mu}{\frac{S_x}{\sqrt{n}}}$$

which has Student's t-distribution based on $n-1$ degrees of freedom. See Chapter 6 for a description of the Student's t-distribution, where S_x represents the sample standard deviation obtained from the data.

When the null hypothesis is true, $\mu = 15.5$ oz and T can be used as a test statistic. As in the previous examples, for a chosen significance level, α, $0 < \alpha < 1$, the *quantiles* of Student's t-distribution are needed to make probability statements concerning the test statistic T. Since these quantiles depend on α as well as on the degrees of freedom $n-1$ (sample size minus one), denote them by $t_{(\alpha, n-1)}$.

Thus, you can write the probability statement

$$P[t_{(\alpha/2, n-1)} \leqslant T \leqslant t_{(1-\alpha/2, n-1)}] = 1 - \alpha$$

for a specified significance level α and sample size n. When H_0 is true, $\alpha = .10$, $n = 8$, and

$$T = \frac{\bar{x} - 15.5}{\frac{S_x}{\sqrt{8}}}$$

and

$$P[t_{(.05, 7)} \leqslant T \leqslant t_{(.95, 7)}] = 1 - .10 = .90$$

The value $t_{(.95,7)}$ can be read from Table B-3 in Appendix B. Corresponding to the degree of certainty $.90 = (1 - .10)$, you read for 7 degrees of freedom $t_{(.95, 7)} = 1.895$. Note that $t_{(\alpha, n-1)} = -t_{(1-\alpha, n-1)}$ so that $t_{(.05, 7)} = -1.895$.

Statistical Hypothesis Testing

(Small-Sample Tests Based on Sample Means–Continued)

Therefore, you reject the null hypothesis, after calculating $\bar{x}$ and S_x from the given data, if and only if

$\quad$ T $\leqslant$ -1.895

or

$\quad$ T $\geqslant$ 1.895

Calculator Solution

If the "DEC 2" indicator appears in the display, press ⌈2nd⌉ ⌈Decimal⌉ before keying in the example.

Procedure	Press	Display
1. Clear calculator and statistical registers.	⌈ON/c⌉ ⌈2nd⌉ STAT	0 STAT
2. Enter data using ⌈Σ+⌉.	15.2 ⌈Σ+⌉	1 STAT
	15 ⌈Σ+⌉	2 STAT
	15.7 ⌈Σ+⌉	3 STAT
	15.9 ⌈Σ+⌉	4 STAT
	15.8 ⌈Σ+⌉	5 STAT
	16.1 ⌈Σ+⌉	6 STAT
	15.6 ⌈Σ+⌉	7 STAT
	15.9 ⌈Σ+⌉	8 STAT
3. Compute $\bar{x}$ minus the hypothesized value $\mu = 15.5$ and store.	⌈$\bar{x}$⌉ ⌈−⌉ 15.5	
	⌈=⌉ ⌈STO⌉	0.15 STAT
4. Compute $S_x/\sqrt{8}$.	⌈σn-1⌉ ⌈÷⌉ 8	
	⌈√x⌉ ⌈=⌉	0.1322876 STAT
5. Compute T.	⌈1/x⌉ ⌈X⌉ ⌈RCL⌉ ⌈=⌉	1.1338934 STAT

(Small-Sample Tests Based on Sample Means–Continued)

Therefore, the computed T statistic is $T = 1.1338934$, as shown in Figure 7-5. Since $-1.895 \leqslant T = 1.1338934 \leqslant 1.895$, do not reject the null hypothesis. Based on the statistical evidence, the manufacturer can be reassured that the tinting process is working well. No adjustment is necessary.

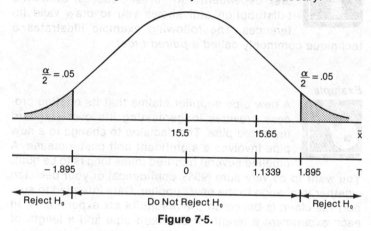

Figure 7-5.

(Small-Sample Tests Based on Sample Means–Continued)

Acceptance Based on Paired t-Test

Concepts

You may desire to compare the means of two populations, but find the observations collected are *dependent*. In these cases, Student's t-distribution still allows you to draw valid inferences. The following example illustrates a technique commonly called a *paired t-test*.

Example

A new pipe supplier claims that its coating process provides longer-lasting life over standard uncoated pipe. The decision to change to a new pipe involves a significant unit cost increase. A pipeline several hundred miles long is to be built. You want to be very sure (95% confidence) of your decision whether to change to the new supplier. Data intended to support the claim is based on the results of six experiments. In each experiment a length of standard pipe and a length of coated pipe were buried side by side in six different locations. The weight loss due to corrosion was measured in ounces per foot per year. The results of the experiments are tabulated below.

Yearly weight loss in ounces/foot/year

Uncoated Steel Pipe	Coated Steel Pipe
3.68	2.68
1.28	0.45
1.84	0.92
3.68	1.69
1.83	0.05
6.00	0.16

It is known that the coated pipe sustains corrosion better than uncoated pipe. The question is whether or not the additional cost justifies the change. By considering differences within the pairs, any differences in soils, climates, or other variables between the pairs are removed.

(Small-Sample Tests Based on Sample Means–Continued)

Is the true difference in weight loss significant to justify a change?

Let μ_D represent the true, average difference in weight loss between the uncoated and coated pipe. Since it is assumed that the coated pipe performs at least as well as the uncoated pipe, appropriate null and alternative hypotheses are:

$H_0: \mu_D = 0$
$H_1: \mu_D > 0$

The null hypothesis specifies that the true difference is negligible, whereas the alternative hypothesis specifies that the true difference is significant.

Let x_i denote the observations on the uncoated pipe and let y_i denote the data values for the coated pipe.

The differences $x_i - y_i$ are from a small sample. Assuming that these differences are normally distributed about the mean μ_D, the random variable

$$T = \frac{\bar{c} - \mu_D}{\dfrac{S_c}{\sqrt{n}}}$$

has Student's t-distribution with $n - 1$ degrees of freedom. Here the sample average weight change is

$$\bar{c} = \frac{1}{n} \sum_{i=1}^{n} c_i = \frac{1}{n} \sum_{i=1}^{n} (x_i - y_i)$$

and

$$S_c = \frac{1}{n-1} \sum_{i=1}^{n} (c_i - \bar{c})^2,$$

where $c_i = x_i - y_i$ represents the sample variance of the paired differences.

Select $\alpha = .05$ as the level of significance. For the given data compute $\bar{c}$ and S_c, and then the T statistic. Reject H_o if and only if $T \geqslant 2.015$ at significance level $\alpha = .05$.

(Small-Sample Tests Based on Sample Means–Continued)

Calculator Solution

First, compute $\bar{c}$ and S_c using the $\boxed{\Sigma+}$ key by entering the differences $x_i - y_i$ for each pair. If the "DEC 2" indicator appears in the display, press $\boxed{\text{2nd}}\boxed{\text{Decimal}}$ before keying in the example.

Procedure	Press	Display
1. Clear calculator and statistical registers.	$\boxed{\text{ON/c}}$ $\boxed{\text{2nd}}$ $\boxed{\text{STAT}}$	**0** _{STAT}
2. Enter paired differences using $\boxed{\Sigma+}$ key.	3.68 $\boxed{-}$ 2.68 $\boxed{=}$$\boxed{\Sigma+}$	**1** _{STAT}
	1.28 $\boxed{-}$ .45 $\boxed{=}$$\boxed{\Sigma+}$	**2** _{STAT}
	1.84 $\boxed{-}$ .92 $\boxed{=}$$\boxed{\Sigma+}$	**3** _{STAT}
	3.68 $\boxed{-}$ 1.69 $\boxed{=}$$\boxed{\Sigma+}$	**4** _{STAT}
	1.83 $\boxed{-}$ .05 $\boxed{=}$$\boxed{\Sigma+}$	**5** _{STAT}
	6 $\boxed{-}$ .16 $\boxed{=}$$\boxed{\Sigma+}$	**6** _{STAT}
3. Compute $S_c/\sqrt{n}$ and store.	$\boxed{\sigma\text{n-1}}$$\boxed{\div}$ 6 $\boxed{\sqrt{x}}$$\boxed{=}$$\boxed{\text{STO}}$	**0.7811914** _{STAT}
4. Compute T.	$\boxed{\bar{x}}$$\boxed{\div}$$\boxed{\text{RCL}}$$\boxed{=}$	**2.6369978** _{STAT}

The computed T statistic is T = 2.637. Since that is greater than or equal to 2.015, reject H_0 in favor of the alternative H_1, and declare that a significant difference in weight loss per foot per year exists between the uncoated and coated pipe. This decision rule results in correct decisions 95% of the time when H_0 is really true, which leads you to believe that you have made the correct decision in this case.

(Small-Sample Tests Based on Sample Means–Continued)

It seems that the additional cost incurred in a change might be feasible. However, other considerations, such as how much more the new pipe costs, how long the pipe needs to last, and the specific soil in which the pipe is laid, affect the decision. Since you believe that the new pipe is better, you can now consider purchasing the new pipe.

Acceptance Based on Unpaired Sample

Concepts

In the next example you apply these concepts to the two different normally distributed populations and compare population means when both populations possess the same variance. These methods and techniques apply to a large variety of practical problems.

Example

A tire manufacturer claims a new line of radials gets more wear than the old line. Since these new radials cost much more than the old line, you want to test this claim. It is reasonable to assume that the populations have equal variances due to the manufacturing process. The following data is given.

Tire Wear (miles)

Sample X Old Line (m = 5)	Sample Y New Line (n = 4)
28,000	33,000
30,700	34,200
31,200	29,700
33,100	32,500
29,700	

Statistical Hypothesis Testing

(Small-Sample Tests Based on Sample Means–Continued)

Test the hypothesis that μ_2, the average wear for the new line, is no better than μ_1, the average wear for the old line of radials. Let σ^2 denote the common unknown variance of the two populations.

The hypotheses are

$$H_0: \mu_1 \geq \mu_2, \text{ or } (0 \leq \mu_1 - \mu_2)$$
$$H_1: \mu_1 < \mu_2, \text{ or } (0 > \mu_1 - \mu_2)$$

To perform this test, use the statistic

$$T = \frac{\bar{x} - \bar{y}}{S_p\sqrt{\frac{1}{m} + \frac{1}{n}}}$$

which has Student's t-distribution with $m + n - 2$ degrees of freedom where

$$S_p^2 = \frac{(m - 1)S_x^2 + (n - 1)S_y^2}{(m + n - 2)}$$

is the pooled estimator of the unknown population variance.

Choose significance level α and reject the null hypothesis H_0 if and only if

$$T < t_{(\alpha, m + n - 2)}$$

Note that $t_{(.05, 7)} = -1.895$.

(Small-Sample Tests Based on Sample Means–Continued)

Calculator Solution

If the "DEC 2" indicator appears in the display, press `2nd` `Decimal` before keying in the example.

Procedure	Press	Display
1. Clear calculator and statistical registers.	`ON/C` `2nd` `STAT`	0
2. Enter X data.	28000 `Σ+`	1
	30700 `Σ+`	2
	31200 `Σ+`	3
	33100 `Σ+`	4
	29700 `Σ+`	5
3. Compute $\bar{x}$.	`x̄`	30540
4. Compute S_x^2.	`σn-1` `2nd` `x²`	3543000
5. Clear statistical registers.	`2nd` `STAT`	3543000
6. Enter Y data.	33000 `Σ+`	1
	34200 `Σ+`	2
	29700 `Σ+`	3
	32500 `Σ+`	4
7. Compute $\bar{y}$.	`x̄`	32350
8. Compute S_y^2.	`σn-1` `2nd` `x²`	3630000
9. Compute $$S_p^2 = \frac{4S_x^2 + 3S_y^2}{7}$$ and store.	4 `×` 3543000 `=` `STO`	14172000
	3 `×` 3630000 `+` `RCL` `=`	25062000
	`÷` 7 `=` `STO`	3580285.7
10. Compute T.	5 `1/x` `+` 4 `1/x` `×` `RCL`	3580285.7
	`=` `1/x` `√x` `STO`	
	30540	30540
	`−` 32350	
	`=` `×` `RCL` `=`	−1.4259801

Statistical Hypothesis Testing

(Small-Sample Tests Based on Sample Means–Continued)

Since T = − 1.4259801, which is greater than − 1.895, accept the null hypothesis and declare that the mean tire wear for the new line is no better than the mean tire wear for the old line. Thus, the additional cost cannot be justified by the consumer.

Tests Involving Proportions

In some testing situations items can be classified as either *defective* or *nondefective*, and your concern may be in the true, but unknown, proportion of defectives items in a given lot. Although destructive testing also exists in some of these situations, a sizeable sample can often be tested without destroying the product. When a large sample size is involved, you can use the result of the Central Limit Theorem to construct tests of hypotheses concerning proportions. The following example illustrates the construction of such a test.

Example

A flashlight manufacturer has just received a first shipment of flashlight bulbs from a new supplier and wants to be sure that the shipment is good before accepting it. Testing the bulbs is quite simple in this case (they either light or do not light), so a sizeable sample of size 250 can easily be tested. The new bulb supplier insists that the shipment (population) contains no more than 12% defective bulbs. At significance level $\alpha = .10$, should the shipment be accepted or rejected?

Let p represent the true, but unknown, proportion of defective bulbs in the shipment. The bulb manufacturer's claim and an appropriate alternative are

H_0: $p \leqslant .12$ vs. H_1: $p > .12$

The sample proportion of defective bulbs, $\hat{p}$, is a good estimate of the population proportion, p, of defective bulbs. Again, it can be shown by the Central Limit Theorem, that

$$P\left[Z_{1-\alpha} \leqslant \frac{\hat{p} - p}{\sqrt{\dfrac{p(1-p)}{n}}} \right] \approx \alpha$$

Suppose the line foreman reports that 43 of 250 bulbs failed. Then $\hat{p}$ = sample proportion of defectives $= \dfrac{43}{250} = .172 = 17.2\%$

Statistical Hypothesis Testing

(Tests Involving Proportions–Continued)

If the null hypothesis is true, an appropriate rejection rule is to reject H_0 in favor of H_1 at significance level $\alpha = .10$ if and only if

$$T = \frac{\hat{p} - .12}{\sqrt{\dfrac{.12(1 - .12)}{250}}} \geq Z_{(.90)} = 1.282$$

$Z_{(.90)} = 1.282$ from Table 7.1.

Calculator Solution

Compute T and compare it with 1.282. If the "DEC 2" indicator appears in the display, press [2nd] [Decimal] before keying in the example.

Procedure	Press	Display
1. Clear calculator.	[ON/C]	0 ˢᵀᵃᵀ
2. Compute T.	1 [−] .12 [×] .12	0.12 ˢᵀᵃᵀ
	[÷] 250 [=] [√x̄] [STO]	0.0205524 ˢᵀᵃᵀ
	43 [÷] 250 [−] .12	0.12 ˢᵀᵃᵀ
	[÷] [RCL] [=]	2.5301216 ˢᵀᵃᵀ

Since $T = 2.5301216$ is greater than 1.282, the statistical evidence indicates that the bulb manufacturer is not meeting the claim. It seems that the true proportion of defective bulbs in the shipment is significantly ($\alpha = .10$) higher than the stated proportion. Therefore, reject the null hypothesis and return the shipment to the supplier.

section III
FINANCE

Time Value of Money

Contents

Introduction

Money not only has a current purchasing value; it also has a time value. Even if you don't consider risk and inflation, a dollar today is worth more than the same dollar a year from now since the dollar can be invested during the year. When the dollar is invested, it earns interest. Interest is the amount of money paid to someone for loaning funds to another individual or business.

This chapter discusses a number of topics dealing with the time value of money. The first topic is simple interest (interest earned only on the principal). The second topic is compounding interest (interest earned on principal and interest). Ordinary annuities, the next topic, involve equal amounts paid at the end of each payment period. The final topic is variable cash flows in which payments are unequal.

Simple Interest

Concepts

Simple interest is the money earned on the principal amount borrowed or invested. It occurs in many financial investments such as 90-day bank notes and certificates of deposit. The terms described below are used when discussing simple interest.

Principal—the original amount of money loaned or borrowed denoted by P.

Term—the length of the loan or the number of time periods for which interest is calculated. Term is usually represented by N.

Rate of interest—the percentage of the principal paid per time period for the use of the money. Rate of interest is usually represented by i.

The following equations are used to solve problems involving simple interest.

$$\text{Total Interest (I)} = \text{i}/100 \times \text{Principal (P)} \times \text{N}$$
Equation (8-1)

$$\text{Total Amount} = \text{Principal (P)} + \text{Total Interest (I)}$$
Equation (8-2)

Example

Example 1—Company A borrows $10,000 at 18% simple annual interest for three years. Assuming interest is paid annually, what is the yearly interest payment and the total interest plus principal paid over the three-year period?

The three inputs required to find the total interest plus principal are given: periodic interest rate = 18%, principal = $10,000, and number of time periods = 3 years. These inputs and the arithmetic functions of your calculator are used to solve the problem.

(Simple Interest–Continued)

Calculator Solution

If the "DEC 2" indicator does not appear in the display, press (2nd) (Decimal) before keying in the example.

Procedure	Press	Display
1. Clear calculator.	(ON/C)	0
2. Enter annual interest rate and convert to decimal.	18 (%)	0.18
3. Multiply by principal to determine annual interest.	(×) 10000 (=)	1800.00
4. Multiply by number of years to determine total interest.	(×) 3 (=)	5400.00
5. Add principal to determine total amount repaid.	(+) 10000 (=)	15400.00

The annual simple interest paid is $1800 with total interest of $5400 paid over the three-year period.

Simple interest is not always computed on an annual basis. The periodic interest rate, for example, can be in terms of months, weeks, or days. The next example illustrates the procedure for computing simple interest on a daily basis.

Example 2—The ABC Company invests $20,000 in a savings certificate that pays 14% annual simple interest rate computed on a 360-day year. What amount does the company withdraw when the certificate matures after 90 days?

In this example, the periodic interest is stated annually and must be converted to a daily rate ($14 \div 360$) before the problem can be solved. The other required inputs are given: principal = $20,000 and number of time periods = 90 days. These inputs and the arithmetic functions of your calculator are then used to solve the problem.

Time Value of Money

(Simple Interest–Continued)

Calculator Solution

If the "DEC 2" indicator does not appear in the display, press ⟦2nd⟧⟦Decimal⟧ before keying in the example.

Procedure	Press	Display
1. Clear calculator.	⟦ON/C⟧	0
2. Divide annual percent interest rate by number of days per year to determine periodic interest rate as a percentage.	14 ⟦÷⟧ 360 ⟦=⟧	0.04
3. Convert to decimal value.	⟦%⟧	0.0003889*
4. Multiply by principal to determine daily interest.	⟦X⟧ 20000 ⟦=⟧	7.78
5. Multiply by number of days to determine total interest.	⟦X⟧ 90 ⟦=⟧	700.00
6. Add principal to determine the total amount.	⟦+⟧ 20000 ⟦=⟧	20700.00

The certificate pays $7.78 interest per day for a total of $700 after 90 days.

*If you have fixed the decimal to two places and the calculated value is less than 0.005, the decimal fix is ignored and the entire value is displayed.

Compound Interest

Although some financial transactions require simple interest, many more use compound interest. Compound interest means that interest is earned on the original principal plus any interest previously earned that is not withdrawn. Interest earned in the previous compounding period becomes part of the principal for the next compounding period. Assume, for example, that $100 is invested for three years earning interest of 10% compounded annually. The investment increases 10% in value each year as shown below.

Year one:

Principal for year one		= $100.00
Interest earned in year one	$100 × 10/100 =	$ 10.00
Balance at end of year one		= $110.00

Year two:

Principal for year two (Balance at end of year one)		= $110.00
Interest earned in year two	$110 × 10/100 =	$ 11.00
Balance at end of year two		= $121.00

Year three:

Principal for year three (Balance at end of year two)		= $121.00
Interest earned in year three	$121 × 10/100 =	$ 12.10
Balance at end of year three		= $133.10

This investment is worth $133.10 after three years. The increase in value is composed of $30 interest earned on the original principal (which is the same as using simple interest) and $3.10 interest earned on interest, as shown below.

	Analysis of Interest Earned		
Year	**Interest earned on Original Principal**	**Interest earned on Interest**	**Total**
1	$10	$0	$10
2	$10	$1	$11
3	$10	$2.10	$12.10
Total	$30	$3.10	$33.10

Time Value of Money

(Compound Interest–Continued)

As shown, interest is computed at the end of each year based on the principal plus any earned interest. If the interest is withdrawn, the example becomes a simple interest problem.

The terms described below are used when discussing problems involving compound interest.

Compounding interest—the process of calculating interest on an initial amount until it increases to a future value. Compounding implies that the amount is moving *forward in time*.

Discounting interest—the process of removing interest from a future value until it equals a present value. Discounting implies moving a value *back in time*. Discounting is the reverse of compounding.

Future value (FV)—the value at the end of the last compounding period of an initial amount (PV) compounded forward at a specified interest rate.

Present value (PV)—the value at the beginning of the first compounding period of a future amount (FV) discounted at a specified interest rate.

Number of compounding periods (N)—the number of time periods for which interest is calculated.

Interest rate (%i)—the percentage of the beginning period amount calculated as interest per time period. The interest rate (%i) that compounds a present value forward to a future value is also the interest rate that discounts that future value back to the present value.

(Compound Interest–Continued)

Using Time-Line Diagrams

    A time-line diagram is a valuable tool for analyzing and understanding financial problems including compound interest problems. Most time-value-of-money problems are easy to diagram with the solution procedure and inputs inferred from the diagram. Consider the following diagram for $100 invested at a 10% annual interest rate for three years.

```
PV = $100                                    FV = $133.10
   ↓                                              ↑
   |_____|_____|_____|
   0          1          2         N = 3
                  %i = 10
```

Time-Line Diagram 8-1

    The horizontal line represents the time scale. Small vertical lines divide the horizontal line into compounding periods. The 0 represents the beginning of the first compounding period. The 1 represents the end of the first compounding period and the beginning of the second compounding period. The total number of compounding periods is indicated by the $N = 3$ below the final vertical line. The compounding periods may be yearly, semiannually, quarterly, monthly, or daily.

    The time-line diagram also represents the amounts paid or received (cash outflows or cash inflows) at various points in time. Cash flows invested have arrows pointing down as shown above the zero period where $100 is invested. Cash flows received are shown with upward-pointing arrows as shown above the end of the third period where $133.10 is received. Present value is indicated by the abbreviation PV and future value by FV. The interest rate per compounding period (%i) is shown below the diagram. In later sections, you learn how to use time-line diagrams to show unknown values and inputs for your calculator.

(Compound Interest–Continued)

Future Value Computations

Concepts

The future value (FV) of an amount borrowed or invested is the initial amount (PV) compounded forward at an appropriate interest rate (%i) for a given number of compounding periods (N). To find the future value of any amount, you must know: PV, the initial amount borrowed or invested; N, the number of compounding periods; and %i, the interest rate per compounding period.

A time-line diagram for the future value of an amount can be drawn as follows.

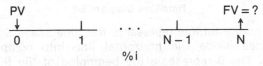

Time-Line Diagram 8-2

The unknown value FV is indicated here by the question mark (?).

A formula for computing the future value of an amount can be written as follows.

$$FV = PV(1 + \%i/100)^N \qquad \textit{Equation (8-3)}$$

Before calculators were easily available to compute the above equation, the process of computation for large values of N was rather tedious. Tables were prepared for the $(1 + \%i/100)^N$ factor which is the *Compound Sum of $1*. This factor is usually referred to as the *Compound Value Interest Factor (CVIF$_{\%i,N}$)**. These tables list the CVIF value for known %i and N values. The table containing the CVIF values is in Appendix A.

The future value formula could alternately be written as:

$$FV = PV(CVIF_{\%i,N}) \qquad \textit{Equation (8-4)}$$

*This factor may also be referred to as (F/P, i, n) or FVIF$_{k,n}$.

(Compound Interest–Continued)

Example

The REW company invests $10,000 in a project that earns 10% compounded annually. Assuming the company allows the interest to compound, what is the investment value at the end of five years?

The first step is to draw the following time-line diagram.

PV = $10,000   FV = ?

```
   ↓      |        |        |        |       ↑
   0      1        2        3        4     N = 5
                   % i = 10
```

Time-Line Diagram 8-3

As shown in the diagram, the three inputs required to solve for future value are given: PV = 10000, %i = 10, and N = 5. The unknown FV value being computed is shown by the question mark (?).

Table Solution

Compound Value Interest Factor (CVIF) tables are included in Appendix A to aid in calculating the future value of an amount. This table solves the value $(1 + \%i/100)^N$ where the %i and N values are specified. To locate the CVIF value for this problem, read down the 10% column to the fifth row and find 1.6105. This is the $(CVIF_{10\%,5})$ value. Using equation (8-4), multiply the present value by 1.6105 to determine the future value.

FV = 10000 × 1.6105
FV = 16105.00

The future value as determined with the table value is $16,105.

Time Value of Money

(Compound Interest–Continued)

Calculator Solution

Equation (8-3) is programmed into your calculator to solve for FV as shown in the following example. If the "DEC 2" indicator does not appear in the display, press ⟨2nd⟩ ⟨Decimal⟩ before keying in the example.

Procedure	Press	Display
1. Clear calculator and select finance mode.	⟨ON/C⟩ ⟨2nd⟩ **FIN**	0
2. Enter number of compounding periods.	5 ⟨N⟩	5.00
3. Enter percent interest rate per compounding period.	10 ⟨%i⟩	10.00
4. Enter present value.	10000 ⟨PV⟩	10000.00
5. Compute future value.	⟨CPT⟩⟨FV⟩	16105.10

The answer when using your calculator is $16,105.10.

You identify the problem input values from the time-line diagram or equation (8-3), and then enter them in the calculator. By pressing ⟨CPT⟩⟨FV⟩, the calculator automatically solves the equation for you. The answers obtained using tables and the calculator differ slightly because the calculator uses 11 digits for internal calculations. In this book, the tables have four decimal places. This is the reason for the $0.10 difference in the table answer of $16,105 and the accurate calculator solution of $16,105.10.

Your calculator is designed to solve general financial problems including annuities (discussed later in this chapter). Ensure that the calculator is ready for a compound interest problem by always pressing ⟨2nd⟩**FIN** or 0 ⟨PMT⟩ at the start of the problem to clear the payment register. If the "ANN" (annuity) indicator is on, the calculator has not been cleared and your results may be incorrect.

(Compound Interest–Continued)

Review

Equation (8-3) is solved when you enter the following input values. Be sure to press ⟨2nd⟩⟨FIN⟩, 0 ⟨PMT⟩, or ⟨ON/C⟩⟨PMT⟩ at the start of the problem so that PMT = 0. If you don't, incorrect answers may result. A zero payment is indicated by the absence of the "ANN" (annuity) indicator in the display.

Equation Value	Meaning	Keystroke
Inputs:		
N	Total number of compounding periods.	⟨N⟩
%i	The percent interest rate per compounding period.	⟨%i⟩
PV	Original investment (at time 0).	⟨PV⟩
Solution:	Solve for future value.	⟨CPT⟩⟨FV⟩

Present Value Computations

Concepts

The present value of an amount is the time zero value of a future cash flow (FV) discounted N periods at a %i interest rate per period. To find the present value of any amount, you must know: FV, the future value of the amount; N, the total number of compounding periods; and %i, the interest rate per compounding period.

(Compound Interest–Continued)

A time-line diagram for present value can be drawn as follows.

PV = ?   FV

0   1   . . .   N − 1   N

%i

Time-Line Diagram 8-4

The general formula for computing the present value is:

$$PV = \frac{FV}{(1 + \%i/100)^N}$$

or

$$PV = FV\,(1 + \%i/100)^{-N} \qquad \text{Equation (8-5)}$$

This equation is derived from formula (8-3) and demonstrates the inverse relationship between PV and FV.

Tables are included in Appendix A for the $(1 + \%i/100)^{-N}$ factor which is the *Present Value of $1*. This factor is usually referred to as the *Present Value Interest Factor* $(PVIF_{\%i,N})$*. These tables give the PVIF for known %i and N values. Note that the PVIF is the reciprocal of the CVIF.

*This factor is sometimes referred to as (P/F, i, n).

The present value formula may also be written as:

$$PV = FV\,(PVIF_{\%i,N}) \qquad \text{Equation (8-6)}$$

Example

The XYZ Company is evaluating an investment that will return $35,000 at the end of two years. Assuming the company wants to earn an annual interest rate of 24% compounded monthly, how much should they pay for this investment?

PV = ?   FV = $35,000

0   1   . . .   23   N = 24

%i = 24/12 = 2

Time-Line Diagram 8-5

(Compound Interest–Continued)

Since interest is compounded monthly, the number of years is multiplied by the number of compounding periods per year to determine the total number of compounding periods (2 yrs × 12 = 24). The interest rate is 2% per month (24%/12 = 2%). The future value is $35,000. The unknown PV value is shown by the question mark (?).

Table Solution

Using the Present Value Interest Factor (PVIF) table in Appendix A, the value at the intersection of the 2% column and the 24th period is:

$(PVIF_{2\%,24}) = 0.6217$

Using equation (8-6), multiply the future value by 0.6217 to determine the present value.

PV = 35000 × 0.6217
PV = 21759.50

Using the table value, the present value is $21,759.50.

Calculator Solution

Equation (8-5) is programmed into your calculator to solve for PV as shown in the following example. If the "DEC 2" indicator does not appear in the display, press [2nd] [Decimal] before keying in the example.

Procedure	Press	Display
1. Clear calculator and select finance mode.	[ON/c] [2nd] [FIN]	0
2. Enter total number of compounding periods.	12 [×] 2 [=] [N]	24.00
3. Enter interest rate per compounding period.	24 [÷] 12 [=] [%i]	2.00
4. Enter future value.	35000 [FV]	35000.00
5. Compute present value.	[CPT] [PV]	21760.25

(Compound Interest–Continued)

To earn 24% annual interest compounded monthly, the company should pay no more than $21,760.25 for the investment. The present value of $21,760.25 after two years is the equivalent time zero value of $35,000 discounted at 2% per month.

Review

Since equation (8-5) is programmed into your calculator, you enter only the input values to compute the answer. Be sure to press (2nd) (FIN), 0 (PMT), or (ON/c)(PMT) at the start of the problem so that PMT = 0. If you do not, incorrect answers may result. A zero payment is indicated by the absence of the "ANN" (annuity) indicator in the display.

Equation Value	Meaning	Keystroke
Inputs:		
N	Total number of compounding periods.	(N)
%i	Interest rate per compounding period as a percent.	(%i)
FV	Cash flow at end of the Nth compounding period.	(FV)
Solution:	Solve for present value.	(CPT)(PV)

(Compound Interest–Continued)

Interest Rate Computations

Concepts

 You can compute the interest rate that makes the present value compound forward to equal a specified future value. Or you can compute the rate that makes a future value discount back to equal a specified present value. To compute the interest rate, you must know: N, the total number of compounding periods; PV, the initial cash flow; and FV, the cash flow at the end of N compounding periods.

A general time-line diagram can be drawn as follows.

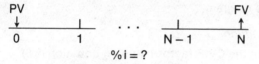

$$\%i = ?$$

Time-Line Diagram 8-6

The general equation for computing %i is:

$$\%i = [(FV/PV)^{1/N} - 1]100 \qquad \textit{Equation (8-7)}$$

The tables in the appendix also may be used in the following manner to solve for %i.

1. Compute the CVIF factor.

$$(CVIF_{\%i = ?,N}) = FV/PV \qquad \textit{Equation (8-8)}$$

2. Read across the N row to find the proper CVIF. If the CVIF value falls between two interest rate values in the table, you may approximate the %i value by interpolating the following equation.

$$\%i = \frac{(CVIF - CVIF_L)\,(Hi\% - Li\%)}{(CVIF_H - CVIF_L)} + Li\%$$

Equation (8-9)

where:

Li% = %i value for the table value $CVIF_L$ which is lower than the desired CVIF value

Hi% = %i value for the table value $CVIF_H$ which is higher than the desired CVIF value

(Compound Interest–Continued)

Example

A company invested $10,000 in a project that returned $18,596 at the end of 10 years. What is the annual interest rate earned on the project?

PV = $10,000   FV = $18,596

```
  |          |     . . .     |          |
  0          1               9        N = 10
                  % i = ?
```

Time-Line Diagram 8-7

The unknown value is the interest rate as indicated on the time-line diagram.

Table Solution

1. Obtain the CVIF factor by using equation (8-8).

   CVIF = 18596/10000 = 1.8596

2. Find the bracket between 6% and 8% on the N = 10 row of the CVIF table in Appendix A and solve equation (8-9).

   Li% = 6%
   $CVIF_L = 1.7908$
   Hi% = 8%
   $CVIF_H = 2.1589$

3. Do the linear interpolation as follows.

   $$i\% = \frac{(1.8596 - 1.7908)\,(8 - 6)}{(2.1589 - 1.7908)} + 6$$

   i% = 6.3738

The approximate interest rate is 6.37%.

(Compound Interest–Continued)

Calculator Solution

Equation (8-7) is programmed into your calculator to solve for %i as shown in the following example. If the "DEC 2" indicator does not appear in the display, press [2nd] [Decimal] before keying in the example.

Procedure	Press	Display
1. Clear calculator and select finance mode.	[ON/C] [2nd] **FIN**	0
2. Enter total number of compounding periods.	10 [N]	10.00
3. Enter present value.	10000 [PV]	10000.00
4. Enter future value.	18596 [FV]	18596.00
5. Compute interest rate.	[CPT] [%i]	6.40

The interest rate is 6.40% per year. It is both the compound interest rate and the discount rate. It compounds the present value forward to equal the future value, and it discounts the future value back to equal the present value. The calculator answer is more accurate than the table answer because the calculator does not assume interest changes are linear.

Time Value of Money

(Compound Interest–Continued)

Review

Since equation (8-7) is programmed into the calculator, you enter only the input values to compute the answer. Be sure to press `2nd` `FIN`, 0 `PMT`, or `ON/c` `PMT` at the start of each problem so that PMT = 0. If you don't, incorrect answers may result. A zero payment is indicated by the absence of the "ANN" (annuity) indicator in the display.

Equation Value	Meaning	Keystroke
Inputs:		
N	Total number of compounding periods.	`N`
PV	Cash flow at the beginning of the first compounding period.	`PV`
FV	Cash flow at the end of the Nth compounding period.	`FV`
Solution:	Solve for interest rate.	`CPT` `%i`

(Compound Interest–Continued)

Number of Compounding Periods Computations

Concepts

You can calculate the total number of compounding periods required to make the present value compound forward to equal a specific future value. You also can calculate the total number of compounding periods required to make the future value discount back to equal a specific present value. The inputs required to calculate the total number of compounding periods are: PV, the beginning cash flow; FV, the ending cash flow; and %i, the interest rate per compounding period.

A general time-line diagram may be drawn as follows.

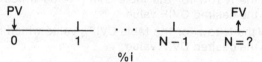

Time-Line Diagram 8-8

The following equation is designed to determine the number of compounding periods.

$$N = \frac{\ln(FV/PV)}{\ln(1 + \%i/100)}$$ *Equation (8-10)*

where ln stands for the natural logarithm (logarithm to the base e, where e is a constant with the value 2.7182818).

(Compound Interest–Continued)

The tables in the appendix may also be used in the following manner to solve for N.

1. Compute the CVIF factor.

$$(CVIF_{\%i,N=?}) = FV/PV \qquad \textit{Equation (8-11)}$$

2. Read down the %i column to find the proper CVIF value. If the CVIF value falls between two compounding periods in the table, you may interpolate for a more accurate N value by using the following equation.

$$N = \frac{(CVIF - CVIF_L)\,(NH - NL)}{(CVIF_H - CVIF_L)} + NL$$

Equation (8-12)

where:

NL = the N row for the table $CVIF_L$ value which is lower than the desired CVIF value

NH = the N row for the table $CVIF_H$ value which is higher than the desired CVIF value

Example

The ABC company invests $10,000 in a project that has an annual earnings rate of 12%. How many compounding periods are required before the initial investment doubles?

PV = $10,000   FV = $20,000

| 0 | 1 | ... | N – 1 | N = ? |

%i = 12

Time-Line Diagram 8-9

Table Solution

1. Calculate the CVIF factor using equation (8-11).

   CVIF = 20000/10000 = 2

(Compound Interest–Continued)

2. Find a bracket between rows 6 and 7 in the 12% column of the CVIF table in Appendix A and solve equation (8-12).

$NL = 6$

$CVIF_L = 1.9738$

$NH = 7$

$CVIF_H = 2.2107$

$$N = \frac{(2 - 1.9738)\ (7 - 6)}{(2.2107 - 1.9738)} + 6$$

$N = 6.1106$

Using linear interpolation, the length of time required is 6.1106 years.

Calculator Solution

Equation (8-10) is programmed into your calculator to solve for N as shown in the following example. If the "DEC 2" indicator does not appear in the display, press [2nd] [Decimal] before keying in the example.

Procedure	Press	Display
1. Clear calculator and select finance mode.	[ON/c] [2nd] [FIN]	0 DEC 2 FIN
2. Enter present value.	10000 [PV]	10000.00 DEC 2 FIN
3. Enter future value.	20000 [FV]	20000.00 DEC 2 FIN
4. Enter percent interest rate per compounding period.	12 [%i]	12.00 DEC 2 FIN
5. Compute number of compounding periods.	[CPT] [N]	6.12 DEC 2 FIN

The investment requires 6.12 years to double in value with interest compounded at 12% annually. The table solution varies slightly from the calculator solution because of the table interpolation error. The calculator solution is correct.

Time Value of Money

(Compound Interest–Continued)

Review

Since equation (8-10) is programmed into your calculator, you enter only the input values to compute the answer. Be sure to press 2nd FIN , 0 PMT , or ON/c PMT at the start of each problem so that PMT = 0. If you don't, incorrect answers may result. A zero payment is indicated by the absence of the "ANN" (annuity) indicator in the display.

Equation Value	Meaning	Keystroke
Inputs:		
PV	Cash flow at beginning of first compounding period.	PV
FV	Cash flow at end of last compounding period.	FV
%i	Percent interest rate per compounding period.	%i
Solution:	Solve for number of compounding periods.	CPT N

Ordinary Annuities

The previous discussions involve only cash flows that occur at time period zero (PV) and at a future time N (FV). No
cash flows occur between time period zero and future time N.
A number of financial transactions, such as loans, involve
payment or receipt of equal amounts of money in addition to
the PV and FV cash flows for a specified number of time
periods. These transactions involve annuities.

An *annuity* is a series of consecutive equal cash flows occurring for N equal time periods with interest calculated at
the end of each cash flow period. The cash flows are usually
called *payments*, even though they might actually represent
an outflow (payment) or an inflow (receipt). The key concepts
to remember in annuities are that all payments must be equal
(excluding PV and FV), they must occur every time period (no
missing payments), and all payments must be of the same
nature (either receipts or payments).

When the payments occur at the end of each period, the
annuity is called an "Ordinary Annuity" or an "Annuity in Ar-
rears." An annuity with payments occurring at the beginning
of each time period is called an "Annuity Due" or an "Advance Payment Annuity." Ordinary annuities are discussed in
this chapter, while annuities due are discussed in the next
chapter.

An annuity having payments compounded forward to accumulate a future sum is often called a "Future Value Annuity" or "Compound Sum of an Annuity." When the payments
are discounted back to a present value, the annuity is often
called a "Present Value Annuity." The terms used for both
types of annuities are described next.

Future value (FV)—the value at the *end* of the last payment
period of a series of equal payments *compounded* forward at
a %i interest rate.
Present value (PV)—the value at the *beginning* of the first
payment period of a series of equal payments *discounted*
back at a %i interest rate.

(Ordinary Annuities–Continued)

Interest rate (%i)—the interest rate per payment period that makes the series of equal payments compound forward to a specified future value, or makes the series of equal payments discount back to a specified present value.

Payments (PMT)—the equal amount paid or received each period for N periods. Payments for ordinary annuities occur at the end of each period and payments for annuities due occur at the beginning of each period.

Number of payments (N)—the total number of equal payments.

The annuities discussed in this chapter assume the number of compounding periods equals the number of payment periods per year. As a result, annual interest rates are divided by the number of payment periods per year to determine %i. So the %i annuity value is both the interest rate per payment period and the interest rate per compounding period.

Chapter 9 shows how to solve annuities when the number of payment periods and compounding periods differs. The procedure used converts the interest rate per compounding period to the equivalent interest rate per payment period and solves the annuities as discussed in this chapter. Because of this procedure, the %i term is defined in this book as the interest rate per payment period.

Future Value Ordinary Annuity

A future value ordinary annuity has a series of equal payments occurring at the end of each payment period. These payments are compounded forward to a future value at the end of the last payment period. An example of a time-line diagram is:

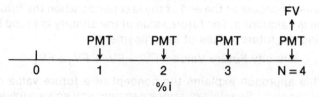

Time-Line Diagram 8-10

The first payment occurs at the *end* of the first payment period, and the final payment occurs at the end of the last payment period. An annuity can be solved as a series of compound interest problems, as shown in the time-line diagrams below.

Decomposed Annuity   **Equivalent Compound Interest**
Time-Line Diagram   **Time-Line Diagram**

PMT_1 $FV_1 = ?$ $PV_1 = PMT_1$ $FV_1 = ?$

| | | | | | | | | |
| 0 | 1 | 2 | 3 | 4 | | 0 | 1 | 2 | N = 3 |

PMT_2 $FV_2 = ?$ $PV_2 = PMT_2$ $FV_2 = ?$

| 0 | 1 | 2 | 3 | 4 | | 0 | 1 | N = 2 |

PMT_3 $FV_3 = ?$ $PV_3 = PMT_3$ $FV_3 = ?$

| 0 | 1 | 2 | 3 | 4 | | 0 | N = 1 |

$PMT_4 = FV_4$ $PMT_4 = FV_4$

| 0 | 1 | 2 | 3 | 4 | | N = 0 |

Time-Line Diagram 8-11

As you see above, the annuity is decomposed into four time-line diagrams. Each has one payment compounded forward to the end of the fourth period. Each decomposed annuity diagram is converted to its equivalent compound interest form by setting the payment equal to a present value. The N

(Future Value Ordinary Annuity–Continued)

value is determined by counting the number of compounding periods between the present value and future value. For example, there are three compounding periods between the first payment period (PMT1) and the last payment period, when FV1 is calculated. The final payment is not compounded because it occurs at the end of the last period when the future value is calculated. The future value of the annuity is found by adding the future values of each payment.

$$\text{Annuity Future Value} = FV_1 + FV_2 + FV_3 + FV_4$$

This approach explains the concept of a future value ordinary annuity. Special equations can help you solve such annuities. These equations can be used because the payments are equal. The following examples show you how to use your calculator or tables to solve for each unknown value (FV, PMT, %i, and N).*

Future Value Computations

Concepts

The future value (FV) of an ordinary annuity is the value of a given number of equal payments (PMT). Each payment is made at the end of each payment period (N) and compounded forward to the end of the last payment period. To calculate the future value of an ordinary annuity, you must know: N, the total number of payments; %i, the interest rate per payment period; and PMT, the equal payment occurring at the *end* of each payment period.

*The future value annuity computations discussed in this section imply that PV = 0. This may not be true in the more general annuity cases discussed in Chapter 9.

(Future Value Ordinary Annuity–Continued)

The time-line diagram for the future value of an annuity may be drawn as follows.

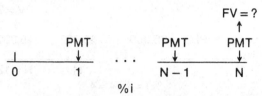

Time-Line Diagram 8-12

The unknown value FV is indicated by the question mark (?).

A general formula for finding the future value of an ordinary annuity is:

$$FV = PMT \left[\frac{(1 + \%i/100)^N - 1}{\%i/100} \right]$$

Equation (8-13)

Tables have been prepared for the sum of an annuity of $1 (the factor of equation (8-13) in brackets). This factor is usually called the Compound Value Interest Factor of an Annuity (CVIFA).* Tables giving the CVIFA for known %i and N values are included In Appendix A.

Using the CVIFA term, equation (8-13) can be rewritten as:

$$FV = PMT\ (CVIFA_{\%i,N})\qquad \textit{Equation (8-14)}$$

Example

The Big D company is depositing $5000 in a sinking fund at the end of each quarter for three years. (Some lenders require the borrowing company to establish a fund to retire a debt issue such as a bond. One method is to make regular deposits in an account called a sinking fund.) Assuming the fund pays 16% annual interest with quarterly compounding, what is the value at the end of three years?

*This factor may also be expressed as (F/A, i, n), $CVIF_a$, $s_{\overline{n}|i}$, $FVIFA_{k,n}$, or s(n,i).

(Future Value Ordinary Annuity–Continued)

The first step is to draw the time-line diagram for the problem.

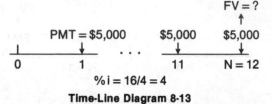

Time-Line Diagram 8-13

As shown in the diagram, the three inputs required to compute the future value are: PMT = 5000, %i = 4, and N = 12. To determine the interest rate per payment period, divide the annual interest rate, 16%, by the number of payment periods per year, 4. Total payments are found by multiplying the number of years, 3, by the number of payments per year, 4. The unknown value, FV, is indicated by the question mark (?).

Table Solution

Using the table for the Compound Value Interest Factor of an Annuity in Appendix A, the value at the intersection of the N = 12 row and 4% column is 15.0258. Use equation (8-14) and multiply the payment amount, $5000, and the CVIFA to obtain the future value.

$$FV = 5000 \times 15.0258$$
$$FV = 75129$$

Using the tables, the future value is $75,129.

(Future Value Ordinary Annuity–Continued)

Calculator Solution

Equation (8-13) is programmed into your calculator to solve for FV as shown in the following example. When solving a future value annuity, you indicate compounding forward by entering the payment as a negative value as shown by the ⊞/⊟ PMT keystrokes. If you forget to key in the negative sign, the computed FV is still correct; however, it has the wrong sign. When *payments* are compounded forward (FV is given or is being computed), you enter the payment as a negative value.*

The solution sequence requires CPT to be pressed before pressing the unknown value key for ordinary annuities. When CPT is pressed, the calculator automatically assumes that the payments occur at the end of each period when solving for any unknown annuity value.

If the "DEC 2" indicator does not appear in the display, press 2nd Decimal before keying in the example.

Procedure	Press	Display
1. Clear calculator and select finance mode.	ON/C 2nd FIN	0
2. Enter number of payments.	3 ✕ 4 ꞊ N	12.00
3. Enter percent interest rate per payment period.	16 ÷ 4 ꞊ %i	4.00
4. Enter payment amount as a negative number to compound interest.	5000 ⊞/⊟ PMT	−5000.00
5. Compute future value.	CPT FV	75129.03

---

*In more general annuity cases where both PV and FV values are involved, this rule is not applicable. The time-line diagrams and entry procedures for future value annuities having a beginning balance at time zero are discussed in Chapter 9.

(Future Value Ordinary Annuity–Continued)

The Big D Company can withdraw $75,129.03 from the sinking fund at the end of three years. Actually, the equation assumes the fund has a balance of $75,129.03 immediately after the last deposit. The final payment is not compounded because it is made at the end of the last payment period. Before the final deposit of $5000, the balance is $70,129.03 ($75,129.03 – $5000).

Review

Since equation (8-13) is programmed into your calculator, you enter only the input values to compute the answer. Be sure to press 2nd FIN , 0 PV , or ON/c PV at the start of each problem so that PV = 0. If you don't, incorrect answers may result.

Equation Value	Meaning	Keystroke
Inputs:		
N	Total number of equal payments.	N
%i	Percent interest rate per payment period.	%i
PMT	Amount of each equal payment.	+/− PMT
Solution:	Solve for future value.	CPT FV

(Future Value Ordinary Annuity–Continued)

Payment Computations
Concepts

The payment of a future value ordinary annuity is the amount paid or received at the end of each payment period for N periods that compounds forward to a specified future value. To compute the payment, you must know: N, the total number of payments; %i, the interest rate per payment period; and FV, the future value of the payments.

A general time-line diagram may be drawn as follows.

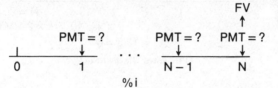

Time-Line Diagram 8-14

The following is a general equation for finding the payment value.

$$PMT = FV \left/ \left[\frac{(1 + \%i/100)^N - 1}{\%i/100} \right] \right.$$

Equation (8-15)

The equation could also be written substituting the CVIFA term as follows.

$$PMT = FV/(CVIFA_{\%i,N})$$ *Equation (8-16)*

Time Value of Money

(Future Value Ordinary Annuity-Continued)

Example

The ABC Company must establish a sinking fund to retire a $1,000,000 bond issue at the end of 10 years. The deposits are to be made at the end of each six-month period. If the 12% annual interest rate is compounded semiannually, what is the amount of each deposit?

$$FV = \$1,000,000$$

```
                                          ↑
        PMT = ?              PMT = ?   PMT = ?
          ↓                    ↓         ↓
 |_____|_____  . . .  _____|_____|
 0        1            19       N = 20
                       (N = 10 Yrs × 2 PMTS/Yr)
          %i = 12/2 = 6
```

Time-Line Diagram 8-15

Table Solution

PMT = 1000000/(CVIFA$_{6\%,20}$)

PMT = 1000000/36.7856

PMT = 27184.55

Using the tables, the payment is $27,184.55.

(Future Value Ordinary Annuity–Continued)

Calculator Solution

Equation (8-15) is programmed into your calculator to solve for payment as shown in the following example. If the "DEC 2" indicator does not appear in the display, press (2nd) (Decimal) before keying in the example.

Procedure	Press	Display
1. Clear calculator and select finance mode.	(ON/c) (2nd) (FIN)	0 DEC 2 FIN
2. Enter number of payments.	10 (X) 2 (=) (N)	20.00 DEC 2 FIN
3. Enter percent interest rate per payment period.	12 (÷) 2 (=) (%i)	6.00 DEC 2 FIN
4. Enter future value.	1000000 (FV)	1000000.0 DEC 2 FIN
5. Compute payment.	(CPT) (PMT)	−27184.56 DEC 2 ANN FIN

The company should deposit $27,184.56 at the end of each six-month period to accrue $1,000,000 after 10 years. The negative answer for payment indicates the payment is *compounding or moving forward in time.*

Review

Equation (8-15) is programmed into your calculator. However, compounding forward gives negative answers when you enter the inputs shown. Be sure to press (2nd)(FIN), 0 (PV), or (ON/c)(PV) at the start of each problem so that PV = 0. If you don't, incorrect answers may result.

(Future Value Ordinary Annuity–Continued)

Equation Value	Meaning	Keystroke
Inputs:		
N	Total number of equal payments.	N
%i	Percent interest rate per payment period.	%i
FV	Future value of payment after N payments.	FV
Solution:	Solve for payment.	CPT PMT

Solving for the Interest Rate

Concepts

 You may calculate the interest rate per payment period that makes the end-of-period payments compound forward to a specified future value. To compute the interest rate of a future value annuity, you must know: N, the total number of payments; PMT, the consecutive equal payment amounts; and FV, the future value of the payments.

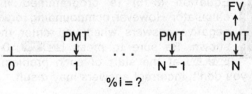

Time-Line Diagram 8-16

A direct equation does not exist to determine the interest rate of an annuity. Instead, a mathematical trial and error process is employed to find an interest rate which balances equation (8-13).

$$FV = PMT \left[\frac{(1 + \%i/100)^N - 1}{\%i/100} \right]$$

Equation (8-13)

(Future Value Ordinary Annuity–Continued)

Your calculator uses a mathematical trial and error process to compute the interest rate.

To solve for the interest rate using the CVIFA tables, use the following procedure.

1. Compute the CVIFA Factor.

$$(CVIFA_{\%i,N}) = FV/PMT \qquad \textit{Equation (8-17)}$$

2. Read across the N table row to find the CVIFA value. If the CVIFA value falls between two interest rates in the table, you may interpolate by using the following equation to obtain an approximation.

$$\%i = \frac{(CVIFA - CVIFA_L)\,(Hi\% - Li\%)}{(CVIFA_H - CVIFA_L)} + Li\%$$

$$\textit{Equation (8-18)}$$

where:

$Li\% = \%i$ for the table $CVIFA_L$ which is lower than the desired CVIFA value

$Hi\% = \%i$ for the table value $CVIFA_H$ which is higher than the desired CVIFA value

Example

To accumulate $420,000, the MA Company wants to deposit $10,000 at the end of each quarter for seven years. What annual interest rate compounded quarterly is necessary to reach the desired future value?

$$FV = \$420{,}000$$

PMT = $10,000 $10,000 $10,000

| 0 | 1 | . . . | 27 | N = 28 |

(N = 7 yrs × 4 PMTS/Yr)

%i

Time-Line Diagram 8-17

(Future Value Ordinary Annuity–Continued)

Table Solution

1. Calculate the CVIFA factor using equation (8-17).

   CVIFA = 420,000/10,000 = 42

2. Find the bracket between 2% and 4% on the N = 28 row of the CVIFA table and solve equation (8-18).

   Li% = 2%

   $CVIFA_L = 37.0512$

   Hi% = 4%

   $CVIFA_H = 49.9676$

   $i\% = \dfrac{(42 - 37.0512)\ (4 - 2)}{49.9676 - 37.0512} + 2$

   i% = 2.7663

   Annual percentage rate = 2.7663 × 4 PMTS/Yr = 11.07% using a linear interpolation procedure.

Calculator Solution

Your calculator automatically uses a mathematical trial and error method to balance equation (8-13) as illustrated in the following example. If the "DEC 2" indicator does not appear in the display, press 2nd Decimal before keying in the example.

Procedure	Press	Display
1. Clear calculator and select finance mode.	ON/C 2nd FIN	0
2. Enter total number of payments.	7 X 4 = N	28.00
3. Enter amount of payment.	10000 +/- PMT	− 10000.00
4. Enter future value.	420000 FV	420000.00
5. Compute interest rate per payment period.	CPT %i	2.85
6. Calculate annual percentage rate.	X 4 =	11.41

(Future Value Ordinary Annuity–Continued)

The company needs an 11.41% annual interest rate compounded quarterly to achieve their sinking fund goal. The calculator answer is more accurate than the table answer of 11.07% which uses the interpolation process. The payment amount is entered as a negative value to indicate compounding forward.

Review

The calculator uses a mathematical trial and error procedure to find an interest rate. Be sure to press $\boxed{2nd}\boxed{FIN}$, 0 $\boxed{PV}$, or $\boxed{ON/C}\boxed{PV}$ before the start of each problem so that PV = 0. If you don't, incorrect answers may result.

Equation Value	Meaning	Keystroke
Inputs:		
N	Total number of payments.	$\boxed{N}$
PMT	End-of-period payment.	$\boxed{+/-}\boxed{PMT}$
FV	Value of N payments at end of last period.	$\boxed{FV}$
Solution:	Solve for interest rate.	$\boxed{CPT}\boxed{\%i}$

(Future Value Ordinary Annuity–Continued)

Solving for the Total Number of Payments
Concepts

You can compute the number of consecutive equal end-of-period payments that compounds forward to a specified future value. To calculate the total number of payments, you must know: %i, the interest rate per payment period; PMT, the equal payment made each period; and FV, the future value of the payments.

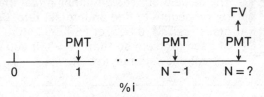

Time-Line Diagram 8-18

The following is a general equation to determine the total number of payments.

$$N = \ln\left[1 + \frac{FV(\%i/100)}{PMT}\right] \Big/ \ln(1 + \%i/100)$$

Equation (8-19)

where ln is the natural logarithm (logarithm to the base e).

The tables in the appendix also may be used to determine the total number of payments in the following manner.

1. Compute the CVIFA Factor.

$$(CVIFA_{\%i,N}) = FV/PMT \qquad \text{Equation (8-20)}$$

2. Read down the %i column to find the CVIFA value. If the CVIFA value falls between two payment periods in the table, you may interpolate for a more accurate N value by using the following equation.

$$N = \frac{(CVIFA - CVIFA_L)(NH - NL)}{(CVIFA_H - CVIFA_L)} + NL$$

Equation (8-21)

(Future Value Ordinary Annuity–Continued)

where:

NL = the N row for the table $CVIFA_L$ which is lower than the desired CVIFA

NH = the N row for the table $CVIFA_H$ which is higher than the desired CVIFA

Example

The XYZ company wants to deposit $5000 per month in a sinking fund. The fund pays 24% annual interest compounded monthly. How many end-of-month deposits are necessary to accumulate $115,000?

$$FV = \$115,000$$

PMT = $5,000 $5,000 $5,000

0	1	...	N – 1	N = ?

%i = 24/12 = 2

Time-Line Diagram 8-19

Table Solution

1. $(CVIFA_{2\%,N})$ = 115000/5000 = 23.

2. Find the bracket between rows 19 and 20 in the 2% column of the CVIFA table and solve equation (8-21).

NL = 19
$CVIFA_L$ = 22.8406
NH = 20
$CVIFA_H$ = 24.2974
$$N = \frac{(23 - 22.8406)\ (20 - 19)}{(24.2974 - 22.8406)} + 19$$
N = 19.1094

Using a linear interpolation procedure, the number of payments is 19.1094.

(Future Value Ordinary Annuity–Continued)

Calculator Solution

Your calculator automatically solves equation (8-19) for the number of payments as shown in the following example. If the "DEC 2" indicator does not appear in the display, press [2nd] [Decimal] before keying in the example.

Procedure	Press	Display
1. Clear calculator and select finance mode.	[ON/C] [2nd] [FIN]	0 DEC 2 FIN
2. Enter percent interest rate per payment period.	24 [÷] 12 [=] [%i]	2.00 DEC 2 FIN
3. Enter payment amount as a negative number.	5000 [+/–] [PMT]	– 5000.00 DEC 2 ANN FIN
4. Enter future value.	115000 [FV]	115000.00 DEC 2 ANN FIN
5. Compute number of payments.	[CPT] [N]	19.11 DEC 2 ANN FIN

To accumulate $115,000 with $5000 end-of-month payments takes 19.11 months.

(Future Value Ordinary Annuity–Continued)

Review

Since equation (8-19) is programmed into your calculator, you only enter the input values to compute the answer. Be sure to press 〔2nd〕〔FIN〕, 0 〔PV〕, or 〔ON/c〕〔PV〕 at the start of each problem so that PV = 0. If you don't, incorrect answers may result.

Equation Value	Meaning	Keystroke
Inputs:		
%i	Interest rate per payment period as a percentage.	〔%i〕
PMT	End-of-period payment.	〔+/−〕〔PMT〕
FV	Future value of payment after N payments.	〔FV〕
Solution:	Solve for number of payments.	〔CPT〕〔N〕

Time Value of Money

Present Value Ordinary Annuity

A present value ordinary annuity has a series of equal end-of-period payments discounted back to a present value. An example of a time-line diagram is:

```
 PV       PMT      PMT      PMT      PMT
  ↑        ↓        ↓        ↓        ↓
──┼────────┼────────┼────────┼────────┼──
  0        1        2        3       N = 4
                   %i
```

Time-Line Diagram 8-20

As with the future value annuity, this annuity can also be solved as a series of compound interest problems as follows.

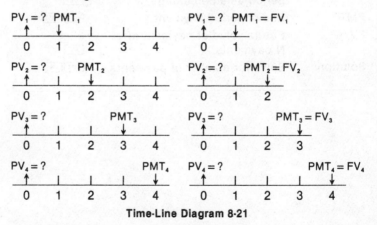

Decomposed Annuity Time-Line Diagram

Equivalent Compound Interest Time-Line Diagram

Time-Line Diagram 8-21

As shown above, the ordinary annuity is broken into four compound interest problems. Once the present value for each payment is determined using procedures discussed in the compound interest section, the present value of the annuity is found by adding the individual values.

$$\text{Annuity present value} = PV_1 + PV_2 + PV_3 + PV_4$$

(Present Value Ordinary Annuity–Continued)

Because payments occur at the end of the payment periods, each payment is discounted at least one period. Using special equations, you can solve for the value of a present value ordinary annuity because the payments are equal. The following discussions show you how, using your calculator or tables, to solve for each unknown value (PV, PMT, %i, and N).*

Solving for Present Value

Concepts

The present value of an ordinary annuity is the value of N payments occurring at the end of each payment period discounted back to the beginning of the first payment period. To compute the present value of an ordinary annuity, you must know: N, the total number of payments; %i, the interest rate per payment period; and PMT, the equal payment amount.

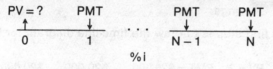

Time-Line Diagram 8-22

The unknown value, PV, is indicated by the question mark (?).

The general equation to solve for the present value of an ordinary annuity follows.

$$PV = PMT \left[\frac{1 - (1 + \%i/100)^{-N}}{\%i/100} \right]$$

Equation (8-22)

*The present value annuity computations discussed in this section imply that FV = 0. This may not be true in the more general annuity cases discussed in Chapter 9.

(Present Value Ordinary Annuity–Continued)

Tables have been prepared that calculate the present value of an annuity of $1 (the factor of equation (8-22) in brackets). This factor is usually referred to as the Present Value Interest Factor of an Annuity (PVIFA)*. These tables, included in the Appendix, give the PVIFA for known %i and N values.

The PVIFA term could be substituted in the general equation (8-22) with the following result.

$$PV = PMT (PVIFA_{\%i,N})$$ *Equation (8-23)*

Example

The Furros Company purchases a machine that provides annual savings of $20,000 per year for the next 10 years. Using an annual discount rate of 10%, compute the present value of the savings.

The first step is to draw the time-line diagram for the problem.

```
PV = ?   PMT = $20,000   $20,000      $20,000
  ↓          ↑             ↑            ↑
  0          1      . . .  9          N = 10
               %i = 10
```
Time-Line Diagram 8-23

As shown in the diagram, the three inputs required to compute the present value are: PMT = 20000, %i = 10, and N = 10.

*PVIFA may also be written as (P/A, i, n) or $PVIF_a$ or $a_{\overline{n}|i}$ or A(n,i).

(Present Value Ordinary Annuity–Continued)

Table Solution

Using the table for the Present Value Interest Factor of an Annuity (PVIFA) in Appendix A, the value at the intersection of the N = 10 row and the 10% column is 6.1446. Multiply the payment of $20,000 by the PVIFA to obtain the present value.

PV = 20000 × 6.1446

PV = 122892

Using the tables, the present value is $122,892.

Calculator Solution

Equation (8-22) is programmed into your calculator to solve for the PV as shown in the following example. When solving a present value annuity, you indicate discounting by entering the payment as a positive value (no sign needs to be entered with the value).* For ordinary annuities, the solution sequence requires [CPT] to be pressed before pressing the unknown value key. When [CPT] is pressed, the calculator automatically assumes that payments occur at the end of each period when solving for an unknown annuity value. If the "DEC 2" indicator does not appear in the display, press [2nd] [Decimal] before keying in the example.

*In more general annuity cases involving both PV and FV values, a negative sign may need to be entered with the payment. The time-line diagrams and entry procedure for present value annuities having a remaining balance are discussed in Chapter 9.

Time Value of Money

(Present Value Ordinary Annuity–Continued)

Procedure	Press	Display
1. Clear calculator and select finance mode.	ON/c 2nd FIN	**0** DEC 2 FIN
2. Enter number of payments.	10 N	**10.00** DEC 2 FIN
3. Enter interest rate per payment period as a percent.	10 %i	**10.00** DEC 2 FIN
4. Enter payment value.	20000 PMT	**20000.00** DEC 2 ANN FIN
5. Compute present value.	CPT PV	**122891.34** DEC 2 ANN FIN

The present value at time zero of the 10 $20,000 payments is $122,891.34, using an annual discount rate of 10%.

Review

Since equation (8-22) is programmed into your calculator, you only enter the input values to compute the answer. Be sure to press 2nd FIN, 0 FV, or ON/c FV at the start of each problem so that FV = 0. If you don't, incorrect answers may result.

Equation Value	Meaning	Keystroke
Inputs:		
N	Total number of equal payments.	N
%i	Interest rate per payment period as a percent.	%i
PMT	Amount of each equal payment.	PMT
Solution:	Solve for present value.	CPT PV

(Present Value Ordinary Annuity–Continued)

Solving for the Payment

Concepts

The payment of a present value ordinary annuity is the amount paid or received at the end of each payment period for N periods that discounts back to a specified present value. To solve for the payment of a present value ordinary annuity, you must know: N, the total number of payments; %i, the interest rate per payment period; and PV, the present value of the payments.

```
PV      PMT = ?              PMT = ?   PMT = ?
↑         ↓          . . .     ↓         ↓
0         1               N − 1        N
                %i
```

Time-Line Diagram 8-24

The following general equation is designed to determine the payment of an ordinary annuity.

$$PMT = PV \left/ \left[\frac{1 - (1 + \%i/100)^{-N}}{\%i/100} \right] \right.$$

Equation (8-24)

Using the PVIFA term, the equation could be rewritten as follows.

$$PMT = PV/(PVIFA_{\%i,N})$$ *Equation (8-25)*

Example

The LD Company is borrowing $125,000 for four years. The loan has a five-year term with end-of-quarter payments. Assuming a 16% annual interest with quarterly compounding, what is the quarterly payment?

```
PV = $125,000  PMT = ?           PMT = ?    PMT = ?
 ↑               ↓        . . .     ↓          ↓
 0               1                 19       N = 20
            %i = 16/4 = 4
```

Time-Line Diagram 8-25

(Present Value Ordinary Annuity–Continued)

Dividing the annual interest rate by the number of compounding and payment periods per year determines the periodic interest (16/4 = 4). The total number of payments is the loan term multiplied by the number of payments per year (5 × 4 = 20).

Table Solution

PMT = 125000/(PVIFA$_{4\%,20}$)

PMT = 125000/13.5903

PMT = 9197.74

Using the tables, the payment is $9197.74.

Calculator Solution

Equation (8-24) is programmed into your calculator to solve for the payment as shown in the next example. If the "DEC 2" indicator does not appear in the display, press [2nd] [Decimal] before keying in the example.

Procedure	Press	Display
1. Clear calculator and select finance mode.	[ON/c] [2nd] [FIN]	0 DEC 2 FIN
2. Enter number of payments.	5 [X] 4 [=] [N]	20.00 DEC 2 FIN
3. Enter the percent interest rate per payment period.	16 [÷] 4 [=] [%i]	4.00 DEC 2 FIN
4. Enter the present value.	125000 [PV]	125000.00 DEC 2 FIN
5. Compute the payment.	[CPT] [PMT]	9197.72 DEC 2 ANN FIN

The end-of-quarter payments are $9197.72. This problem can also be stated as follows: $125,000 invested at 4% per quarter will allow $9197.72 to be withdrawn at the end of each quarter for five years.

(Present Value Ordinary Annuity–Continued)

Review

Since equation (8-24) is built into your calculator, you only enter the input values and compute the answer. Be sure to press 2nd FIN, 0 FV, or ON/c FV at the start of each problem so that FV = 0. If you don't, incorrect answers may result.

Equation Value	Meaning	Keystroke
Inputs:		
N	Total number of payments.	N
%i	Interest rate per payment period as a percentage.	%i
PV	Present value of N payments at beginning of first payment period.	PV
Solution:	Solve for payment.	CPT PMT

Solving for the Interest Rate

Concepts

You can calculate the interest rate per payment period that makes the end-of-period payments discount back to a specified present value. To compute the interest rate per payment period of a present value annuity, you must know: N, the total number of payments; PMT, the equal payment amount; and PV, the present value of the payments.

PV   PMT   PMT   PMT
↑   ↓   . . .   ↓   ↓
0   1   N − 1   N
           %i = ?

Time-Line Diagram 8-26

Time Value of Money

(Present Value Ordinary Annuity–Continued)

A direct equation to determine the interest rate of an annuity does not exist. Instead, a mathematical trial and error process is used to find an interest rate that balances equation (8-22).

$$PV = PMT \left[\frac{1 - (1 + \%i/100)^{-N}}{\%i/100} \right]$$

Equation (8-22)

The tables in the appendix also may be used in the following manner to solve for the interest rate.

1. Compute the PVIFA Factor.

$$(PVIFA_{\%i,N}) = PV/PMT \qquad \textit{Equation (8-26)}$$

2. Read across the N table row to find PVIFA. If the PVIFA value falls between two interest rate values in the table, you may interpolate for a more accurate %i value by using the following equation.

$$\%i = \frac{(PVIFA - PVIFA_L)(Hi\% - Li\%)}{(PVIFA_H - PVIFA_L)} + Li\%$$

Equation (8-27)

where:

Li% = %i for the table value $PVIFA_L$ which is higher than the desired PVIFA value

Hi% = %i for the table value $PVIFA_H$ which is lower than the desired PVIFA value

Example

The Altas Coal Company is purchasing a new strip mine auger for $700,000. This machine is expected to have end-of-year savings equal to $144,000 for nine years. What annual interest rate is earned on this machine?

PV = $700,000 PMT = $144,000 $144,000 $144,000

| 0 | 1 | . . . | 8 | N = 9 |

%i = ?

Time-Line Diagram 8-27

(Present Value Ordinary Annuity–Continued)

Table Solution

1. Calculate the (PVIFA) factor using equation (8-26).

   $(PVIFA_{\%i,9}) = 700000/144000 = 4.8611$

2. Reading across the N = 9 row, find the bracket between the 14% and 16% column on the PVIFA table and solve equation (8-27).

   $Li\% = 14\%$

   $PVIFA_L = 4.9464$

   $Hi\% = 16\%$

   $PVIFA_H = 4.6065$

   $i\% = \dfrac{(4.8611 - 4.9464)\,(16 - 14)}{4.6065 - 4.9464} + 14$

   $i\% = 14.5019$

   Using a linear interpolation procedure, the interest rate is 14.5019%.

Calculator Solution

Your calculator automatically employs a mathematical trial and error process to solve equation (8-22) as shown in the following example. If the "DEC 2" indicator does not appear in the display, press ⟨2nd⟩ ⟨Decimal⟩ before keying in the example.

Procedure	Press	Display
1. Clear calculator and select finance mode.	⟨ON/C⟩ ⟨2nd⟩ ⟨FIN⟩	0
2. Enter total number of payments.	9 ⟨N⟩	9.00
3. Enter amount of payment.	144000 ⟨PMT⟩	144000.00
4. Enter present value.	700000 ⟨PV⟩	700000.00
5. Compute interest rate per payment period.	⟨CPT⟩ ⟨%i⟩	14.48

An interest rate of 14.48% discounted the nine payments of $144,000 back to an amount equal to the original outlay of $700,000.

(Present Value Ordinary Annuity–Continued)

Review

The calculator uses a mathematical trial and error procedure to find an interest rate. Be sure to press `2nd` `FIN`, 0 `FV`, or `ON/c` `FV` at the start of each problem so that FV = 0. If you don't, incorrect answers may result.

Equation Value	Meaning	Keystroke
Inputs:		
N	Total number of equal payments.	`N`
PMT	End-of-period payment.	`PMT`
PV	Value of N payments at beginning of first payment period.	`PV`
Solution:	Solve for percent interest rate.	`CPT` `%i`

Solving for the Number of Payments

Concepts

You may compute the number of equal end-of-period payments that discount back to a specified present value. To solve for the number of payments, you must know: %i, the interest rate per payment period; PMT, the equal payment amount; and PV, the present value of the payments.

```
PV        PMT              PMT       PMT
↑          ↓                ↓         ↓
0          1       . . .    N – 1    N = ?
                %i
```

Time-Line Diagram 8-28

(Present Value Ordinary Annuity–Continued)

The following general formula is designed to determine the number of payments of an ordinary annuity.

$$N = -\ln\left[1 - \frac{PV(\%i/100)}{PMT}\right] \Big/ \ln(1 + \%i/100)$$

Equation (8-28)

where ln is the natural logarithm (logarithm to the base e).

The tables in the appendix also may be used in the following manner to solve for the number of payments.

1. Compute the PVIFA factor.

   $(PVIFA_{\%i,N}) = PV/PMT$

2. Read down the %i column to find the PVIFA. If the PVIFA value falls between two payment periods in the table, you may interpolate for a more accurate N value by using the following equation.

$$N = \frac{(PVIFA - PVIFA_L)\,(NH - NL)}{(PVIFA_H - PVIFA_L)} + NL$$

Equation (8-29)

where:

NL = the N row for the table $PVIFA_L$ which is higher than the desired PVIFA value

NH = the N row for the table $PVIFA_H$ which is lower than the desired PVIFA value

Example

The BG Company wants to set up an annuity paying $4000 at the end of each quarter. If $45,000 is deposited and the 16% annual interest is compounded quarterly, how many payments are received?

PV = $45,000 PMT = $4000 $4000 $4000

```
       ↓              ↑        . . .      ↑          ↑
       0              1                 N − 1      N = ?
```

%i = 16/4 = 4

Time-Line Diagram 8-29

(Present Value Ordinary Annuity–Continued)

Table Solution

1. $(PVIFA_{4\%,N}) = 45000/4000 = 11.25$.

2. Find the bracket between rows 15 and 16 in the 4% column of the PVIFA table and solve equation (8-29).

    $NL = 15$
    $PVIFA_L = 11.1184$
    $NH = 16$
    $PVIFA_H = 11.66523$
    $$N = \frac{(11.25 - 11.1184)(16 - 15)}{(11.6523 - 11.1184)} + 15$$
    $N = 15.2465$

Using a linear interpolation procedure, the number of payments is 15.2465.

Calculator Solution

Equation (8-28) is solved automatically for the number of payments as shown in the following example. If the "DEC 2" indicator does not appear in the display, press [2nd] [Decimal] before keying in the example.

Procedure	Press	Display
1. Clear calculator and select finance mode.	[ON/c] [2nd] [FIN]	0 DEC 2 FIN
2. Enter interest rate per payment period.	16 [÷] 4 [=] [%i]	4.00 DEC 2 FIN
3. Enter payment amount.	4000 [PMT]	4000.00 DEC 2 ANN FIN
4. Enter present value.	45000 [PV]	45000.00 DEC 2 ANN FIN
5. Compute number of payments.	[CPT] [N]	15.24 DEC 2 ANN FIN

The investment of $45,000 at 4% per quarter pays $4000 for 15.24 quarters.

(Present Value Ordinary Annuity–Continued)

Review

Since equation (8-28) is programmed into your calculator, you only enter the input values to compute the answer. Be sure to press [2nd] [FIN], 0 [FV], or [ON/c] [FV] at the start of each problem so that FV = 0. If you don't, incorrect answers may result.

Equation Value	Meaning	Keystrokes
Inputs:		
%i	Interest rate per payment period.	[%i]
PMT	End-of-period payment.	[PMT]
PV	Value of N payments at beginning of first payment period.	[PV]
Solution:	Solve for number of payments.	[CPT] [N]

Variable Cash Flows

In annuities, all payments are equal, periodic, and of the same nature (inflow or outflow). A more general case, however, is a series of unequal cash flows, each either an inflow or an outflow. These unequal cash flows are usually called *variable cash flows* or uneven cash flows.

You can solve for the present value by treating the variable cash flows as a series of compound interest payments. Your calculator, however, does not solve directly for the interest rate of a series of variable cash flows. You can manually obtain a bracket and interpolate to approximate the interest rate.

Solving for Present Value
Concepts

 The present value of variable cash flows is the value of the cash flows occurring at the end of each payment period discounted back to the beginning of the first cash flow period (time zero).

$$PV = ? \qquad CF_1 \qquad \ldots \qquad CF_{j-1} \qquad CF_j$$

$$\overline{\underset{0}{\downarrow} \qquad \underset{1}{\uparrow} \qquad \qquad \underset{N-1}{\uparrow} \qquad \underset{N}{\uparrow}}$$

$$\%\,i$$

Time-Line Diagram 8-30

The following general formula determines the present value of a variable cash flow.

$$PV = CF_1/(1 + \%\,i/100)^1 + CF_2/(1 + \%\,i/100)^2 + \ldots + CF_j/(1 + \%\,i/100)^j$$

This formula can be rewritten using summation notation as:

$$PV = \sum_{j=1}^{N} CF_j \Big/ (1 + \%\,i/100)^{-j} = \sum_{j=1}^{N} CF_j(1 + \%\,i/100)^{-j}$$

Equation (8-30)

The tables in the appendix also may be used with the following formula.

$$PV = \sum_{j=1}^{N} CF_j(PVIF_{\%\,i,j})$$

Equation (8-31)

(Variable Cash Flows–Continued)

Example

The ABC Company purchases a machine that saves the following end-of-year amounts.

Year	1	2	3	4
Amount	$5000	$7000	$8000	$10000

Assuming a discount rate of 10%, does the present value of the cash flows exceed the original cost of $23,000?

PV = ?	$5000	$7000	$8000	$10,000
0	1	2	3	N = 4

The present value of the variable cash flows is found by first decomposing the time-line diagram above into four separate compound interest problems, as shown below.

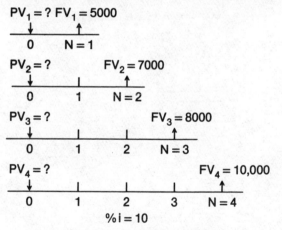

Time-Line Diagram 8-31

After developing the four compound interest diagrams, the present value of each is computed. The sum of the four individual present values is the total present value of the cash flows.

Time Value of Money

(Variable Cash Flows–Continued)

Table Solution

After determining the PVIF values for N = 1, 2, 3, and 4, the present value is solved as:

$$PV = 5000\ (PVIF_{10\%,1}) + 7000\ (PVIF_{10\%,2})$$
$$+ 8000\ (PVIF_{10\%,3}) + 10000(PVIF_{10\%,4})$$

$$PV = 5000(0.9091) + 7000\ (0.8264) + 8000\ (0.7513)$$
$$+ 10000\ (0.6830)$$

$$PV = 23170.70$$

Calculator Solution

If the "DEC 2" indicator does not appear in the display, press [2nd] [Decimal] before keying in the example.

(Variable Cash Flows–Continued)

Procedure	Press	Display
1. Clear calculator and select finance mode.	[ON/c] [2nd] [FIN]	0 DEC 2 FIN
2. Enter interest rate per cash flow period.	10 [%i]	10.00 DEC 2 FIN
3. First cash flow a. Enter amount.	5000 [FV]	5000.00 DEC 2 FIN
b. Enter first period.	1 [N]	1.00 DEC 2 FIN
c. Compute present value of first cash flow and store.	[CPT] [PV] [STO]	4545.45 DEC 2 FIN
4. Second cash flow a. Enter next amount.	7000 [FV]	7000.00 DEC 2 FIN
b. Enter cash flow period number.	2 [N]	2.00 DEC 2 FIN
c. Compute present value and sum to memory.	[CPT] [PV] [SUM]	5785.12 DEC 2 FIN
5. Third cash flow a. Amount.	8000 [FV]	8000.00 DEC 2 FIN
b. Period number.	3 [N]	3.00 DEC 2 FIN
c. Compute present value and sum to memory.	[CPT] [PV] [SUM]	6010.52 DEC 2 FIN
6. Fourth cash flow a. Amount.	10000 [FV]	10000.00 DEC 2 FIN
b. Period number.	4 [N]	4.00 DEC 2 FIN
c. Compute present value and sum to memory.	[CPT] [PV] [SUM]	6830.13 DEC 2 FIN
7. Recall present value of variable cash flows.	[RCL]	23171.23 DEC 2 FIN
8. Subtract original cost to determine excess present value.	[–] 23000 [=]	171.23 DEC 2 FIN

(Variable Cash Flows–Continued)

The present value of the cash flows is $23,171.23, which exceeds the machine's cost by $171.23. This is a profitable investment for the company.

If you are solving for the interest rate, try various guesses for i until you bracket the original cash flow. Next interpolate to find an approximate value for the interest rate. See Chapter 11 for the procedure.

Review

Be sure to press [2nd] [FIN], 0 [PMT], or [ON/C] [PMT] at the start of each problem so that PMT = 0. If you don't, incorrect answers may result. A zero payment is indicated by the absence of the "ANN" (annuity) indicator from the display.

Equation Value	Meaning	Keystrokes
Step 1:		
%i	Enter interest rate.	[%i]
N_1	First cash flow period.	[N]
CF_1	First cash flow amount.	[FV]
PV_1	Present value of first cash flow.	[CPT] [PV] [STO]
Step 2:		
N_j	Cash flow period for CF_j.	[N]
CF_j	Cash flow CF_j.	[FV]
PV_j	Present value of CF_j.	[CPT] [PV] [SUM]
Step 3:	Repeat step 2 for each cash flow.	
Step 4:	Total present value.	[RCL]

Chapter 9

ADVANCED TIME VALUE OF MONEY TOPICS

Advanced Time Value of Money Topics

Contents

Introduction

In Chapter 8, compound interest and ordinary annuities are discussed. In this chapter, further annuity topics are discussed. One topic to be explored is annuities due, in which payments occur at the beginning of each payment period.

The second topic relates to ordinary annuities and annuities due involving both a present value (PV) and future value (FV). In Chapter 8, annuity situations, such as home loans, always amortize to zero and payments are made for the entire term of the loan. In some cases, however, the loan is prepaid and an ending lumpsum payment (called a balloon payment) is made. Such situations involve both PV and FV in the computations and are the most general cases of present value annuities.

Another topic covered involves a beginning balance and regular payments as either a future value ordinary annuity or a future value annuity due. An example of this type of problem is a savings account. For a savings account, the number of payment periods may differ from the number of compounding periods. In this case the interest rates must be converted to the interest rate per payment period. The remainder of the chapter deals with the conversion of interest rates.

Annuities Due

In many practical annuity cases, such as leases, periodic payments may be made at the beginning of each period rather than at the end of the period. Annuities with payments occurring at the beginning of each period are called *annuities due* or *advance payment annuities*.

Both ordinary annuities and annuities due assume an equal number of payment and compounding periods per year with interest compounded at the end of each payment period. As a result, the only difference between an annuity due and an ordinary annuity is the number of compounding periods. Since the first payment occurs at different times, the compounding effects produce different PV or FV values when compared to ordinary annuities.

An annuity due with payments compounded forward to accumulate a future sum is a *future value annuity due*. When the beginning-of-period payments are discounted back to a present value, the annuity is a *present value annuity due*. The following terms are used when discussing annuities due.

Future value due (FV)—the value, at the *end* of the last payment period, of a series of beginning-of-period payments *compounded* forward at a given interest rate (%i) for a given number of periods (N).

Present value due (PV)—the value, at the *beginning* of the first payment period, of a series of beginning-of-period payments *discounted* back at a given interest rate (%i) for a given number of periods (N).

Interest rate (%i)—the interest rate per payment period that compounds a series of beginning-of-period payments forward to a specified future value, or the interest rate that discounts a series of beginning-of-period payments back to a specified present value. Interest is calculated at the end of each payment period.

Payment due (PMT)—the amount of the equal beginning-of-period amounts paid or received for N periods.

Number of payments (N)—the total number of equal payments.

Future Value Annuities Due

A future value annuity due has a series of equal payments, occurring at the beginning of each payment period, that are compounded forward to a future value. An illustrative time-line diagram is:

```
PMT      PMT    . . .   PMT      FV
 ↓        ↓              ↓        ↑
 0        1            N – 1      N
               %i
```
Time-Line Diagram 9-1

By drawing a time-line diagram you can easily determine if your annuity is an ordinary annuity or an annuity due. As shown in the time-line diagram, an annuity due has N payments with the first payment made at the beginning of the first payment period (time zero) and the last payment made at the *beginning* of the last payment period (N). As a result, the future value is calculated one period after the last payment.

In an ordinary annuity, the future value is calculated when the last payment is made (at the *end* of period N) and includes the last payment. Thus, the difference between an ordinary annuity and an annuity due is only one compounding period. Both have the same number of payments and both have the future value (FV) occurring at the end of the last payment period. (In future value annuities due and future value ordinary annuities, PV = 0 is implied.)

Advanced Time Value of Money Topics

(Future Value Annuities Due–Continued)

Solving for the Future Value of an Annuity Due
Concepts

The future value of an annuity due is the value of N beginning-of-period payments compounded forward to the end of the last payment period. To solve for the future value, you must know: N, the total number of payments; %i, the interest rate per payment period; and PMT, the equal payment made at the beginning of each payment period.

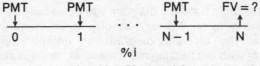

Time-Line Diagram 9-2

A general equation to determine the future value of an annuity due follows.

$$FV = PMT(1 + \%i/100)\left[\frac{(1 + \%i/100)^N - 1}{\%i/100}\right]$$

Equation (9-1)

Comparing equation (9-1) to the future value ordinary annuity equation (8-13), the difference is the term $[(1 + \%i/100)]$. As a result, equation (9-1) can be expressed as:

$$FV(due) = FV(ordinary)(1 + \%i/100)$$

(Future Value Annuities Due–Continued)

Example

At the beginning of each month for six years, your aunt plans to deposit $250 in a savings account. If the 6% annual interest rate is compounded monthly, how much money is in the account at the end of six years?

```
$250      $250            $250       FV = ?
  ↓         ↓               ↓          ↑
  0         1              71        N = 72
                          (N = 6 yrs × 12 PMTS/Yr)
        % i = 6/12 = 0.5
```
Time-Line Diagram 9-3

The number of payments is determined by multiplying the total number of years and the number of payments per year. The annual interest rate is converted to the rate per payment period by dividing the annual rate by the number of compounding periods per year. Since the number of payment and compounding periods per year are equal, the 0.5% is also the interest rate per payment period.

Calculator Solution

Your calculator is programmed to solve equation (9-1) as shown in the following example. When solving a future value annuity (annuity due or ordinary annuity), you indicate compounding forward by entering the payment as a negative value as shown by the [+/-] [PMT] keystrokes. If you forget to key in the negative sign, the computed FV still is correct; however, it has the wrong sign. A rule to remember is that when *payments* are compounded forward (FV is given or being computed) you enter the payment as a negative value.*

*This rule is *not* applicable in general annuity cases involving both PV and FV values. The time-line diagrams and entry procedures for future value annuities having a beginning balance are discussed later in this chapter.

(Future Value Annuities Due–Continued)

An unknown value for an annuity due is calculated by pressing DUE before pressing the unknown value key. When DUE is pressed, the calculator automatically assumes the payments occur at the beginning of each period. When CPT is pressed, the calculator solves for an ordinary annuity unknown value.

If the "DEC 2" indicator does not appear in the display, press 2nd Decimal before keying in the example.

Procedure	Press	Display
1. Clear calculator and select finance mode.	ON/C 2nd FIN	0 DEC 2 FIN
2. Enter total number of deposits.	6 X 12 = N	72.00 DEC 2 FIN
3. Enter percent interest rate per payment period.	6 ÷ 12 = %i	0.50 DEC 2 FIN
4. Enter deposit amount as negative value.	250 +/− PMT	− 250.00 DEC 2 ANN FIN
5. Compute future value of annuity due.	DUE FV	21710.22 DEC 2 ANN FIN

Your aunt has $21,710.22 in her account at the end of six years, one month after her last deposit.

(Future Value Annuities Due–Continued)

Review

Since equation (9-1) is programmed into your calculator, you enter the input values and compute the answer using ⟨DUE⟩ for an annuity due. Be sure to press ⟨2nd⟩⟨FIN⟩, 0 ⟨PV⟩, or ⟨ON/C⟩⟨PV⟩ at the start of each problem so that PV = 0. If you don't, incorrect answers may result.

Equation Value	Meaning	Keystroke
Inputs:		
N	Total number of payments.	⟨N⟩
%i	Percent interest rate per payment period.	⟨%i⟩
PMT	Amount of each beginning-of-period payment as negative value.	⟨+/−⟩⟨PMT⟩
Solution:	Solve for future value of annuity due (FV).	⟨DUE⟩⟨FV⟩

Going Further With Future Value Annuities Due

The procedure to solve for remaining variables of future value annuity due cases is identical to the procedure for ordinary annuities except that ⟨DUE⟩ is pressed before the unknown value key. A detailed example is not given for each unknown value; however, the equation and basic keystrokes for each follows.

(Future Value Annuities Due–Continued)

Be sure to clear the financial registers at the start of each problem by pressing [2nd][FIN], 0 [PV], or [ON/c][PV] so that PV = 0. If you don't, incorrect answers may result.

Solving for the Payment

General Equation

$$PMT = FV \Bigg/ \left\{ (1 + \%i/100) \left[\frac{(1 + \%i/100)^N - 1}{\%i/100} \right] \right\}$$

Equation (9-2)

Calculator Keys
Inputs: [FV], [N], [%i]
Solution: [DUE][PMT]
(Answer is negative)

Solving for the Interest Rate

General Equation (9-1)

$$FV = PMT(1 + \%i/100) \left[\frac{(1 + \%i/100)^N - 1}{\%i/100} \right]$$

Calculator Keys
Inputs: [FV], [N], [+/-][PMT]
Solution: [DUE][%i]

Solving for the Number of Payments

General Equation

$$N = \ln \left[\frac{- FV(\%i/100)}{PMT(1 + \%i/100)} \right] \Bigg/ \ln(1 + \%i/100)$$

Equation (9-3)

Calculator Keys
Inputs: [FV], [%i], [+/-][PMT]
Solution: [DUE][N]

Present Value Annuities Due

A present value annuity due has a series of beginning-of-period payments discounted back to a present value. A general time-line diagram is:

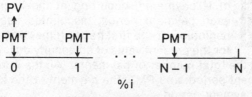

Time-Line Diagram 9-4

As shown in the time-line diagram, N payments occur with the first payment made at the beginning of the first payment period (time zero) and the last payment made at the *beginning* of the final payment period (N). As a result, the present value is calculated at the same time the first payment is made and includes the first payment.

In an ordinary annuity, the present value is calculated at time zero, but the first payment is not made until period one. Thus, the difference between an ordinary annuity and an annuity due is only one compounding period. Both have the same number of payments and both have the present value (PV) occurring at time zero. (In present value annuity due and present value ordinary annuity cases, FV = 0 is implied.)

Advanced Time Value of Money Topics

(Present Value Annuities Due–Continued)

Solving for the Present Value of an Annuity Due
Concepts

The present value of an annuity due is the value of N payments, occurring at the beginning of each payment period, discounted back to the beginning of the first period (time zero). To solve for the present value of an annuity due, you must know: N, the total number of payments; %i, the interest rate per payment period; and PMT, the payment at the beginning of each payment period.

```
PV?
 ↓
PMT      PMT          PMT
 ↑        ↑     ...    ↑        ⌐
 0        1          N – 1      N
              %i
```
Time-Line Diagram 9-5

A present value annuity due time-line diagram can be broken into two diagrams: an initial payment at time zero and an ordinary annuity with (N – 1) payments.

```
PMT
 ↑        ⌐           ⌐         ⌐
 0        1     ...  N – 1      N
PV       PMT          PMT
 ↓        ↑     ...    ↑        ⌐
 0        1          N – 1      N
```
Time-Line Diagram 9-6

Thus, PV is the sum of PMT and the PV of an ordinary annuity with (N – 1) payments.

The following general formula is designed to solve the present value of an annuity due.

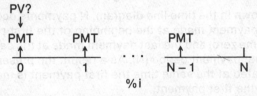

$$PV = PMT\,(1 + \%i/100)\left[\frac{1 - (1 + \%i/100)^{-N}}{\%i/100}\right]$$

Equation (9-4)

FINANCE
9-12

(Present Value Annuities Due–Continued)

An ordinary annuity table can be used to find the table values for an annuity due. Subtract one from the number of payments, find the table value for PVIF, and add one to the answer. However, your calculator directly solves annuities due, as shown in the following section.

Example

A company is leasing an asset that has 36 quarterly payments of $4000. Each payment is made at the beginning of each quarter. Using an annual interest rate of 18% compounded quarterly, determine the present value of the lease payments.

PV = ?

$4000 $4000   . . . $4000

0   1   35   N = 36

%i = 18/4 = 4.5

Time-Line Diagram 9-7

The interest rate per payment period is found by dividing the annual rate, 18%, by the number of compounding periods per year, four. Notice that the first $4000 payment occurs at time zero, and that the unknown present value (PV), including the first payment, also occurs at time zero.

Calculator Solution

Equation (9-4) is programmed into your calculator to solve for present value as shown in the following example. The solution sequence requires ⟨DUE⟩ to be pressed before the unknown value key for annuities due. When ⟨DUE⟩ is pressed, the calculator automatically assumes that payments occur at the beginning of each payment period when solving for an unknown annuity value. If the "DEC 2" indicator does not appear in the display, press ⟨2nd⟩ ⟨Decimal⟩ before keying in the example.

(Present Value Annuities Due–Continued)

Procedure	Press	Display
1. Clear calculator and enter finance mode.	ON/c 2nd FIN	0 DEC 2 FIN
2. Enter total number of payments.	36 N	36.00 DEC 2 FIN
3. Enter percent interest rate per payment period.	18 ÷ 4 = %i	4.50 DEC 2 FIN
4. Enter lease payment.	4000 PMT	4000.00 DEC 2 ANN FIN
5. Compute present value of annuity due.	DUE PV	73844.05 DEC 2 ANN FIN

The present value of the lease payments is $73,844.05. This amount represents the equivalent value at time zero of the 36 beginning-of-period payments.

Review

Since equation (9-4) is programmed into your calculator, you enter the input values and compute the answer. Be sure to press 2nd FIN , 0 FV , or ON/c FV at the start of each problem so that FV = 0. If you don't, incorrect answers may result.

Equation Value	Meaning	Keystroke
Inputs:		
N	Total number of payments.	N
%i	Percent interest rate per payment period.	%i
PMT	Cash payment occurring at beginning of each period entered as a positive value.	PMT
Solution:	Solve for present value of annuity due (PV).	DUE PV

(Present Value Annuities Due–Continued)

Solving for the Interest Rate of a Present Value Annuity Due

Concepts

You may calculate the interest rate per payment period that makes the beginning-of-period payments discount back to a specified present value. To calculate the interest rate, you need to know: N, the total number of payments; PMT, the beginning-of-period payment; and PV, the present value of the N beginning-of-period payments.

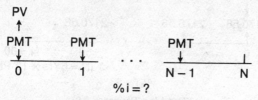

Time-Line Diagram 9-8

A direct equation does not exist to determine the interest rate of an annuity due. Instead, a mathematical trial and error procedure is programmed into the calculator to find an interest rate that balances equation (9-4).

$$PV = PMT\,(1 + \%\,i/100)\left[\frac{1 - (1 + \%\,i/100)^{-N}}{\%\,i/100}\right]$$

(Present Value Annuities Due–Continued)

Example

The ABC Company purchased a machine for $85,000 and immediately leased it to the XYZ Company for five years. The XYZ Company's beginning-of-month lease payment is $2170.58. What are the monthly and annual nominal interest rates used by the ABC Company to compute lease payments? Note that accountants often call this rate the *implicit interest rate*.

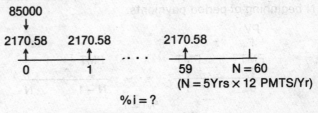

Time-Line Diagram 9-9

Calculator Solution

Your calculator uses a mathematical trial and error procedure to balance equation (9-4), as shown in the following example. If the "DEC 2" indicator does not appear in the display, press **2nd** **Decimal** before keying in the example.

(Present Value Annuities Due–Continued)

Procedure	Press	Display
1. Clear calculator and select finance mode.	ON/c 2nd FIN	**0** DEC 2 · FIN
2. Enter total number of payments.	5 ✕ 12 = N	**60.00** DEC 2 · FIN
3. Enter present value (cost of asset).	85000 PV	**85000.00** DEC 2 · FIN
4. Enter beginning-of-period payment.	2170.58 PMT	**2170.58** DEC 2 ANN FIN
5. Compute annuity due interest rate per payment period (monthly).	DUE %i	**1.58** DEC 2 ANN FIN
6. Enter number of payments per year and calculate annual percentage rate.	✕ 12 =	**19.00** DEC 2 ANN FIN

The interest rate per month on this lease is 1.58%, equivalent to an annual percentage rate of 19%. The ABC Company used an annual rate of 19% compounded monthly to determine the lease payments.

(Present Value Annuities Due–Continued)

Review

Using the procedure shown below, your calculator finds the interest rate that balances equation (9-4). Be sure to press [2nd] [FIN], 0 [FV], or [ON/c] [FV] at the start of each problem so that FV = 0. If you don't, incorrect answers may result.

Equation Value	Meaning	Keystroke
Inputs:		
N	Total number of payments.	[N]
PV	Present value of annuity due.	[PV]
PMT	Beginning-of-period payment.	[PMT]
Solution:	Solve for percent interest rate.	[DUE] [%i]

The interest rate computed using the above procedure is the rate per payment period. To determine the annual percentage rate, multiply the computed rate and the number of payment periods per year.

(Present Value Annuities Due–Continued)

Going Further With Present Value Annuities Due

The procedure for solving for the remaining present value annuity due values (N and PMT) is identical to the procedure for solving for ordinary annuities except that ⟨DUE⟩ is pressed before the unknown value key. As a result, a detailed example is not given for each unknown value. However, the equation and basic keystrokes are shown below.

Be sure to clear the financial registers at the start of each problem by pressing ⟨2nd⟩⟨FIN⟩, 0 ⟨FV⟩, or ⟨ON/c⟩⟨FV⟩ so that FV = 0. If you don't, incorrect answers may result.

Solving for the Payment

General Equation

$$PMT = PV \bigg/ \left\{ (1 + \%i/100) \left[\frac{1 - (1 + \%i/100)^{-N}}{\%i/100} \right] \right\}$$

Equation (9-5)

Calculator Keys
Inputs: ⟨PV⟩, ⟨%i⟩, ⟨N⟩
Solution: ⟨DUE⟩⟨PMT⟩

Solving for the Number of Payments

General Equation

$$N = -\ln\left[1 - \frac{PV\,(\%i/100)}{PMT\,(1 + \%i/100)} \right] \bigg/ \ln(1 + \%i/100)$$

Equation (9-6)

Calculator Keys
Inputs: ⟨PV⟩, ⟨%i⟩, ⟨PMT⟩
Solution: ⟨DUE⟩⟨N⟩

Present Value Annuities with an Ending Balloon or Salvage Value

A number of time value of money applications, such as bonds, capital budgeting, leasing, and balloon mortgages, require combining a present value annuity and compound interest. These annuities are called present value annuities with an ending balloon payment. The term present value annuities is used not because they have only a present value (PV), but because the future value (FV) and payment (PMT) are of the same nature (both inflows or outflows) and are *discounted back* to equal the present value. The annuity involved may be either an ordinary annuity or an annuity due. The concept is easily explained using time-line diagrams. First, assume a mortgage has N end-of-period payments with a remaining balance (called FV) payable after N payments.

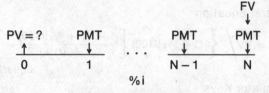

Time-Line Diagram 9-10

Conceptually, the present value is the sum, for N periods, of the present values for an ordinary annuity and a cash flow (remaining balance). This is easily seen when the time-line diagram is decomposed as follows.

PV1 = ? PMT ... PMT PMT
0 1   N − 1 N
%i

PV2 = ?   ...   FV
0 1   N − 1 N
%i

Time-Line Diagram 9-11

The mortgage's present value is the sum of PV1 and PV2.

The same approach is used with annuities due. Annuities due require regular payments at the start of each period.

(Present Value Annuities with an Ending Balloon or Salvage Value–Continued)

A lease is a common application of beginning-of-period payments with a residual value. The residual value is the value of the leased asset at the end of the final payment period. The general time-line diagram is:

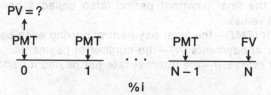

Time-Line Diagram 9-12

Decomposing the time-line diagram results in an annuity due and a cash flow occurring at the end of the final payment period.

```
PV1 = ?
  ↑
PMT       PMT      ...    PMT
 ↓         ↓               ↓        |
 0         1              N – 1     N
              %i

PV2 = ?
  ↑
  |         |        ...    |       FV
  |         |               |       ↓
  0         1              N – 1    N
              %i
```

Time-Line Diagram 9-13

The present value of the lease is the sum of PV1 and PV2.

Notice that in both examples, the value for FV occurs at the end of the final payment period. Also, both the payments and future value are either paid or received. Both are either cash outflows or inflows (represented by the up arrow or down arrow). These are two important assumptions built into the calculator. As a result, if you have a cash flow analysis that fits either of the above general time-line diagrams, your calculator solves directly for PV, %i, N, PMT, or FV. You do not have to solve for PV1 and PV2 and then add them; your calculator automatically does it. The following terms are used when discussing this type of annuity.

(Present Value Annuities with an Ending Balloon or Salvage Value–Continued)

Present value (PV)—the present value of N payments plus the present value of the cash flow (FV) occurring at the end of the final payment period.

Future value (FV)—the remaining balance occurring at the end of the final payment period (also called a balloon or salvage value).

Payment (PMT)—the level payment occurring each period.

Number of payments (N)—the number of payments.

Interest rate (%i)—the interest rate per payment period.

Solving for the Present Value of an Annuity with a Remaining Balance

Concepts

The total present value is the sum of the present value for an annuity with N payments and the present value of a future cash flow (FV) occurring at the end of the last payment period. To solve for present value, you must know: N, the number of equal payments; %i, the interest rate per payment period; PMT, the equal payment amount; and FV, the value at the end of the Nth payment period.

Payments occurring at the *end* of each period (*ordinary annuity*):

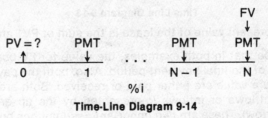

Time-Line Diagram 9-14

Advanced Time Value of Money Topics Chapter 9

(Present Value Annuities with an Ending Balloon or Salvage Value–Continued)

Payments occurring at the *beginning* of each period (*annuity due*):

PV = ?

PMT	PMT	...	PMT	FV
0	1		N − 1	N

%i

Time-Line Diagram 9-15

The following general equation is designed to determine the present value of an annuity with a remaining balance.

$$PV = (1 + (\%i/100)\,K)\,PMT \left[\frac{1 - (1 + \%i/100)^{-N}}{\%i/100} \right]$$
$$+ FV(1 + \%i/100)^{-N} \qquad \textit{Equation (9-7)}$$

where:

K = 0 if PMT occurs at the *end* of each payment period (ordinary annuity).

K = 1 if PMT occurs at the *beginning* of each payment period (annuity due).

The introduction to this section states that the present value of an annuity with an ending balloon or salvage value can be decomposed into two time-line diagrams. One of the diagrams is for the annuity and the other diagram is for the remaining balance. Equation (9-7) can also be decomposed into two equations discussed in Chapters 8 and 9. The first part of equation (9-7) is the equation for the present value of an annuity, equation (8-22) or (9-4). The second part of equation (9-7) is the compound interest present value formula, equation (8-5).

FINANCE

9-23

(Present Value Annuities with an Ending Balloon or Salvage Value–Continued)

Example

The Big Oil Company is buying land from you. They have offered to pay for the land by making 120 monthly payments of $5000 with a balloon payment of $150,000 in addition to the last $5000 payment. You have the choice of receiving the monthly payments at the beginning or end of each month. Using an annual interest rate of 18% compounded monthly, determine which payment method gives you the largest present value.

Payments occurring at the *end* of each period (ordinary annuity):

```
                                              FV = $150,000
                                                   ↑
   PV = ?      $5000           $5000    $5000
     ↓           ↑               ↑        ↑
     0           1      . . .   119     N = 120
                  % i = 18/12 = 1.5
```

Time-Line Diagram 9-16

Payments occurring at the *beginning* of each period (annuity due):

```
   PV = ?
     ↓
   $5000      $5000           $5000    FV = $150,000
     ↑          ↑               ↑        ↑
     0          1      . . .   119     N = 120
                 % i = 18/12 = 1.5
```

Time-Line Diagram 9-17

(Present Value Annuities with an Ending Balloon or Salvage Value–Continued)

Calculator Solution

Your calculator is programmed to solve equation (9-7), as shown in the following example. If the "DEC 2" indicator does not appear in the display, press ⟨2nd⟩ ⟨Decimal⟩ before keying in the example.

Procedure	Press	Display
1. Clear calculator and select finance mode.	⟨ON/c⟩ ⟨2nd⟩ ⟨FIN⟩	0 DEC 2 FIN
2. Enter number of equal payments.	120 ⟨N⟩	120.00 DEC 2 FIN
3. Enter percent interest rate per payment period.	18 ⟨÷⟩ 12 ⟨=⟩ ⟨%i⟩	1.50 DEC 2 FIN
4. Enter amount of equal payment.	5000 ⟨PMT⟩	5000.00 DEC 2 ANN FIN
5. Enter balloon at end of last payment period.	150000 ⟨FV⟩	150000.00 DEC 2 ANN FIN
6. a) Compute present value with equal payments occurring at *end* of each month.	⟨CPT⟩ ⟨PV⟩	302620.75 DEC 2 ANN FIN
b) Compute present value with equal payments occurring at *beginning* of each month.	⟨DUE⟩ ⟨PV⟩	306783.13 DEC 2 ANN FIN

If you accept beginning-of-period payments, the present value is $306,783.13 compared to $302,620.75 for end-of-period payments.

Advanced Time Value of Money Topics

(Present Value Annuities with an Ending Balloon or Salvage Value–Continued)

Review

Equation (9-7) is solved using the procedure below when you enter the inputs shown in the time-line diagram. Be sure to clear the financial registers at the start of each problem by pressing 2nd FIN .

Equation Value	Meaning	Keystroke
Inputs:		
N	Number of equal payments.	N
%i	Percent interest rate per payment period.	%i
PMT	Equal payment per period.	PMT
FV	Cash flow occurring at *end* of Nth payment period.	FV
Solution:	a)Solve for PV if payment occurs at *end* of each period.	CPT PV
	b)Solve for PV if payment occurs at *beginning* of each period.	DUE PV

(Present Value Annuities with an Ending Balloon or Salvage Value–Continued)

Going Further With Present Value Annuities and a Remaining Balance or Balloon

Your calculator solves for any one of the five values (N, %i, PMT, PV, and FV) if the other four values are entered. Press CPT for an ordinary annuity or press DUE for an annuity due before pressing the unknown value key. Earlier, when solving present value annuities, the following equations were used. However, a zero was entered in the FV register since you cleared the financial registers (N, %i, PMT, PV, and FV) and did not enter a value for FV. Pressing CPT makes K = 0, and pressing DUE makes K = 1.

Solving for the Payment

General Equation

$$PMT = \frac{\left[PV - FV(1 + \%i/100)^{-N} \right]}{(1 + \%iK/100)\left[\dfrac{1 - (1 + \%i/100)^{-N}}{\%i/100} \right]}$$

Equation (9-8)

Calculator Keys

Inputs: PV , FV , %i , N

Solution: a) End-of-period payments, CPT PMT
          b) Beginning-of-period payments, DUE PMT

Solving for the Remaining Balance or Balloon

General Equation

$$FV = PV(1 + \%i/100)^N - (1 + \%iK/100)PMT$$
$$\times \left[\frac{(1 + \%i/100)^N - 1}{\%i/100} \right]$$

Equation (9-9)

Calculator Keys

Inputs: PV , %i , N , PMT

Solution: a) End-of-period payments, CPT FV
          b) Beginning-of-period payments, DUE FV

Advanced Time Value of Money Topics

(Present Value Annuities with an Ending Balloon or Salvage Value–Continued)

Solving for the Interest Rate

General Equation (9-7)

$$PV = (1 + (\%i/100)\,K)\,PMT \left[\frac{1 - (1 + \%i/100)^{-N}}{\%i/100} \right] + FV\,(1 + \%i/100)^{-N}$$

A direct equation does not exist to determine the interest rate of an annuity with a remaining balance. Instead, a mathematical trial and error procedure is employed to find an interest rate that balances equation (9-7).

Calculator Keys

Inputs: $\boxed{PV}$, $\boxed{FV}$, $\boxed{PMT}$, $\boxed{N}$

Solution: a) End-of-period payments, $\boxed{CPT}\boxed{\%i}$
           b) Beginning-of-period payments, $\boxed{DUE}\boxed{\%i}$

Solving for the Number of Time Periods

General Equation

$$N = \frac{\ln\left[\dfrac{\%i\,FV/100 - (1 + \%iK/100)\,PMT}{\%i\,PV/100 - (1 + \%iK/100)\,PMT} \right]}{\ln(1 + \%i/100)}$$

Equation (9-10)

Calculator Keys

Inputs: $\boxed{PV}$, $\boxed{FV}$, $\boxed{PMT}$, $\boxed{\%i}$

Solution: a) End-of-period payments, $\boxed{CPT}\boxed{N}$
           b) Beginning-of-period payments, $\boxed{DUE}\boxed{N}$

Future Value Annuities with a Beginning Balance

Some time-value-of-money applications have beginning cash flows and a series of equal payments being compounded forward to a future value. Sinking funds and savings accounts are two such examples.

These time-value-of-money applications are solved by combining a future value annuity and the compound amount of the beginning cash flow. The future value annuity term is used not only because it has a future value (FV), but because the present value (PV) and payment (PMT) are of the same nature (both inflows or outflows) and are *compounded forward* to equal the future value. To illustrate, assume a savings account has a beginning balance (PV) and a series of end-of-period deposits.

The general time-line diagram for ordinary annuities is:

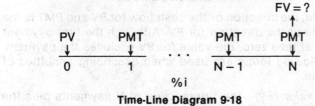

Time-Line Diagram 9-18

Decomposing the above diagram into two diagrams for the concept results in:

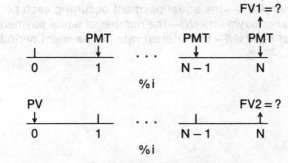

Time-Line Diagram 9-19

Advanced Time Value of Money Topics

*(Future Value Annuities with a Beginning Balance–
Continued)*

The total present value is the sum of FV1 and FV2. Notice that the future value is calculated at the end of the final payment period. Also, the PV and PMT are both either paid or received.

An annuity due with a beginning balance is analyzed using the same approach.

Time-Line Diagram 9-20

Again, the direction of the cash flow for PV and PMT is the opposite of the direction for FV. Although the first payment occurs at time zero, the value for PV excludes the payment. The following terms are used when describing annuities of this type.

Future value (FV)—the future value of N payments plus the future value of the initial cash flow (PV).
Present value (PV)—the cash flow occurring at time zero, excluding regular payments.
Payment (PMT)—the equal payment occurring each period.
Number of payments (N)—the number of equal payments.
Interest rate (%i)—the interest rate per payment period.

*(Future Value Annuities with a Beginning Balance–
Continued)*

Solving for the Interest Rate of a Future Value Annuity with a Beginning Balance

Concepts

 You may calculate the interest rate per payment period that compounds forward N equal payments and a beginning balance (PV) to equal a specified future value. The inputs you need are: N, the number of equal payments; PV, the initial balance or cash flow; PMT, the equal payment each period; and FV, the value at the end of N payment periods plus the value of the initial cash flow (PV).

Payments occurring at the *end* of each period (ordinary annuity):

$$\text{\%i} = \text{?}$$

Time-Line Diagram 9-21

Payments occurring at the *beginning* of each period (annuity due):

$$\text{\%i} = \text{?}$$

Time-Line Diagram 9-22

Advanced Time Value of Money Topics

(Future Value Annuities with a Beginning Balance–Continued)

The following equation determines the interest rate of a future value annuity with a beginning balance.

$$FV = (1 + \%iK/100)\, PMT \left[\frac{(1 + \%i/100)^N - 1}{\%i/100} \right]$$
$$+ PV\,(1 + \%i/100)^N \qquad \text{Equation (9-11)}$$

where:

K = 0 if PMT occurs at the end of each payment period

K = 1 if PMT occurs at the beginning of each payment period

In the introduction to this section, you saw that the future value of an annuity with a beginning balance could be decomposed into two time-line diagrams. One of the diagrams is for the annuity and the other diagram is for the beginning balance. Equation (9-11) can also be decomposed into two equations discussed in Chapters 8 and 9. The first part of equation (9-11) is the equation for the future value of an annuity, equation (8-13) or (9-1). The second part of equation (9-11) is the compound interest future value formula, equation (8-3).

*(Future Value Annuities with a Beginning Balance–
Continued)*

Example

Your savings account has a $4000 balance on
January 1st. You plan to deposit $50 a month for
five years to accumulate $10,000. What interest
rate is necessary to satisfy your goals if you a)
make end-of-month deposits or b) make
beginning-of-month deposits?

Payments made at the *end* of each period (ordinary annuity):

FV = $10,000

PV = $4000 $50 $50 $50

0   1   59   N = 60
(N = 5 yrs × 12 P/yr)
%i = ?

Time-Line Diagram 9-23

Payments made at the *beginning* of each period (annuity due):

PV = $4000

$50 $50 $50   FV = $10,000

0   1   59   N = 60
(N = 5 yrs × 12 P/yr)
%i = ?

Time-Line Diagram 9-24

Calculator Solution

Your calculator uses a mathematical trial and error procedure to balance equation (9-11) as shown in the following
example. The payment is entered as a negative value to indicate compounding forward. To ensure that negative payment values need to be entered, check the cash flow pattern
(inflows and outflows) of the general time-line diagram 9-21 or
9-22. If the cash flow pattern is the same or completely opposite to time-line diagram 9-21 or 9-22, negative payment
values are required. Pressing CPT places the payments at the
end of each period, while pressing DUE places the payments
at the beginning of each period.

Advanced Time Value of Money Topics

(Future Value Annuities with a Beginning Balance–Continued)

If the "DEC 2" indicator does not appear in the display, press [2nd] [Decimal] before keying in the example.

Procedure	Press	Display
1. Clear calculator and select finance mode.	[ON/C] [2nd] [FIN]	0
2. Enter number of equal payments.	5 [X] 12 [=] [N]	60.00
3. Enter initial balance.	4000 [PV]	4000.00
4. Enter amount of regular payment as negative value.	50 [+/−] [PMT]	− 50.00
5. Enter future value.	10000 [FV]	10000.00
6. Solve for: a) Interest rate per month with end-of-period payments.	[CPT] [%i]	0.74
b) Annual rate.	[X] 12 [=]	8.92
7. Solve for: a) Interest rate per month with beginning-of-period payments.	[DUE] [%i]	0.74
b) Annual rate.	[X] 12 [=]	8.85

An annual interest rate of 8.92% is required if the $50 is deposited at the end of each month. Making the payments at the beginning of each month, however, requires a lower rate of 8.85%. Note that the interest rate per month with end-of-period payments and with beginning-of-period payments appears the same (0.74) due to the decimal two rounding.

*(Future Value Annuities with a Beginning Balance–
Continued)*

Review

A direct equation does not exist to determine the
interest rate. Using the following inputs, the
calculator employs a mathematical trial and error procedure that balances equation (9-11). Be
sure to clear the financial registers at the start of
each problem by pressing 2nd FIN.

Equation Value	Meaning	Keystroke
Inputs:		
N	Total number of equal payments.	N
PV	Initial cash flow separate from payment at time zero.	PV
PMT	Equal payment per period entered as negative value.	+/− PMT
FV	Future value of payment and initial cash flow (PV) at end of last payment period.	FV
Solution:	Solve for percent interest rate per payment period	
	a) End-of-period payments	CPT %i
	b) Beginning-of-period payments.	DUE %i

The payment is entered as a negative value to indicate
compounding forward. To ensure that negative payment
values need to be entered, check the cash flow pattern (inflows and outflows) of the general time-line diagram 9-21 or
9-22. If the cash flow pattern is the same or completely opposite to time-line diagram 9-21 or 9-22, negative payment
values are required. Pressing CPT places the payments at the
end of each period, while pressing DUE places the payments
at the beginning of each period.

*(Future Value Annuities with a Beginning Balance–
Continued)*

Going Further With Future Value Annuities and a Beginning Balance

Your calculator solves for any one of the five values (N, %i, PMT, PV, and FV) if the other four values are entered. Press ⟨CPT⟩ for an ordinary annuity or ⟨DUE⟩ for an annuity due before pressing the unknown value key. When you previously solved future value annuities, the following equations were used. A zero was entered in the PV register when the calculator was cleared. Pressing ⟨CPT⟩ automatically sets K = 0, while pressing ⟨DUE⟩ automatically sets K = 1.

Solving for Future Value

General Equation (9-11)

$$FV = (1 + \%iK/100)\, PMT \left[\frac{(1 + \%i/100)^N - 1}{\%i/100} \right]$$
$$+ PV(1 + \%i/100)^N$$

Calculator Keys

Inputs: ⟨PV⟩, ⟨+/−⟩⟨PMT⟩, ⟨%i⟩, ⟨N⟩

Solution: a) End-of-period payments, ⟨CPT⟩⟨FV⟩
          b) Beginning-of-period payments, ⟨DUE⟩⟨FV⟩

Solving for the Payment

General Equation

$$PMT = \frac{FV - PV(1 + \%i/100)^N}{(1 + \%iK/100) \left[\dfrac{(1 + \%i/100)^N - 1}{\%i/100} \right]}$$

Equation (9-12)

Calculator Keys

Inputs: ⟨PV⟩, ⟨FV⟩, ⟨N⟩, ⟨%i⟩

Solution: a) End-of-period payments, ⟨CPT⟩⟨PMT⟩
          b) Beginning-of-period payments, ⟨DUE⟩⟨PMT⟩
          (Answer is negative)

(Future Value Annuities with a Beginning Balance–Continued)

Solving for the Present Value

General Equation

$$PV = FV(1 + \%i/100)^{-N} - (1 + \%iK/100)\,PMT$$
$$\times \left[\frac{1 - (1 + \%i/100)^{-N}}{\%i/100} \right]$$

Equation (9-13)

Calculator Keys

Inputs: `FV`, `+/−` `PMT`, `%i`, `N`

Solution: a) End-of-period payments, `CPT` `PV`
b) Beginning-of-period payments, `DUE` `PV`

Solving for the Number of Payments

General Equation (9-10)

$$N = \frac{\ln\left[\dfrac{\%i\,FV/100 - (1 + \%iK/100)\,PMT}{\%i\,PV/100 - (1 + \%iK/100)\,PMT} \right]}{\ln(1 + \%i/100)}$$

Calculator Keys

Inputs: `PV`, `+/−` `PMT`, `FV`, `%i`

Solution: a) End-of-period payments, `CPT` `N`
b) Beginning-of-period payments, `DUE` `N`

Advanced Time Value of Money Topics

Perpetual Annuities

A perpetual annuity has even payments that continue indefinitely. An example of a perpetual annuity is a preferred stock which yields a constant dollar dividend forever. The following terms are used when discussing perpetual annuities.

Present value (PV) — the present value of perpetual payments.
Interest rate (%i) — the interest rate per payment period.
Payment (PMT) — the perpetual payment amount.

Because the term $(1 + i)^{-N}$ in the present value annuity equation approaches zero as N becomes larger, the present value equation can be expressed as:

$$PV = \frac{PMT}{(\%i/100)} \quad \text{(End-of-Period Payments)}$$
Equation (9-14)

$$PV = PMT + \frac{PMT}{(\%i/100)} \quad \text{(Beginning-of-Period Payments)}$$
Equation (9-15)

You can verify these equations by solving a present value annuity, with an N of 200, 500, 1000, and 2000, while studying the effect on the present value.

The following general time-line diagrams represent a perpetual annuity as an ordinary annuity and as an annuity due.

End-of-period payments (ordinary annuity):

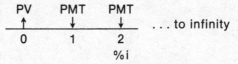

Time-Line Diagram 9-25

Beginning-of-period payments (annuity due):

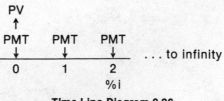

Time-Line Diagram 9-26

(Perpetual Annuities–Continued)

Solving for the Present Value of a Perpetual Annuity

Example

The Land of OZ has issued perpetual bonds for replacing bricks in their highway system. The bonds pay $110 per $1000 bond. You plan to purchase the bonds if you can earn 15% annually. What price should you pay for the bonds, assuming the first payment occurs in one year?

```
PV = ?    $110    $110
  ↑        ↓       ↓
  ─────────────────────── . . . to infinity
  0        1       2
            %i = 15
```

Time-Line Diagram 9-27

Calculator Solution

To solve for the present value of a perpetual annuity, use the arithmetic functions of the calculator. If the "DEC 2" indicator does not appear in the display, press [2nd] [Decimal] before keying in the example.

Procedure	Press	Display
1. Clear calculator.	[ON/c]	0
2. Enter payment.	110	110
3. Divide by percent interest rate to determine present value.	[÷] 15 [%] [=]	733.33

The present value is $733.33 for perpetual payments of $110 using a 15% interest rate.

Converting Annual Interest Rates

In the United States, annual interest rates are normally defined as Annual Percentage Rates (APR) or Annual Nominal Rates. The annual rate is found by multiplying the interest rate per compounding period and the number of compounding periods per year. A loan having a 1% monthly compounding rate has an annual rate of 12%.

So far, the number of payment periods and the number of compounding periods per year have been equal. This is a valid assumption in many situations, but it is not valid in others. For example, savings and loan associations may compound interest daily while deposits are made monthly.

Furthermore, in many investment situations the number of compounding periods per year may differ from investment to investment. This means the comparison of APRs is misleading. In such situations, a comparison of the annual effective rates is the true measure. This section shows you how to convert an APR to an annual effective rate and vice versa using the calculator's built-in conversion keys.

Consider an investment of $1 for 12 months with an APR of 12% compounded monthly. The value of the investment at the year's end is $1.12682503. This is summarized on the time-line diagram below.

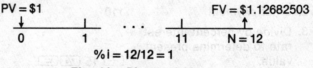

Time-Line Diagram 9-28

You can also ask the following question, "What annual interest rate compounded once a year yields the same future value?" Drawing a second time-line diagram:

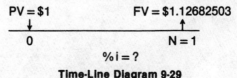

Time-Line Diagram 9-29

(Converting Annual Interest Rates–Continued)

The answer to the question is the interest rate that makes $1 grow to $1.12682503 in one compounding period. Since $1 is invested, the interest earned is $.12682503, or expressed as a percent, 12.682503%. Hence, the annual effective interest rate is 12.682503%. By definition, the annual effective rate is compounded annually. This annual effective rate is equivalent to a monthly rate of 1% compounded 12 times a year, which is also a nominal rate (or APR) of 12%. You cannot make a meaningful comparison of APRs by ranking them if each APR has a different number of compounding periods per year. The annual effective rate of each should be calculated before ranking the projects. The following terms are used when discussing interest rate conversions.

c/yr—number of compounding periods per year for APR.
$\%i_c$—the nominal rate per compounding period.
APR—the annual percentage rate where APR = $\%i_c$ (c/yr).
EFF—the annual effective rate.

Converting an APR to an Annual Effective Rate

Concepts

The annual effective rate is the interest rate compounded once a year that equals the future value of an annual percentage rate with a periodic rate of APR/(c/yr) compounded c/yr times. To solve for the annual effective interest rate, you need to know: APR, annual percentage rate; and c/yr, number of compounding periods per year for APR.

The following general equation is designed to convert an APR to an annual effective rate.

$$EFF = \left\{ \left[1 + \frac{\%APR}{100\,(c/yr)} \right]^{c/yr} - 1 \right\} \times 100$$

Equation (9-16)

(Converting Annual Interest Rates–Continued)

Example

A bank is offering a certificate that pays an APR of 15% with monthly compounding. What is the annual effective rate?

Calculator Solution

If the "DEC 2" indicator does not appear in the display, press [2nd] [Decimal] before keying in the example.

Procedure	Press	Display
1. Clear calculator and select finance mode.	[ON/c] [2nd] [FIN]	0
2. Enter number of compounding periods per year for APR.	12 [2nd] [APR►]	12.00
3. Enter APR and calculate annual effective rate.	15 [=]	16.08

An APR of 15% compounded monthly is equivalent to an annual effective rate of 16.08%.

Review

Your calculator has a special key to convert APRs to annual effective rates using the procedure shown below.

Equation Value	Meaning	Keystroke
Inputs:		
c/yr	Number of compounding periods per year for APR.	c/yr [2nd] [APR►]
APR	Enter APR as percent.	APR
Solution:	Calculate annual effective rate.	[=]

(Converting Annual Interest Rates–Continued)

Converting Annual Effective Rates to APRs
Concepts

The APR is the effective interest rate APR/(c/yr) compounded c/yr times that results in the same future value as an annual effective rate compounded annually. To solve for the APR, you need to know: EFF, the annual effective rate; and c/yr, the number of compounding periods per year for APR.

Convert an annual effective rate to an APR by simply answering the question, "What interest rate compounded c/yr times gives the same future value as the annual effective rate (EFF)?" Consider a situation where $1 invested for one year at an annual effective rate of 18% is worth $1.18 at the year's end. The time-line diagram for converting this to an APR follows.

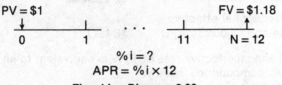

Time-Line Diagram 9-30

Determine the *monthly* periodic rate and multiply it by 12 (c/yr) for the APR.

The general equation for converting an annual effective rate to an APR follows.

$$APR = \left[(1 + \%EFF/100)^{1/(c/yr)} - 1 \right] \times (c/yr)(100)$$

Equation (9-17)

(Converting Annual Interest Rates–Continued)

Example

You are considering an investment that earns an annual effective rate of 18%. What is the equivalent APR with weekly compounding?

Calculator Solution

If the "DEC 2" indicator does not appear in the display, press [2nd] [Decimal] before keying in the example.

Procedure	Press	Display
1. Clear calculator and select finance mode.	[ON/c] [2nd] FIN	0 DEC 2 FIN
2. Enter number of compounding periods per year (52 weeks) for APR.	52 [2nd] ◄EFF	52.00 DEC 2 FIN
3. Enter annual effective rate and calculate APR.	18 [=]	16.58 DEC 2 FIN

An annual effective rate of 18% is equivalent to an APR of 16.58% compounded weekly.

Review

Your calculator has a special key to convert EFFs to APRs using the procedure shown below.

Equation Value	Meaning	Keystroke
Inputs:		
c/yr	Number of compounding periods per year for APR.	c/yr [2nd] ◄EFF
EFF	Enter annual effective rate as percent.	EFF
Solution:	Calculate APR.	[=]

Cash Flows with Compounding Periods Different from Payment Periods Per Year

In some time value of money problems, the number of payment periods differs from the number of compounding periods per year. Solving such problems is simple using the interest rate conversions discussed in the preceding section.

Since the annuity routines in the calculator assume the number of compounding periods per year (c/yr) equals payment periods per year (p/yr), you can convert the interest rate per compounding period to the equivalent interest rate per payment period using `APR►` and `◄EFF`. Once you have the equivalent interest rate per payment period, the problem is solved as an annuity or variable cash flow problem. If you are determining the interest rate, solve for the interest rate per payment period and then convert to the equivalent rate per compounding period.

Consider the following example of a payment made *semiannually* for a year with *quarterly* compounding.

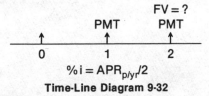

$$\%i = APR_{c/yr}/4$$
Time-Line Diagram 9-31

The diagram shows two payments and four compounding periods. The $\%i$ is equal to the quarterly rate, but the input for `%i` must be the interest rate per payment period (semiannually). Converting the $APR_{c/yr}$ compounded quarterly to the equivalent $APR_{p/yr}$ compounded semiannually, the time-line diagram is shown as:

```
                        FV = ?
              PMT       PMT
        ↑       ↑        ↑
 ───────┼───────┼────────┼───────
        0       1        2
```
$$\%i = APR_{p/yr}/2$$
Time-Line Diagram 9-32

Advanced Time Value of Money Topics

(Cash Flows with Compounding Periods Different from Payment Periods Per Year–Continued)

Once the interest rate per payment period is determined, the problem can be solved as an ordinary annuity as previously discussed.

Conversion of an interest rate compounded c/yr to an interest rate compounded p/yr can be accomplished by converting to annual effective interest rate. Conversion achieved by dividing the APR by p/yr is *not* correct since compounding effects have not been taken into account. The conversion procedure can be shown as follows:

| APR (compounded c/yr) | ► | EFF (compounded 1/yr) | ► | APR (compounded p/yr) |

This section discusses the conversion methods necessary in annuity cases where p/yr is not equal to c/yr. The terms used in this section are:

$APR_{c/yr}$—annual percentage rate compounded c/yr times.
$APR_{p/yr}$—annual percentage rate compounded p/yr times.
c/yr—number of compounding periods per year for APR.
p/yr—number of payment periods per year.
$\%i_c$—interest rate per compounding period, $\%i_c = APR/(c/yr)$.
$\%i_p$—interest rate per payment period.

(Cash Flows with Compounding Periods Different from Payment Periods Per Year–Continued)

Converting the Interest Rate Per Compounding Period to the Interest Rate Per Payment Period and Solving For PV, FV, PMT, or N

Concepts

Before solving for PV, FV, PMT, or N, the annual rate compounded c/yr times must be converted to an annual rate compounded p/yr times. After determining the interest rate per payment period, solve the problem in the normal manner. You need to know: $APR_{c/yr}$, the annual percentage rate; c/yr, the number of compounding periods per year for APR; and p/yr, the number of payment periods per year.

The following general equation is designed to determine the interest rate per payment period.

$$\%i_p = \left\{ \left[1 + \frac{APR}{100\,(c/yr)} \right]^{(c/yr)/(p/yr)} - 1 \right\} \times 100$$

Equation (9-18)

Example

On November 1st, Fred has $5000 in a savings account. He plans to deposit $100 at the beginning of each month. How much money is in the account after 22 months if the annual interest rate is 6.6% compounded quarterly?

```
$5000
  ↓
$100        $100            $100       FV = ?
  ↓           ↓      . . .    ↓          ↑
  0           1              21        N = 22
```

$$\%i_c = 6.6/4 = 1.65$$
$$\%i_p = ?$$

Time-Line Diagram 9-33

As indicated in the time-line diagram, the interest rate per payment period (i_p) must be determined before solving for FV.

Advanced Time Value of Money Topics

(Cash Flows with Compounding Periods Different from Payment Periods Per Year–Continued)

Calculator Solution

After the interest rate is converted, the future value of an annuity due is computed using normal procedures. If the "DEC 2" indicator does not appear in the display, press [2nd] [Decimal] before keying in the example.

Procedure	Press	Display
1. Clear calculator and select finance mode.	[ON/c] [2nd] [FIN]	0 _{DEC 2} _{FIN}
2. Enter number of compounding periods per year for APR_{c/yr}.	4 [2nd] [APR▶]	4.00 _{DEC 2} _{FIN}
3. Enter APR_{c/yr}, calculate EFF and store.	6.6 [=] [STO]	6.77 _{DEC 2} _{FIN}
4. Enter number of payments per year.	12 [2nd] [◀EFF]	12.00 _{DEC 2} _{FIN}
5. Recall EFF to compute equivalent rate compounded p/yr.	[RCL] [=]	6.56 _{DEC 2} _{FIN}
6. Divide by p/yr and enter interest rate.	[÷] 12 [=] [%i]	0.55 _{DEC 2} _{FIN}
7. Enter beginning balance.	5000 [PV]	5000.00 _{DEC 2} _{FIN}
8. Enter number of payments.	22 [N]	22.00 _{DEC 2} _{FIN}
9. Enter payment as a negative value to compound forward.	100 [+/−] [PMT]	−100.00 _{DEC 2} _{ANN} _{FIN}
10. Compute future value.	[DUE] [FV]	7981.39 _{DEC 2} _{ANN} _{FIN}

Fred has $7981.39 in his account after 22 payments.

(Cash Flows with Compounding Periods Different from Payment Periods Per Year–Continued)

Review

Convert the interest rates as shown below and then solve the problem using the standard procedures.

Equation Value	Meaning	Keystroke
c/yr	Number of compounding periods for $APR_{c/yr}$.	c/yr [2nd] [APR▶]
EFF	Enter $APR_{c/yr}$ and calculate annual effective rate and store.	$APR_{c/yr}$ [=] [STO]
p/yr	Enter number of payment periods per year.	p/yr [2nd] [◀EFF]
$APR_{p/yr}$	Recall annual effective rate and convert to annual rate compounded p times per year.	[RCL] [=]
p/yr	Divide by number of payments per year and enter as %i. Solve rest of problem.	[÷] p/yr [=] [%i]

Advanced Time Value of Money Topics

(Cash Flows with Compounding Periods Different from Payment Periods Per Year–Continued)

Solving for the Interest Rate per Compounding Period when Payments and Compounding Periods Per Year Differ

Concepts

Solve for the interest rate per payment period, then convert it to the equivalent rate per compounding period. You must know: i_p, the interest rate per payment period; p/yr, the number of payments per year; and c/yr, the number of compounding periods per year.

The following general equation is designed to determine the interest rate per compounding period.

$$\%i_C = \left\{ \left[1 + \%i_p/100 \right]^{(p/yr)/(c/yr)} - 1 \right\} \times 100$$

Equation (9-19)

$$APR_{c/yr} = \%i_C (c/yr) \qquad \text{Equation (9-20)}$$

Example

You paid $56,000 for an Armadillo Beer truck that will earn $1500 a month for the next five years. Assuming the cash flows occur at the end of each month, what is the annual interest rate compounded weekly on this investment?

PV = $56,000 $1500 $1500 $1500

0   1   . . .   59   N = 60

$$\%i_p = ?$$
$$\%i_c = ?$$
$$APR_{c/yr} = \%i_c \times c/yr$$

Time-Line Diagram 9-34

As indicated in the time-line diagram, the interest rate per payment period must be found before the $APR_{c/yr}$ can be determined.

(Cash Flows with Compounding Periods Different from Payment Periods Per Year–Continued)

Calculator Solution

First, the interest rate per payment period is found using standard procedures. Then it is converted to an $APR_{c/yr}$ compounded 52 times per year. If the "DEC 2" indicator does not appear in the display, press 2nd Decimal before keying in the example.

	Procedure	Press	Display
1.	Clear calculator and select finance mode.	ON/c 2nd FIN	0 DEC 2 FIN
2.	Enter number of payments.	5 ✕ 12 = N	60.00 DEC 2 FIN
3.	Enter present value.	56000 PV	56000.00 DEC 2 FIN
4.	Enter monthly payment.	1500 PMT	1500.00 DEC 2 ANN FIN
5.	Compute percent interest rate per payment period.	CPT %i	1.71 DEC 2 ANN FIN
6.	Multiply by number of payments per year and store ($APR_{p/yr}$).	✕ 12 = STO	20.52 DEC 2 ANN FIN
7.	Enter number of payments per year.	12 2nd APR▸	12.00 DEC 2 ANN FIN
8.	Recall annual rate compounded 12 times per year; calculate EFF and store.	RCL = STO	22.57 DEC 2 ANN FIN
9.	Enter number of compounding periods per year.	52 2nd ◂EFF	52.00 DEC 2 ANN FIN
10.	Recall annual effective rate and calculate $APR_{c/yr}$ compounded weekly.	RCL =	20.39 DEC 2 ANN FIN

Your investment earns an annual rate of 20.39% compounded weekly, which is equivalent to an annual effective rate of 22.57% at an annual rate compounded monthly of 20.52%.

Advanced Time Value of Money Topics

(Cash Flows with Compounding Periods Different from Payment Periods Per Year–Continued)

Review

Equation Value	Meaning	Keystroke
i	Solve for i.	
APR$_{p/yr}$	Enter number of payments per year and store.	☒ p/yr ═ STO
p/yr	Enter number of payments per year.	p/yr 2nd APR▶
EFF	Recall annual rate compounded p times and compute annual effective rate and store.	RCL ═ STO
c/yr	Enter number of compounding periods per year.	c/yr 2nd ◀EFF
APR$_{c/yr}$	Recall annual effective rate and convert to APR$_{c/yr}$ compounded c times per year.	RCL ═

Chapter 10
VALUATION OF BONDS AND STOCKS

Valuation of Bonds and Stocks

Contents

Introduction

Long-term securities such as bonds, preferred stock, and common stock are issued by firms to help meet the needs for funds. The valuation of stocks and bonds is of interest to a number of people including financial managers of firms, current and prospective owners, and security analysts. It is important for the firm's financial managers to know how the value of the firm's securities is affected by their decisions. The firm's current and prospective owners compare their firm's securities to the market prices to make rational decisions. Similarly, security analysts study the value of the long-term securities and other factors when making investment recommendations.

The value of a long-term security such as a bond, preferred stock, or common stock is based on the expected cash returns generated during the period that the asset is held. These cash returns may be interest or dividend payments. Thus, the value of a bond, preferred stock, or common stock is the present value of all future cash receipts discounted at an appropriate interest rate. The procedure to determine an asset's value is known as the *capitalization-of-income* method of valuation.

The first step in the valuation process is to determine an appropriate discount rate. This discount rate includes the riskless rate of return plus a risk premium dependent upon the β (risk factor) of an individual security. A detailed discussion of the discount rate can be found in various finance texts. In this book, valuation of a security is based on a given discount rate.

The terminology used when dealing with bonds and stocks is slightly different. For example, the interest rate that discounts future cash flows back to an amount equal to the present value is called "Yield to Maturity" for a bond and "Rate of Return" for stocks. However, the basic techniques are identical to the valuation procedures discussed in Chapters 8 and 9.

Bonds

A bond is a financial obligation made by a corporation or a government agency. The purchaser of a bond receives fixed periodic interest payments, usually semiannually, and receives the face value of the bond on the redemption or maturity date.

Each period's interest payment equals the interest rate printed on the bond divided by the number of payments per year, then multiplied by the face value of the bond. For example, each six months a $1000 bond earning 10% annual interest compounded semiannually pays:

$$\frac{.10}{2} \times \$1000 = \$50$$

This semiannual interest payment is often called the coupon payment. (The word coupon refers to the fact that the semiannual payment is frequently collected by presenting a coupon from a printed sheet that is part of the bond). In this case, each coupon payment is $50 or 5% of the face value of the bond. This payment amount and the coupon rate remain constant. Bonds, however, often sell at prices above or below the face value. A bond selling for an amount greater than the face (or par) value sells at a *premium*, while a bond priced below par sells at a *discount*.

The actual selling price is determined by the return paid on money invested as specified by the general level of interest plus a premium that incorporates the investment's risk. For example, a bond was originally sold when 9% was an acceptable return. If 12% is required currently in the market, the bond must be sold below par (at a discount) to allow for the change in the return required by financial markets. This return required by financial markets is called *yield to maturity*. The yield to maturity desired by an investor is a function of many factors: the issuer's bond rating, the state of the economy, and the maturity of the bonds purchased, to name a few.

(Bonds–Continued)

The approaches included here are commonly used for computing bond price and yield to maturity. However, the examples shown are specific illustrations and do not consider all of the factors that may affect the bond market. Historically, bond transactions incorporate a variety of approximations. Many of these different types of calculations are used today. Because of this, the answers obtained by the following methods may not be identical to answers from other sources.

Price of a Bond Sold on a Coupon Payment Date

Concepts

The price of a bond sold on a coupon payment date is the present value of the coupon payments and the redemption value. Yield to maturity is used to discount the payments and redemption value to the present value.

Your calculator uses equation (9-8), present value of an ordinary annuity with an ending balloon value, to compute the price of a bond sold on an interest date. For bonds, periodic payments are coupon payments (C) and the future value is the redemption value (M); thus, the equation for the price of a bond (P) is:

$$P = (1 + (\%i/100)K)C \left[\frac{1 - (1 + \%i/100)^{-N}}{\%i/100} \right]$$
$$+ M(1 + \%i/100)^{-N}$$

Equation (10-1)

where:

K = 0 in equation (10-1) because the coupon payments occur at the end of each period (ordinary annuity).

%i = the required rate of return per period.

Some texts use the symbol k or r for the required rate of return. In this book, %i is used.

Valuation of Bonds and Stocks

(Bonds–Continued)

Example

The ABC Company issued 20-year bonds to finance a new plant. The bonds have a 10% coupon rate with semiannual payments, but the yield to maturity when the bonds were issued was 11%. What was the bond price per $1000?

The following input values are given or must be calculated to solve the problem.

Interest rate per coupon period (%i)

$$= \frac{11\% \text{ Annual yield to maturity}}{2 \text{ coupon payments per year}}$$

$$= 5.5\%$$

Amount of coupon payment (C)

$$= \frac{\$1000 \text{ Par} \times 0.10 \text{ Annual coupon rate as a decimal}}{2 \text{ coupon payments per year}}$$

$$= \$50$$

Number of coupon payments (N)

$$= 20 \text{ years} \times 2 \text{ coupon payments per year}$$

$$= 40 \text{ payments}$$

Redemption value (M) = $1000 par

```
                                          M = $1000
                                              ↑
    P = ?      $50          $50      $50
      ↓         ↑            ↑        ↑
    ┌───────────────── ... ──────────────┐
    0           1            39     N = 40
```

Yield per coupon period = %i = 5.5%

Time-Line Diagram 10-1

The payments are at the end of each coupon period because interest is paid at the end of each six month period. The bond price is the present value of 40 end-of-period $50 payments plus a final balloon payment of $1000. These cash flows are discounted using the 5.5% yield-to-maturity per coupon period.

(Bonds–Continued)

Calculator Solution

If the "DEC 2" indicator does not appear in the display, press 2nd Decimal before keying in the example.

Procedure	Press	Display
1. Clear calculator and select finance mode.	ON/c 2nd FIN	0 DEC 2 FIN
2. Calculate and enter yield per coupon period.	11 ÷ 2 = %i	5.50 DEC 2 FIN
3. Calculate and enter coupon payment.	1000 X 10 % ÷ 2 = PMT	50.00 DEC 2 ANN FIN
4. Calculate and enter number of coupon payments.	20 X 2 = N	40.00 DEC 2 ANN FIN
5. Enter redemption value.	1000 FV	1000.00 DEC 2 ANN FIN
6. Compute bond price (present value).	CPT PV	919.77 DEC 2 ANN FIN

The price is $919.77. This is the present value of 40 end-of-period $50 payments and of the $1000 redemption value received at the end of the 40th period, discounted at 5.5% per semiannual period.

(Bonds–Continued)

Review

Be sure to clear the financial registers at the start of each problem by pressing [2nd] [FIN].

Equation Value	Meaning	Keystroke
Inputs:		
%i	Annual yield to maturity divided by number of coupon payments per year.	[%i]
C	Par times annual coupon rate divided by number of coupon payments per year.	[PMT]
N	Bond life in years times number of coupon payments per year.	[N]
M	Redemption value.	[FV]
Solution:	Solve for bond price.	[CPT] [PV]

(Bonds–Continued)

Yield to Maturity for a Bond Sold on a Coupon Payment Date

Concepts

The yield to maturity is the interest rate per coupon period that discounts the coupon payments and redemption value back to a present value equaling the bond price. This yield calculation assumes the bond is held until it matures. Yield to maturity is an earnings rate only when the coupon payments are reinvested at the yield-to-maturity rate.

Your calculator, using a mathematical trial-and-error procedure, finds the interest rate that balances equation (10-1).

$$P = (1 + (\%i/100)K)C \left[\frac{1 - (1 + \%i/100)^{-N}}{\%i/100} \right]$$
$$+ M(1 + \%i/100)^{-N}$$

where:

K = 0 because payments occur at the end of each period (ordinary annuity).

%i = the required rate of return or coupon rate per period.

(Bonds–Continued)

Example

A $1000 semiannual bond with a 12% coupon rate maturing in 10 years is quoted at $1050. At this price, what is the yield to maturity?

The following input values are given or must be calculated to solve the problem.

Bond price (P) = $1050

Amount of coupon payment (C)

$$= \frac{\$1000 \text{ Par} \times 0.12 \text{ Annual coupon rate as a decimal}}{2 \text{ coupon payments per year}}$$

= $60

Number of coupon payments (N)

= 10 years × 2 coupon payments per year

= 20

Redemption value (M) = $1000 par

```
                                            M = $1000
                                                ↑
P = $1050      $60                $60          $60
    ↓           ↑       . . .      ↑            ↑
    0           1                  19        N = 20
```

Yield per coupon period = %i = ?

Time-Line Diagram 10-2

As shown in the time-line diagram, the unknown value is the yield rate per coupon period, as indicated by the question mark. The cash flow pattern is an ordinary annuity with an ending balloon value.

(Bonds–Continued)

Calculator Solution

If the "DEC 2" indicator does not appear in the display, press `2nd` `Decimal` before keying in the example.

Procedure	Press	Display
1. Clear calculator and select finance mode.	`ON/c` `2nd` `FIN`	**0** DEC 2 FIN
2. Enter bond price.	1050 `PV`	**1050.00** DEC 2 FIN
3. Calculate and enter coupon payment.	1000 `X` 12 `%` `÷` 2 `=` `PMT`	**60.00** DEC 2 ANN FIN
4. Calculate and enter number of coupon payments.	10 `X` 2 `=` `N`	**20.00** DEC 2 ANN FIN
5. Enter redemption value.	1000 `FV`	**1000.00** DEC 2 ANN FIN
6. Calculate yield per coupon period.	`CPT` `%i`	**5.58** DEC 2 ANN FIN
7. Enter number of coupon payments per year and calculate annual yield to maturity.	`X` 2 `=`	**11.16** DEC 2 ANN FIN

The annual yield to maturity is 11.16%. It is lower than the annual coupon rate of 12% because the bond is selling at a premium.

Valuation of Bonds and Stocks

(Bonds–Continued)

Review

Be sure to clear the financial registers at the start of each problem by pressing 〈2nd〉〈FIN〉.

Equation Value	Meaning	Keystroke
Inputs:		
P	Bond price.	〈PV〉
C	Par times annual coupon rate divided by number of coupon payments per year.	〈PMT〉
N	Bond life in years times number of coupon payments per year.	〈N〉
M	Redemption value.	〈FV〉
Solution:	a) Solve for yield to maturity per coupon period.	〈CPT〉〈%i〉
	b) Multiply by number of coupon payments per year (cpn/yr) to compute annual yield to maturity.	〈X〉 cpn/yr 〈=〉

(Bonds–Continued)

Perpetual Bonds

Concepts

Occasionally governments and companies issue bonds that never mature, but pay interest indefinitely. These bonds are called perpetual bonds. A perpetual bond is equivalent to a perpetual annuity.

You solve for the price of a perpetual bond using equation (9-17). Since payments are coupon payments (C), equation (9-17) can be rewritten as:

$$P = C \ / \ (\%i/100) \qquad \textit{Equation (10-2)}$$

The periodic interest rate as a percentage is found by rearranging the equation.

$$\%i = (C \times 100)/P \qquad \textit{Equation (10-3)}$$

These simple equations are solved on your calculator using the arithmetic functions as shown in the following example.

Example

The NOD government is issuing 14% perpetual bonds paying semiannual interest. You can purchase a $1000 bond for $950, but you also want a yield of 15%. What price should you pay for a 15% yield, and what is the yield on the bonds priced at $950?

The following input values are given or must be calculated to solve the problem.

Bond price (P) = $950

Coupon payment (C)

$$= \frac{\$1000 \ \text{Par} \times 0.14 \ \text{Annual coupon rate as a decimal}}{2 \ \text{coupon payments per year}}$$

$$= \$70$$

Valuation of Bonds and Stocks

(Bonds–Continued)

Desired yield (%i)
  = 15%/2 coupon payments per year
  = 7.5%

a) Solving for Price

$$P = ? \quad \$70 \quad \$70$$

```
 ↓      ↑      ↑
─┼──────┼──────┼──── . . . to infinity
 0      1      2
```

Yield per coupon period = %i = 7.5%

Time-Line Diagram 10-3

b) Solving for Yield

$$P = \$950 \quad \$70 \quad \$70$$

```
 ↓      ↑      ↑
─┼──────┼──────┼──── . . . to infinity
 0      1      2
```

Yield per coupon period = %i = ?

Time-Line Diagram 10-4

The $1000 redemption value is omitted because it is never repaid. The interest payments are made forever.

(Bonds–Continued)

Calculator Solution

If the "DEC 2" indicator does not appear in the display, press (2nd) (Decimal) before keying in the example.

Procedure	Press	Display
1. Clear calculator.	(ON/C)	**0** DEC 2 FIN
Solve for Price		
2. Enter coupon payment and divide by yield per coupon period in decimal form to calculate price.	70 (÷) 7.5 (%) (=)	**933.33** DEC 2 FIN
Solve for Yield		
3. Enter coupon payment and divide by bond price. Multiply by 100 to determine yield per coupon period as percent.	70 (÷) 950 (×) 100 (=)	**7.37** DEC 2 FIN
4. Multiply by number of coupon payments per year to calculate annual yield.	(×) 2 (=)	**14.74** DEC 2 FIN

You should pay $933.33 to earn 15%. The bonds selling at $950 earn 14.74%.

Preferred Stock

Concepts

Preferred stock has features of both bonds and common stocks. A fixed cash dividend is paid on preferred stock, just as a fixed coupon payment is paid on bonds. Holders of preferred stock, however, own equity in the company as do common stockholders. Preferred stockholders normally have precedence over common stockholders if the company liquidates. Preferred stock is limited to its stated dividend when sharing in the company's income, while common stock is unlimited. Although the preferred dividends may be missed, the preferred stockholder's position is normally protected by the provision that no dividends be paid to common stockholders until the skipped payment is made to preferred stockholders.

This section deals with preferred stock issued *without* expectation of being redeemed. Thus, the valuation is identical to perpetual bonds. Preferred stock values are determined using the perpetual annuity equation (9-17).

To find the present value to the company of the preferred stock, the flotation costs are subtracted from the present value obtained using this equation. The flotation costs are the costs of issuing the securities. In the following example, the flotation costs are ignored. Since the payment is the dividend (d) in preferred stock applications, equation (9-17) could be rewritten as:

$$P = d \left/ (\%i/100) \right. \qquad \textit{Equation (10-4)}$$

The interest rate as a percentage is found by rearranging equation (10-4).

$$\%i = (d \times 100) \left/ P \right. \qquad \textit{Equation (10-5)}$$

(Preferred Stock–Continued)

These simple equations are solved on your calculator using the arithmetic functions as shown in the following example.

Example

The Golly Gee Company preferred stock pays a $4.25 annual dividend. In 1975 you purchased 100 shares at $53.25. The stock is selling at a price yielding 9.75% annually. What is the current stock price, and what is the yield on the stock you purchased in 1975?

The inputs needed to solve the problem are given.

Stock price (P) = $53.25
Dividend (d) = $4.25
Desired yield (%i) = 9.75%

a) Solving for Price

$$
\begin{array}{cccc}
P=? & \$4.25 & \$4.25 & \\
\downarrow & \uparrow & \uparrow & \ldots \text{to infinity} \\
\hline
0 & 1 & 2 &
\end{array}
$$

Annual Yield = %i = 9.75%

Time-Line Diagram 10-5

b) Solving for Yield

$$
\begin{array}{cccc}
P=\$53.25 & \$4.25 & \$4.25 & \\
\downarrow & \uparrow & \uparrow & \ldots \text{to infinity} \\
\hline
0 & 1 & 2 &
\end{array}
$$

Annual Yield = %i = ?

Time-Line Diagram 10-6

Valuation of Bonds and Stocks

(Preferred Stock–Continued)

Calculator Solution

If the "DEC 2" indicator does not appear in the display, press `2nd` `Decimal` before keying in the example.

Procedure	Press	Display
1. Clear calculator.	`ON/c`	**0** DEC 2 FIN
Solve for Price		
2. Enter dividend payment and divide by yield.	4.25 `÷` 9.75 `%` `=`	**43.59** DEC 2 FIN
Solve for Yield		
3. Enter dividend payment and divide by stock price. Multiply by 100 to determine annual yield.	4.25 `÷` 53.25 `X` 100 `=`	**7.98** DEC 2 FIN

The current stock price is \$43.59, yielding 9.75% annually. The return on the stock purchased in 1975 for \$53.25 is 7.98% annually.

Common Stock

Common stock represents ownership in a company. As a result, common stockholders normally have voting rights and share in company's income either through dividends or through an increase in the stock price. They also share in the risk. Their liquidation rights come after bond and preferred stockholder's rights.

The dividend is not guaranteed because it is determined by the board of directors. It may be decreased or omitted if net income is down or an operating loss is incurred. Some companies pay no dividends so they can reinvest all income.

In general, the stock price is the present value of the dividends plus the present value of the stock's future selling price. Because of the uncertainty in predicting future cash flows and other external factors, stock valuation models at best provide "ball park" estimates. Properly used, however, the models can provide insight into a stock's value.

Four stock valuation models are discussed in this section: stock without dividends, stock with constant dividends, stock with constant growth dividends, and stock with supernormal growth dividends.

The rate of return on a stock is the interest rate that discounts the stock's dividends and future selling price back to an amount equaling the original price. Examples are shown to determine the rate of return on stocks without dividends and with constant dividends.

Valuation of Bonds and Stocks

(Common Stock–Continued)

Value of Stocks Paying No Dividends

Concepts

The value of a stock paying no dividends is the present value of its future sales price discounted at an appropriate interest rate.

Since no periodic payments (dividends) are made, the compound interest equation (8-5) can be used to determine the price (P) of the stock.

$$P = FV (1 + \%i/100)^{-N} \qquad Equation\ (10\text{-}6)$$

where FV is the future selling price.

Example

You are planning to purchase XYZ Company stock to sell for $125 in two years. Assuming you want a 17% annual rate of return, what is the most you should pay for the stock?

The inputs needed to solve the problem are given.

Future selling price of stock (FV) = $125

Number of compounding periods (N) = two years

Rate of return per compounding period (%i) = 17%

P = ?   FV = $125

    0   1   N = 2

Rate of Return = %i = 17%

Time-Line Diagram 10-7

(Common Stock–Continued)

Calculator Solution

If the "DEC 2" indicator does not appear in the display, press 2nd Decimal before keying in the example.

Procedure	Press	Display
1. Clear calculator and select finance mode.	ON/c 2nd FIN	0 DEC 2 FIN
2. Enter estimated future selling price.	125 FV	125.00 DEC 2 FIN
3. Enter rate of return per compounding period.	17 %i	17.00 DEC 2 FIN
4. Enter number of compounding periods.	2 N	2.00 DEC 2 FIN
5. Solve for stock price (present value).	CPT PV	91.31 DEC 2 FIN

If you can buy the stock for $91.31 or less and the stock is sold for $125, you achieve the minimum 17% rate of return.

Review

Be sure to clear the financial registers at the start of each problem by pressing 2nd FIN.

Equation Value	**Meaning**	**Keystroke**
Inputs:		
FV	Future stock selling price.	FV
%i	Rate of return per compounding period.	%i
N	Number of compounding periods.	N
Solution:	Solve for stock price (P).	CPT PV

(Common Stock–Continued)

Rate of Return on Stock Paying No Dividends

Concepts

The rate of return on a non-dividend-paying stock is the interest rate that discounts the selling price back to a present value equal to the purchase price.

The rate of return is found using equation (8-7). Since the present value is the purchase price (P), equation (8-7) is:

$$\%i = [(FV/P)^{1/N} - 1]\,100 \qquad \text{Equation (10-7)}$$

Example

Three years ago you bought several shares of stock in the OX Company paying $93 per share. This year the stock is selling for $132 per share. The stock has paid no dividends. What is the rate of return on this stock if you sell it and ignore any sales fees on the transaction?

The inputs needed to solve the problem are given.

Original purchase price (P) = $93

Selling price (FV) = $132

Number of compounding periods (N) = Three years

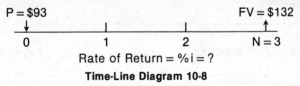

Rate of Return = %i = ?

Time-Line Diagram 10-8

(Common Stock–Continued)

Calculator Solution

If the "DEC 2" indicator does not appear in the display, press 2nd Decimal before keying in the example.

Procedure	Press	Display
1. Clear calculator and select finance mode.	ON/c 2nd FIN	0 DEC 2 FIN
2. Enter purchase price.	93 PV	93.00 DEC 2 FIN
3. Enter selling price.	132 FV	132.00 DEC 2 FIN
4. Enter number of compounding periods.	3 N	3.00 DEC 2 FIN
5. Solve for rate of return (interest rate).	CPT %i	12.38 DEC 2 FIN

The stock earned an annual rate of return equal to 12.38%.

Review

Be sure to clear the financial registers at the start of each problem by pressing 2nd FIN.

Equation Value	Meaning	Keystroke
Inputs:		
P	Original purchase price.	PV
FV	Selling price.	FV
N	Number of compounding periods.	N
Solution:	Solve for rate of return.	CPT %i

(Common Stock–Continued)

Value of a Stock Paying Constant Dividends

Concepts

The value placed on a stock varies depending on how long it is held and the amount of dividends paid. If you assume the stock is held indefinitely, then its value is the present value of a perpetuity as discussed in Chapter 8. Here, it is assumed the stock can be sold for an estimated future price. Under this assumption, the value is the present value of the future dividends and selling price.

The price is the present value of an ordinary annuity with a balloon payment. It is found using equation (9-8). For common stock, periodic payments are dividends (d). Thus the equation for the price of the stock (P) is:

$$P = (1 + (\%i/100)K)d \left[\frac{1 - (1 + \%i/100)^{-N}}{\%i/100} \right]$$
$$+ FV(1 + \%i/100)^{-N} \qquad \textit{Equation (10-8)}$$

where:

K = 0 in equation (10-8) because payments occur at the end of each quarter (ordinary annuity)

%i = rate of return per period

N = number of dividend payments.

(Common Stock–Continued)

Example

You have an opportunity to purchase a stock paying a $1.25 dividend at the end of each quarter. You have estimated that the stock can sell for $135 at the end of five years. If you want an annual rate of return of 15% compounded quarterly, what is the amount you are willing to pay for the stock, disregarding taxes and commissions?

The following inputs are given or must be calculated to solve the problem.

Rate of return per dividend period (%i) = 15%/4 = 3.75%

Dividend (d) = $1.25

Number of dividend payments (N) = 5 years × 4 dividends per year
= 20

Estimated future sales price (FV) = $135

```
                                              FV = $135
                                                  ↑
   P = ?        $1.25           $1.25      $1.25
     ↓            ↑               ↑          ↑
  ───┼────────────┼─────  . . .  ─┼──────────┼───
     0            1               19       N = 20
```

Rate of return per dividend period %i = 15%/4 = 3.75%

Time-Line Diagram 10-9

Valuation of Bonds and Stocks

(Common Stock–Continued)

Calculator Solution

If the "DEC 2" indicator does not appear in the display, press `2nd` `Decimal` before keying in the example.

Procedure	Press	Display
1. Clear calculator and select finance mode.	`ON/c` `2nd` `FIN`	**0** DEC 2 FIN
2. Enter annual rate of return and divide by number of dividends paid per year.	15 `÷` 4 `=` `%i`	**3.75** DEC 2 FIN
3. Enter dividend payment.	1.25 `PMT`	**1.25** DEC 2 ANN FIN
4. Enter years and multiply by number of dividends paid per year to calculate total dividends paid.	5 `X` 4 `=` `N`	**20.00** DEC 2 ANN FIN
5. Enter estimated future sales price.	135 `FV`	**135.00** DEC 2 ANN FIN
6. Compute stock price (present value).	`CPT` `PV`	**82.02** DEC 2 ANN FIN

Assuming your estimate of the dividends and future selling price is accurate, you should pay $82.02 for the stock.

(Common Stock–Continued)

Review

Be sure to clear the financial registers at the start of each problem by pressing [2nd] [FIN].

Equation Value	Meaning	Keystroke
Inputs:		
%i	Annual rate of return divided by number of dividend payments per year.	[%i]
d	Dividend payment.	[PMT]
N	Number of dividends paid.	[N]
FV	Estimated future value.	[FV]
Solution:	Solve for stock price.	[CPT] [PV]

Rate of Return for Stock Paying Constant Dividends

Concepts

If the stock is assumed to be held indefinitely, then its rate of return is the interest rate of a perpetuity as discussed in Chapter 9. Here it is assumed that the stock is sold. Thus, the rate of return is the interest rate that discounts the dividends and sales price back to a present value equal to the purchase price.

(Common Stock–Continued)

The rate of return is the interest rate of an ordinary annuity with a balloon payment. The unknown value is the interest rate that balances equation (10-8).

$$P = (1 + (\%i/100)K)d \left[\frac{1 - (1 + \%i/100)^{-N}}{\%i/100} \right]$$
$$+ FV (1 + \%i/100)^{-N}$$

where $K = 0$ because dividends are paid at the end of each quarter (ordinary annuity).

Example

Four years ago you purchased some stock for $53 per share. The stock paid dividends of $0.35 at the end of each quarter. You sold the stock for $65 at the end of the fourth year. Ignoring taxes and commissions, find the annual rate of return compounded quarterly.

The following inputs are given or must be calculated to solve the problem.

Purchase price of stock (P) = $53

Dividend payment (d) = $0.35

Number of dividend payments (N) = 4 years × 4 dividends
                                                    per year
                                              = 16

Selling price at end of four years = $65

FV = $65
↑
P = $53 $.35 $.35 $.35
↓   ↑   ...   ↑   ↑
0   1   15   N = 16

Rate of return per dividend period = $\%i$ = ?

Time-Line Diagram 10-10

(Common Stock–Continued)

Calculator Solution

If the "DEC 2" indicator does not appear in the display, press [2nd][Decimal] before keying in the example.

Procedure	Press	Display
1. Clear calculator and select finance mode.	[ON/c] [2nd] **FIN**	**0** _{DEC 2} _{FIN}
2. Enter purchase price.	53 [PV]	**53.00** _{DEC 2} _{FIN}
3. Enter dividend payment.	.35 [PMT]	**0.35** _{DEC 2} _{ANN} _{FIN}
4. Enter years and multiply by number of dividends paid per year to calculate total dividends paid.	4 [X] 4 [=] [N]	**16.00** _{DEC 2} _{ANN} _{FIN}
5. Enter selling price.	65 [FV]	**65.00** _{DEC 2} _{ANN} _{FIN}
6. Compute rate of return per dividend period.	[CPT] [%i]	**1.89** _{DEC 2} _{ANN} _{FIN}
7. Enter number of dividends paid per year and calculate annual rate of return.	[X] 4 [=]	**7.54** _{DEC 2} _{ANN} _{FIN}

The annual rate of return for the four years you owned the stock is 7.54%.

Valuation of Bonds and Stocks

(Common Stock–Continued)

Review

Be sure to clear the financial registers at the start of each problem by pressing [2nd] [FIN].

Equation Value	Meaning	Keystroke
Inputs:		
P	Purchase price.	[PV]
d	Dividend payment.	[PMT]
N	Number of dividends paid.	[N]
FV	Sales price.	[FV]
Solution:	a) Solve for rate of return per dividend period.	[CPT] [%i]
	b) Multiply by number of dividends paid per year to calculate annual return.	[X] p/yr [=]

(Common Stock–Continued)

Value of Stock with Normal (Constant) Growth

Concepts

A stock with normal or constant growth has dividends increasing at a specified interest rate indefinitely. Thus, the stock price (value) is the present value of dividend payments increasing at a compound rate. As shown below, the equation for the present value of a perpetuity is modified to determine the stock price.

$$P = [d / (\%i - \%G)]\,100 \qquad \textit{Equation (10-9)}$$

where:

%G = the growth rate per payment period.

%i > %G, the two interest rates cannot be equal and if %i is less than %G, a negative answer results.

This simple equation is solved on your calculator using the arithmetic functions as shown in the next example.

Example

You are considering the purchase of a stock that has dividends expected to grow indefinitely at a 4% compound interest rate. The last annual dividend is $10 per share. Assuming you want an annual return of 12%, what is the stock's value?

The inputs needed to solve the problem are given.

Last dividend paid (d) = $10

Required rate of return (%i) = 12%

Constant growth rate (%G) = 4%

$$
\begin{array}{ccc}
P = ? & \$10(1.04)^1 & \$10(1.04)^2 \\
\downarrow & \uparrow & \uparrow \qquad \ldots \text{to infinity} \\
0 & 1 & 2
\end{array}
$$

Rate of Return = %i = 12%

Time-Line Diagram 10-11

(Common Stock–Continued)

Calculator Solution

If the "DEC 2" indicator does not appear in the display, press [2nd] [Decimal] before keying in the example.

Procedure	Press	Display
1. Clear calculator.	[ON/c]	**0** DEC 2 FIN
2. Enter required rate of return and subtract growth rate.	12 [−] 4 [=] [%] [1/x]	**12.50** DEC 2 FIN
3. Enter last dividend and multiply by reciprocal of the difference in interest rates.	[×] 10 [=]	**125.00** DEC 2 FIN

The stock's value is $125.00 assuming the dividends grow indefinitely at a 4% rate.

Value of a Stock with Supernormal Growth

Concepts

Sometimes a particular stock is expected to experience "supernormal growth." For a limited, predictable period, it grows at a much faster rate than the economy as a whole and then drops back to a lower growth rate that continues indefinitely. The stock's value is the present value of the growing dividends discounted back using a specified rate of return.

(Common Stock–Continued)

Solving for the present value requires breaking the cash flows into two groups. First the present value of the normal growth dividends are found at the *end* of the *last* supernormal growth period. This value is often called the "Terminal Value."

$$\text{Terminal Value} = \frac{d(1 + gs)^N (1 + gn)}{(i - gn)}$$

Equation (10-10)

where:

gs = supernormal growth in decimal form

gn = normal growth rate in decimal form

N = number of supernormal growth periods

d = periodic dividend amount

i ≠ gn, the interest rates are unequal.

Next, the present value of the stock is found using:

$$P = d \left[\frac{1 - (1 + I)^{-N}}{I} \right] + \left[\frac{d(1 + gs)^N (1 + gn)}{(i - gn)} \right]$$
$$\times \left[\frac{1}{(1 + i)^N} \right]$$

Equation (10-11)

where:

$$I = \left[\frac{1 + i}{1 + gs} \right] - 1$$

The above equation, however, can be reduced to use your calculator for an easy solution. The terminal value is changed as shown below.

$$P = d \left[\frac{1 - (1 + I)^{-N}}{I} \right] + \left[\frac{d(1 + gn)}{(i - gn)} \right] (1 + I)^{-N}$$

Equation (10-12)

With the equation in this form, it can be solved as an ordinary annuity with a balloon using $d(1 + gn)/(i - gn)$ as the future value.

Valuation of Bonds and Stocks

(Common Stock–Continued)

Example

You are investigating a stock that pays a dividend of $2.20 annually, but is expected to grow at a supernormal rate of 25% per year for the next eight years. You expect it then to drop to a normal growth rate of 5% per year that continues indefinitely. Your company requires an annual rate of return of 11% per year on all investments. What is the value of the stock?

The inputs needed to solve the problem are shown below.

Last dividend payment (d) = $2.20

Supernormal growth rate (gs) = 25%

Number of supernormal growth periods (N) = 8

Normal growth rate (gn) = 5%

Required rate of return (%i) = 11%

PV = ? $2.2(1.25)^1$ $2.2(1.25)^8$ $2.2(1.25)^8(1.05)^1$

```
  ↓         ↑        . . .        ↑              ↑          . . . to infinity
  0         1                     8              9
```

Rate of return per dividend period = %i = 11%

Time-Line Diagram 10-12

(Common Stock–Continued)

Calculator Solution

If the "DEC 2" indicator does not appear in the display, press 〔2nd〕〔Decimal〕 before keying in the example.

Procedure	Press	Display
1. Clear calculator and select finance mode.	〔ON/C〕〔2nd〕〔FIN〕	**0** <small>DEC 2 FIN</small>
2. Calculate equivalent interest rate. a. Enter supernormal growth rate and store.	25 〔%〕〔+〕 1 〔=〕〔STO〕	**1.25** <small>DEC 2 FIN</small>
b. Enter rate of return.	11 〔%〕〔+〕 1 〔=〕	**1.11** <small>DEC 2 FIN</small>
c. Divide by results of step 2a, subtract one, multiply by 100 and enter.	〔÷〕〔RCL〕〔−〕 1 〔×〕 100 〔=〕〔%i〕	**− 11.20** <small>DEC 2 FIN</small>
3. Subtract normal growth rate from rate of return and store.	11 〔−〕 5 〔=〕〔%〕〔STO〕	**0.06** <small>DEC 2 FIN</small>
4. Enter dividend.	2.2 〔PMT〕	**2.20** <small>DEC 2 ANN FIN</small>
5. Enter normal growth rate and divide by results of Step 3 and enter future value.	〔+〕 5 〔%〕 〔÷〕〔RCL〕〔=〕〔FV〕	**38.50** <small>DEC 2 ANN FIN</small>
6. Enter number of supernormal growth periods.	8 〔N〕	**8.00** <small>DEC 2 ANN FIN</small>
7. Solve for value of stock (present value).	〔CPT〕〔PV〕	**130.74** <small>DEC 2 ANN FIN</small>

The value of the stock is $130.74.

(Common Stock–Continued)

Review

Be sure to clear the financial registers at the start of each problem by pressing [2nd] [FIN].

Equation Value	Meaning	Keystroke
Inputs:		
$(1 + gs)$	Enter supernormal growth rate and store.	gs [%] [+] 1 [=] [STO]
$(1 + i)$	Enter rate of return.	i [%] [+] 1 [=]
$\left[\dfrac{(1+i)-1}{(1+gs)}\right]\times 100$	Calculate equivalent interest rate.	[÷] [RCL] [−] 1 [×] 100 [=] [%i]
d	Last dividend payment.	[PMT]
$(i - gn)$	Subtract normal growth rate from rate of return and store.	i [−] gn [=] [%] [STO]
$\dfrac{d(1+gn)}{(i-gn)}$	Value entered for terminal value.	d [+] gn [%] [÷] [RCL] [=] [FV]
N	Number of supernormal dividend periods.	[N]
Solution:	Solve for value of stock.	[CPT] [PV]

Chapter 11
CAPITAL BUDGETING TECHNIQUES

Capital Budgeting Techniques

Contents

Introduction

Capital budgeting deals with the process of planning and financing capital outlays with returns for more than one year. Land, buildings, and equipment are examples of capital outlays. In contrast, returns from normal operating expenditures are realized during the next one-year period. Even though the one-year period is an arbitrary choice, it does provide a convenient cutoff point. Specifically, capital budgeting deals with determining incremental cash flows associated with the investment proposal and evaluating the profitability of these cash flows over the cost of the project.

Because the capital budgeting technique uses cash flows as inputs, the first discussion in this chapter is how to determine the three basic categories of cash flows. The techniques used to evaluate these projects—payback, net present value, internal rate of return, profitability index, and equivalent annuity value—are discussed next followed by a discussion of the merits of net present value versus the internal rate of return. The chapter concludes with a discussion of risk and uncertainty in cash flows.

Measuring Cash Flows

When measuring cash flows, remember several important concepts. First, the cash flow is measured on an *incremental basis*. If the project is adopted, only the *changes* in cash flows are considered.

Secondly, the cash flows are on an *after-tax basis*. The true cost of a tax deductible item is not the actual dollars paid but the amount of payment, considering taxes. Capital budgeting decisions are based on after-tax cash flows since those are the amounts retained by the investor. Because the computation of taxes under the tax code is complex and the tax paid can vary from investor to investor, an effective tax rate is used in this chapter. The effective tax rate is the actual taxes paid divided by income before taxes. An effective rate for the cash flows during the life of a project and a separate effective rate for capital gains are used in this chapter because many capital budgeting decisions have revenue from normal operations and a gain or loss on the sale of an asset.

Finally, all of the *indirect effects* of a project are considered before determining the cash flows. For example, the introduction of a new product may require increased inventory costs. Thus the net effect, direct or indirect, is used in calculating the cash flows.

Cash flows from a project can be divided into three categories.

   a) Initial investment
   b) Cash flows during the life of the project
   c) Final cash flow, gain or loss, from the sale of an asset.

In determining the cash flows from each of the categories, the three basic principles described above are applied.

(Measuring Cash Flows–Continued)

Initial Investment

Concepts

Initial investment has four component costs.
1. Asset cost including installation and shipping costs
2. Any increase in working capital requirements
3. After-tax cash flows associated with the sale of an old asset
4. Cash flows from investment tax credit

The following word formula represents a net initial investment.

Net Initial Investment = Installed cost of an asset
+ Increase in working capital required
− After-tax cash flows from the sale of the old asset
− Investment tax credit.

When calculating net initial investment, items one and two are simple; however, item three involves some complex tax laws. A simplified procedure involving three possible situations for determining cash flows is described below.

1. *Sale of an asset for book value*
   In this case, no taxes result since there is no gain or loss on the asset. The after-tax cash flow is equal to the sale price.
2. *Sale of an asset for less than net book value*
   In this case, the difference between the net book value (original cost − accumulated depreciation) and the sale price can be used to offset income, resulting in a tax savings. For example, if the current net book value is $5000 and the asset is sold for $3000, the $2000 difference can offset other income.

Capital Budgeting Techniques

(Measuring Cash Flows–Continued)

3. *Sale of an asset for more than net book value*
   The difference between the sale price and the net book value is taxed at the firm's capital gains tax rate. For example, the old machine was purchased for $10,000. The current net book value is $5000, and the sale price is $7000. In this case, $5000 is non-taxable and $2000 ($7000-$5000) is taxed at the capital gains income rate.

   After-tax cash flows from the sale of an asset can be written as:

   After tax cash flow = Asset sale price – [(Asset sale price – Net book value) × Tax rate]

   or

   After tax cash flow = Asset sale price × (1 – Tax rate) + Net book value × (Tax rate)

   Equation (11-1)

Example

Company XYZ is considering the purchase of a new machine for $50,000. The new machine replaces a fully depreciated machine originally purchased for $100,000 with a net book value and salvage value of $10,000. Installation charges of $2000 and shipping charges of $3000 are required on the new machine. The old machine can be sold for $15,000. The effective capital gains tax rate is 15%. The new machine requires an increase in inventory of $5000 because of increased capacity. What is the initial investment?

The inputs needed to solve this problem are shown below.

   Installed cost of the new machine (AC) = $55000 ($50000 + $3000 + $2000)

   Net book value of old machine (NBV) = $10000

   Asset sale price (SP) = $15000

   Tax Rate = 15%

   Increase in working capital required (WC) = $5000

(Measuring Cash Flows–Continued)

Calculator Solution

If the "DEC 2" indicator does not appear in the display, press 2nd Decimal before keying in the example.

Procedure	Press	Display
1. Clear calculator.	ON/C	0
2. Calculate asset sale price and store value.	15000 − 15 %= STO *	12750.00
3. Calculate NBV × Tax Rate %.	10000 × 15 %=	1500.00
4. Calculate after-tax cash flow from sale of old machine and store value.	+ RCL = STO	14250.00
5. Enter installed cost of new machine.	55000	55000
6. Add increase in working capital required.	+ 5000	5000
7. Subtract after-tax cash flows from sale of old machine.	− RCL	14250.00
8. Compute net initial investment.	=	45750.00

The net after-tax cash outflow resulting from the sale of the old machine and the purchase of the new machine is $45,750.

*This is the same as calculating (1 − TR%) × SP.

(Measuring Cash Flows–Continued)

Review

Equation Value	Meaning	Keystroke
(1 – Tax Rate)SP	Asset sale price.	SP ⊟ TR [%] [=] [STO]
NBV(Tax Rate)	Net book value. After-tax cash flow from the sale of old asset.	NBV [X] TR [%] [=] [+] [RCL] [=] [STO]
AC	Installed cost of an asset.	AC [+]
WC	Increase in working capital required.	WC ⊟
	After-tax cash flows from sale of an old machine.	[RCL] ⊟
IC*	Investment tax credit.	IC
Solution:	Net initial investment.	[=]

* Due to the complexity of investment tax credit laws, this topic is not discussed here. However, it can be found in other texts.

(Measuring Cash Flows–Continued)

Cash flows during the life of the project

Concepts

Cash flows during the life of an asset are affected by the operating revenues, the cash operating costs, and the depreciation tax shield.

Example

Consider the following example with $1000 revenue, $400 of cash expenses, and $200 of depreciation.

The first step in the traditional method is computing taxes as follows.

Revenue		$1000
Less:		
Cash expenses	400	
Depreciation	200	600
Income before tax		400
Tax at 40%		160
Income after tax		$ 240

Next, the non-cash deductions are added to income after tax to determine after-tax cash flows.

Income after tax	$240
Depreciation	200
After-tax cash flow	$440

Capital Budgeting Techniques

(Measuring Cash Flows–Continued)

An alternative calculation procedure which is often easier in capital budgeting problems can be used. This method computes the taxes paid or avoided (sheltered) on the individual cash flows and on the non-cash expenses such as depreciation. As an explanation, consider the following procedure for the preceding example.

	Before Tax Cash	Non-cash	Tax paid at 40%	Tax avoided at 40%	After-tax cash flow
Revenue	$1000		− $400		$600
Cash Expenses	− 400			+ $160	− 240
Net Amount	600				360
Depreciation	0	$200		+ 80	+ 80
Total after-tax cash flow					$440

As you see, the after-tax cash flow from revenue, less cash expenses of $360 ($600-$240) plus the tax of $80 avoided because of depreciation, equals the total after-tax cash flow of $440. Depreciation is not a source of cash but shelters cash flows from taxes. The depreciation deduction of $200 sheltered $80 of cash flow. Because of the $200 deduction, $80 of taxes were not paid that otherwise would have been paid. In general, the after-tax cash flow resulting from cash inflows or outflows (revenues or expenses) is calculated using:

After-Tax Cash Flow = Cash Flow × (1 − Tax Rate)

Equation (11-2)

(Measuring Cash Flows–Continued)

The cash sheltered by non-cash deductions, such as depreciation, is determined using:

Cash Sheltered = Non-cash Expense × Tax Rate
(Depreciation)

Equation (11-3)

The example is now solved using equations (11-2) and (11-3).

Calculator Solution

If the "DEC 2" indicator does not appear in the display, press [2nd] [Decimal] before keying in the example.

Procedure	Press	Display
1. Clear calculator.	[ON/c]	0 DEC 2 FIN
2. Calculate net cash flow.	1000 [−] 400 [=]	600.00 DEC 2 FIN
3. Calculate after-tax cash flow and store.	[−] 40 [%] [=] [STO]	360.00 DEC 2 FIN
4. Calculate cash shelter benefit from depreciation.	200 [×] 40 [%] [=]	80.00 DEC 2 FIN
5. Calculate total after-tax cash flow.	[+] [RCL] [=]	440.00 DEC 2 FIN

Capital Budgeting Techniques

(Measuring Cash Flows–Continued)

Review

Equation Value	Meaning	Keystroke
Cash Flow × (1 – Tax Rate)	After-tax flows from cash flow.	CF ⊟ Tx ⅌ ⊟ STO
Depreciation × Tax Rate	Tax benefit from depreciation.	DEP ⊠ Tx ⅌ ⊞
After-tax cash flow	Total after-tax cash flow.	RCL ⊟

(Measuring Cash Flows–Continued)

Final cash flow, gain or loss, from the sale of an asset

Concepts

This cash flow generally includes the salvage value of the asset plus or minus any taxable gains or losses at the time of the sale. To determine tax gain or loss, the procedure described in the "initial investment" section equation (11-2) or (11-3) is used.

Example

An asset having a net book value of $2000 is sold for $3000. The original purchase price of the machine was $5000. The effective tax rate for the firm is 48%. What is the final cash flow?

The inputs necessary to solve this problem are given below.

> Sale price of the machine (SP) = $3000
> Net book value (NBV) = $2000
> Tax Rate = 48%

Calculator Solution

If the "DEC 2" indicator does not appear in the display, press [2nd] [Decimal] before keying in the example.

Procedure	Press	Display
1. Clear calculator.	[ON/C]	0
2. Calculate asset sale price and store.	3000 [−] 48 [%] [=] [STO]	1560.00
3. Calculate NBV (Tax Rate %).	2000 [×] 48 [%] [=]	960.00
4. After-tax final cash flow.	[+] [RCL] [=]	2520.00

The after-tax cash inflow from selling the asset is $2520.

Cash Flow Examples

Three categories of cash flows and their calculation procedures have been discussed so far. Two common kinds of cash flow problems are discussed next.

Equal Cash Flows with Straight Line Depreciation

Example

 The ABC Company purchases a machine for $25,000. It has a five-year life for depreciation with a $5000 salvage value. The annual depreciation deduction is $4000. The machine should save $7000 each year before taxes and depreciation. At the end of five years, the machine is sold for $1000. Compute the after-tax cash flows assuming a 40% tax rate on operating income and a 20% rate on the asset sale.

(Cash Flow Examples–Continued)

Calculator Solution

If the "DEC 2" indicator does not appear in the display, press [2nd] [Decimal] before keying in the example.

Procedure	Press	Display
1. Clear calculator.	[ON/C]	0

Solve for total annual after-tax flows

2. Calculate after-tax cash flow and store.	7000 [−] 40 [%] [=] [STO]	4200.00
3. Calculate tax benefit from depreciation.	4000 [×] 40 [%] [=]	1600.00
4. Add results of Step 2 to calculate total annual after-tax cash flows.	[+] [RCL] [=]	5800.00

Solve for cash flow from sale of asset

5. Enter asset sale price and tax rate; store results.	1000 [−] 20 [%] [=] [STO]	800.00
6. Enter net book value and tax rate.	5000 [×] 20 [%]	0.20
7. Add results of Step 5 to determine after-tax cash flow from sale of asset.	[+] [RCL] [=]	1800.00

The after-tax cash flows from operation for years one to five are $5800 with an additional $1800 at the end of year five. The sale of the asset resulted in a $4000 tax loss ($1000 − $5000) which shelters other income equal to $800 ($4000 × .2). As a result, the $1000 received plus the tax shelter of $800 equals $1800.

(Cash Flow Examples–Continued)

Once the after-tax cash flows are determined, the next step is to draw a time-line diagram. The cash flows are now in a form that is suitable for computing the net present value or internal rate of return.

After-tax flow:

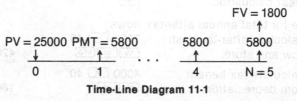

Time-Line Diagram 11-1

From the time-line diagram, the following inputs could be obtained: sale, FV = 1800; savings, PMT = 5800; outlay, PV = 25,000.

Note that the procedures for calculating net present value and internal rate of return are explained later in this chapter.

Uneven Cash Flows with Accelerated Depreciation

When cash flows vary period by period, or when an accelerated depreciation method is selected, each period's after-tax cash flows must be computed separately.

Example

The XYZ Company purchased a new molding machine for $50,000 that has a five-year life and zero salvage and market values. The annual cash savings and depreciation deduction are:

Year	1	2	3	4	5
Cash savings	$ – 5,000	$10,000	$25,000	$30,000	$25,000
Depreciation	$16,667	$13,333	$10,000	$ 6,667	$ 3,333

Using a 30% effective tax rate, compute the after-tax cash flows.

(Cash Flow Examples–Continued)

Calculator Solution

If the "DEC 2" indicator does not appear in the display, press (2nd) (Decimal) before keying in the example.

Procedure	Press	Display
1. Clear calculator.	(ON/c)	0
2. Calculate first year's after-tax cash flow.		
a. Enter net cash flow and tax rate	5000 (+/−) (−) 30 (%) (=) (STO)	− 3500.00
b. Enter depreciation and tax rate	16667 (×) 30 (%) (+)	5000.10
c. Add results of Step 2a to calculate after-tax cash flow	(RCL) (=)	1500.10
3. Calculate second year's after-tax cash flow.		
a. Cash flow	10000 (−) 30 (%) (=) (STO)	7000.00
b. Depreciation	13333 (×) 30 (%) (+)	3999.90
c. Net cash flow	(RCL) (=)	10999.90
4. Calculate third year's after-tax cash flow.		
a. Cash flow	25000 (−) 30 (%) (=) (STO)	17500.00
b. Depreciation	10000 (×) 30 (%) (+)	3000.00
c. After-tax cash flow	(RCL) (=)	20500.00

(continued)

Capital Budgeting Techniques

(Cash Flow Examples–Continued)

(continued)

Procedure	Press	Display
5. Calculate fourth year's after-tax cash flow.		
a. Cash flow	30000 ⊟ 30	
	[%] [=] [STO]	**21000.00** DEC 2 FIN
b. Depreciation	6667 [×] 30	
	[%] [+]	**2000.10** DEC 2 FIN
c. After-tax cash flow	[RCL] [=]	**23000.10** DEC 2 FIN
6. Calculate fifth year's after-tax cash flow.		
a. Cash flow	25000 ⊟ 30	
	[%] [=] [STO]	**17500.00** DEC 2 FIN
b. Depreciation	3333 [×] 30	
	[%] [+]	**999.90** DEC 2 FIN
c. After-tax cash flow	[RCL] [=]	**18499.90** DEC 2 FIN

After determining the after-tax cash flows, a time-line diagram can be prepared as below.

```
-50000   1500.10  10999.10  20500.00  23000.10  18499.90
  ↓          ↑         ↑         ↑         ↑         ↑
  0          1         2         3         4       N=5
```
Time-Line Diagram 11-2

Note that the first year's after-tax cash flow is positive while the cash flow before tax is negative. The depreciation shelters taxable income by $5000. After deducting the $3500 after-tax cash flow, the net effect is a $1500 shelter that benefits other taxable income.

Evaluating Investment Proposals

Investment proposals are often evaluated by computing the payback period, the net present value, the profitability index, or the internal rate of return. These four methods are discussed in this section, along with the calculator procedures for computing them. This section concludes with a discussion of the net present value method versus the internal rate of return method.

Payback Period

Concepts

The payback period is the number of years necessary for projected cash flows to equal the investment cost. While easy to compute, the payback period ignores the time value of money, the timing of cash flows, as well as the number of cash flows. Some companies, however, do use the payback period when the cash invested must be recovered in a relatively short time period. The payback period is calculated as follows.

Equal Annual Cash Flows

$$\text{Payback period} = \frac{\text{Cost}}{\text{Annual cash flows}}$$

Equation (11-4)

Uneven Annual Cash Flows

1. Sum the cash flows until the total exceeds the cost. Label the last cash flow as HCF, its number as HN, and the total as TCF.

2. Calculate the payback period using the following interpolation equation.

$$\text{Payback period} = \frac{(\text{Cost} - \text{TCF} + \text{HCF})}{\text{HCF}} + \text{HN} - 1$$

Equation (11-5)

(Evaluating Investment Proposals–Continued)

Example

The Keep-um-Flying Company is considering the purchase of two flight simulators. The Type A simulator costs $10,000 and saves $2000 annually for 10 years. The Type B simulator costs $8000. It saves $2000 for the first three years and $3000 for the remaining seven years. What is the payback period for each simulator?

Calculator Solution

If the "DEC 2" indicator does not appear in the display, press [2nd] [Decimal] before keying in the example.

Procedure	Press	Display
1. Clear calculator.	[ON/C]	**0** DEC 2 FIN
Payback period with even cash flows		
2. Enter cost.	10000	**10000** DEC 2 FIN
3. Divide by annual savings to determine payback period.	[÷] 2000 [=]	**5.00** DEC 2 FIN
Payback period with uneven cash flows		
4. Enter cost.	8000	**8000** DEC 2 FIN
5. Subtract annual savings until the total becomes negative.		
a) Year one savings	[−] 2000 [=]	**6000.00** DEC 2 FIN
b) Year two savings	[−] 2000 [=]	**4000.00** DEC 2 FIN
c) Year three savings	[−] 2000 [=]	**2000.00** DEC 2 FIN
d) Year four savings	[−] 3000 [=]	**−1000.00** DEC 2 FIN
Total becomes negative in year four.		
6. Add year four savings and divide by year four savings.	[+] 3000 [STO] [÷] [RCL] [=]	**0.67** DEC 2 FIN
7. Add number of year where savings exceed cost and subtract one to determine payback period.	[+] 4 [−] 1 [=]	**3.67** DEC 2 FIN

(Evaluating Investment Proposals–Continued)

Simulator A has a payback period of five years while simulator B has a payback period of 3.67 years.

Review

Equation Value	Meaning	Keystrokes
Even Cash Flows		
$\dfrac{\text{Cost}}{\text{Annual savings}}$	Payback period.	Cost ⌹ Annual Savings ⌸
Uneven Savings		
Cost	Enter cost.	Cost
Cost − TCF	Subtract projected savings until difference is negative.	⊟ Annual Savings ⌸
$\dfrac{\text{Cost} - \text{TCF} + \text{HCF}}{\text{HCF}}$	Add savings for year where difference becomes negative and divide by same amount.	⊞ HCF [STO] ⌹ [RCL]
$\dfrac{\text{Cost} - \text{TCF} + \text{HCF}}{\text{HCF}} + \text{HN} - 1$	Add last year where difference is negative and subtract one to determine payback.	⊞ HN ⊟ 1 ⌸

Capital Budgeting Techniques

(Evaluating Investment Proposals–Continued)

Net Present Value

Net present value is the present value of future cash flows discounted at the opportunity cost of capital minus the initial outlay. The opportunity cost of capital or hurdle rate for an investment project is the rate of return investors could expect to earn on securities of equivalent risk.

A positive net present value (NPV) indicates a profitable investment while a negative NPV indicates a loss. As a result, the NPV represents the project's contribution to investors' wealth in current dollars and allows comparison to other projects' NPVs when it is necessary to resolve conflicts among mutually exclusive projects.

Use of NPV for project selection is theoretically correct and should be preferred. Most NPV problems can be solved on your calculator using one of the two following methods.

Equal Cash Flows

Concepts

First, a number of NPV problems have an initial cash outflow, a series of equal cash flows, and a final extra cash flow as shown in the time-line diagram below.

```
                                              FV
                                              ↑
   PV        PMT              PMT            PMT
   ↓          ↑                ↑              ↑
   0          1       . . .   N−1             N
                    %i
```

Time-Line Diagram 11-3

When computing NPV, the %i is the hurdle rate and the PV is the present value of the equal payments and extra cash flow (FV). The NPV is the original investment subtracted from the present value of the equal payments.

(Evaluating Investment Proposals–Continued)

The payments are the equal after-tax cash flows occurring at the end of each period. The final extra cash flow is the after-tax cash flow resulting from liquidating the project at the end of the last cash flow period. Examining the cash flow pattern in the time-line diagram, you see that it is identical to a present value ordinary annuity with a final extra payment. Any of the annuity values (PV, PMT, FV, N, and %i) can be computed on your calculator using equation (9-7).

$$PV = (1 + (\%i/100)\,K)\,PMT \left[\frac{1 - (1 + \%i/100)^{-N}}{\%i/100} \right]$$
$$+ FV(1 + \%i/100)^{-N}$$

where:

K = 0 for end-of-period payments

K = 1 for beginning-of-period payments.

Net present value is found by first computing PV using equation (9-7) and then subtracting the cost.

$$NPV = PV - Cost \qquad \textit{Equation (11-6)}$$

Example

The Enterprise Paper Company is planning to pay $19,600 for a paper folding machine that should save the company $7000 a year for the next 10 years. The machine has a $1600 salvage value for depreciation and should have a $2000 market value after 10 years. This new machine replaces a current machine which has zero market and net book values. Enterprise requires a 20% rate of return on investments of this type and expects to pay an average tax rate equal to 30%. Assuming straight line depreciation, compute the net present value.

(Evaluating Investment Proposals–Continued)

Using the procedure for straight line depreciation in Chapter 15, the annual depreciation is $1800. The after-tax cash flows are:

Annual cash flow
$$\$7000 \times (1 - .3) = \$4900$$

Depreciation tax shield
$$\$1800 \times (.3) \quad = \underline{\$\ 540}$$

Total annual after-
tax cash flows $\quad = \underline{\$5440}$

The cash flow from selling the machine after 10 years is:

Cash flow after taxes from $\quad = \$2000 - [\$2000 - \$1600](.3)$
selling machine after 10 $\quad = \$1880$
years

Next, the time-line diagram is drawn to determine the inputs to solve for NPV.

```
                                                       FV = 1880
                                                          ↑
  PV = ?      PMT = 5440          5440          5440
    ↓            ↑        . . .     ↑             ↑
    0            1                  9           N = 10
                         %i = 20
```

Time-Line Diagram 11-4

(Evaluating Investment Proposals–Continued)

After completing the time-line diagram, the inputs to determine the present value are identified as PMT = 5440, FV = 1880, N = 10, and %i = 20. The NPV can be calculated as shown below.

Calculator Solution

If the "DEC 2" indicator does not appear in the display, press [2nd] [Decimal] before keying in the example.

Procedure	Press	Display
1. Clear calculator and select finance mode.	[ON/C] [2nd] **FIN**	0 DEC 2 FIN
2. Enter number of equal cash flows.	10 [N]	10.00 DEC 2 FIN
3. Enter hurdle rate.	20 [%i]	20.00 DEC 2 FIN
4. Enter annual equal cash flow.	5440 [PMT]	5440.00 DEC 2 ANN FIN
5. Enter after-tax proceeds from selling asset.	1880 [FV]	1880.00 DEC 2 ANN FIN
6. Compute present value of after-tax cash flows.	[CPT] [PV]	23110.68 DEC 2 ANN FIN
7. Subtract asset cost to determine net present value.	[−] 19600 [=]	3510.68 DEC 2 ANN FIN

The positive net present value means the investment earns 20% and has a NPV of $3510.68.

(Evaluating Investment Proposals–Continued)

Review

Be sure to clear the financial registers at the start of each problem by pressing `2nd` `FIN`.

Equation Value	Meaning	Keystrokes
Inputs:		
N	Number of equal cash flows.	`N`
%i	Hurdle rate per cash flow period.	`%i`
PMT	Equal after-tax cash flow.	`PMT`
FV	After-tax cash flow from selling asset at end of N periods.	`FV`
PV	Compute present value of cash flows.	`CPT` `PV`
Solution:		
PV − COST	Subtract cost to determine NPV.	`−` COST `=`

(Evaluating Investment Proposals–Continued)

Unequal Cash Flows
Concepts

When the project's cash flows vary or an accelerated depreciation method is selected, the net present value must be computed using the variable cash flow equation (8-30).

$$PV = \sum_{j=1}^{N} CF_j \Big/ (1 + \%i/100)^{-j}$$

$$NPV = PV - Cost \qquad \textit{Equation (11-7)}$$

Any cash flow resulting from liquidating the project is added to the final cash flow CF_N. After determining the after-tax cash flows, the NPV is found as shown in the following example.

Example

The Big Tex Boat Company is evaluating a new automated boat-making machine that costs $60,000. This machine has a five-year life and a zero salvage value for depreciation. The machine will be replaced after five years at which time it is expected to have a $10,000 market value. Depreciation is computed using the appropriate IRS accelerated cost recovery percentages (15, 22, 21, 21, 21). The machine also qualifies for the full 10% investment tax credit. The operating cash flows before taxes and the depreciation for each year are:

Year Operating	1	2	3	4	5
Cash flows	$25,000	30,000	35,000	33,000	31,000
Depreciation	$ 9,000	13,200	12,600	12,600	12,600

The company expects an effective tax rate of 35% on operating income and 20% on gains resulting from asset disposal. Assuming a hurdle rate of 18%, compute the net present value.

Capital Budgeting Techniques

(Evaluating Investment Proposals–Continued)

Using equations (11-2) and (11-3) with a 35% operating income tax rate, the resulting after-tax cash flows are:

Year After-tax Operating Cash Flows	$16,250	19,500	22,750	21,450	20,150
Tax Benefit from Depreciation	$ 3,150	4,620	4,410	4,410	4,410
Total	$19,400	24,120	27,160	25,860	24,560

Next, the after-tax cash flow resulting from selling the asset for $10,000 after 10 years is calculated using equation (11-3).

Cash flow after taxes from selling asset:

$$= \$10,000 - [\$10,000 - 0] (.2)$$
$$= \$8000$$

Finally, the tax benefit resulting from the investment tax credit of 10% at the end of the first year is calculated.

Investment tax credit = $60,000 (.1) = $6000

After determining the relevant cash flows, the next step is to develop the time-line diagram for the calculator solution.

Disposal of Asset					8,000
Investment Tax Credit	6,000				
After-Tax Operating Cash Flows	19,400	24,120	27,160	25,860	24,560
Cost of Asset	− 60,000				
Total	− 60,000	25,400	24,120	27,160	25,860	32,560
Years	0	1	2	3	4	N = 5

%i = 18

Time-Line Diagram 11-5

(Evaluating Investment Proposals–Continued)

Calculator Solution

If the "DEC 2" indicator does not appear in the display, press **2nd** **Decimal** before keying in the example.

Procedure	Press	Display
1. Clear calculator and select finance mode.	ON/C 2nd FIN	0 DEC2 FIN
2. Enter hurdle rate per cash flow period.	18 %i	18.00 DEC2 FIN
3. Calculate present value of first year's cash flow.		
a. Period	1 N	1.00 DEC2 FIN
b. Cash flow	25400 FV	25400.00 DEC2 FIN
c. Compute present value and store	CPT PV STO	21525.42 DEC2 FIN
4. Calculate present value for second year's cash flow.		
a. Period	2 N	2.00 DEC2 FIN
b. Cash flow	24120 FV	24120.00 DEC2 FIN
c. Compute present value and sum	CPT PV SUM	17322.61 DEC2 FIN
5. Calculate present value for third year's cash flow.		
a. Period	3 N	3.00 DEC2 FIN
b. Cash flow	27160 FV	27160.00 DEC2 FIN
c. Compute present value and sum	CPT PV SUM	16530.41 DEC2 FIN

(continued)

Capital Budgeting Techniques

(Evaluating Investment Proposals–Continued)

(continued)

Procedure	Press	Display
6. Calculate present value for fourth year's cash flow.		
a. Period	4 `N`	4.00
b. Cash flow	25860 `FV`	25860.00
c. Compute present value and sum	`CPT` `PV` `SUM`	13338.30
7. Calculate present value for fifth year's cash flow.		
a. Period	5 `N`	5.00
b. Cash flow	32560 `FV`	32560.00
c. Compute present value and sum	`CPT` `PV` `SUM`	14232.28
8. Recall total present value of after-tax cash flows.	`RCL`	82949.02
9. Subtract cost to determine net present value.	`−` 60000 `=`	22949.02

The present value of the cash flows is $82,949.02 and the net present value is $22,949.02. This means the investment is profitable for the company.

(Evaluating Investment Proposals–Continued)

Review

Be sure to clear the financial registers at the start of each problem by pressing 2nd FIN .

Equation Value	Meaning	Keystroke
A. %i	Hurdle rate.	%i
B. PV of CF$_1$	Present value of first cash flow.	1 N CF$_1$ FV CPT PV STO
C. PV of CF$_j$	Present value of jth cash flow. Repeat Step C until present value of all cash flows is computed.	j N CF$_j$ FV CPT PV SUM
D. NPV	Subtract cost to determine NPV.	RCL − Cost =

(Evaluating Investment Proposals–Continued)

Internal Rate of Return

The interest rate that makes the net present value equal to zero is called the Internal Rate of Return (IRR). For cash flows having an outlay at time zero and a series of inflows, IRR is the interest rate that discounts the inflows back to an amount equal to the outflow. While this latter definition satisfies many cash flow patterns, the former definition encompasses all cash flow patterns. IRR is not an earnings rate unless all cash flows are reinvested at the IRR. For example, a project with a 25% IRR does not earn that rate unless the cash flows are reinvested at 25%. Nor does IRR indicate the magnitude or number of the cash flows. It only indicates the interest rate that makes the NPV equal to zero.

(Evaluating Investment Proposals–Continued)

Equal Cash Flows

Concepts

Your calculator computes the IRR directly for cash flow patterns that can be solved using either compound interest, ordinary annuities, or annuities due. These cash flow patterns are:

Compound Interest

Ordinary Annuity with Ending Balloon

Annuity Due with Ending Balloon

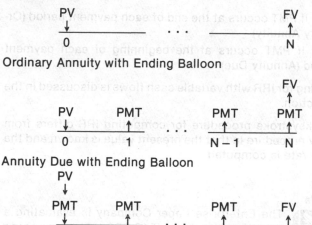

Time-Line Diagram 11-6

Capital Budgeting Techniques

(Evaluating Investment Proposals–Continued)

The interest rate that satisfies these cash flow patterns is the IRR.

The annuity equation (9-7) is:

$$PV = (1 + (\%i/100)\,K)\,PMT \left[\frac{1 - (1 + \%i/100)^{-N}}{\%i/100} \right]$$
$$+ FV (1 + \%i/100)^{-N}$$

where:

K = 0 if PMT occurs at the end of each payment period (Ordinary Annuity)

K = 1 if PMT occurs at the beginning of each payment period (Annuity Due)

Solving for IRR with variable cash flows is discussed in the next section.

The keystroke procedure for computing IRR differs from the NPV procedure in that the present value is known and the interest rate is computed.

Example

The Enterprise Paper Company is evaluating a machine costing $19,600. The machine generates annual savings of $5440 after taxes at the end of each year for 10 years. An additional after-tax cash flow of $1880 results from selling the machine at the end of 10 years. What is the Internal Rate of Return?

(Evaluating Investment Proposals–Continued)

Since the after-tax cash flows are known, the IRR can be computed after developing the time-line diagram.

Time-Line Diagram 11-7

Because the equal cash flows occur at the end of each period, this is an ordinary annuity with a balloon.

Calculator Solution

If the "DEC 2" indicator does not appear in the display, press [2nd] [Decimal] before keying in the example.

Procedure	Press	Display
1. Clear calculator and select finance mode.	[ON/c] [2nd] [FIN]	0 DEC 2 FIN
2. Enter number of equal cash flows.	10 [N]	10.00 DEC 2 FIN
3. Enter amount of equal cash flows.	5440 [PMT]	5440.00 DEC 2 ANN FIN
4. Enter initial cash outflow.	19600 [PV]	19600.00 DEC 2 ANN FIN
5. Enter cash flow from selling the asset.	1880 [FV]	1880.00 DEC 2 ANN FIN
6. Compute IRR.	[CPT] [%i]	25.04 DEC 2 ANN FIN

The interest rate of 25.04% that makes the net present value equal zero is the IRR.

(Evaluating Investment Proposals–Continued)

Review

Your calculator automatically solves equation (9-7) when you enter the inputs shown on the time-line diagram using the following procedure. Be sure to clear the financial registers at the start of each problem by pressing 2nd FIN.

Equation Value	Meaning	Keystroke
Inputs:		
N	Total number of equal after-tax cash flows.	N
PMT	Amount of after-tax equal cash flows.	PMT
PV	Cash outflow at time zero.	PV
FV	Extra after-tax cash flow at end of last equal payment period.	FV
Solution:		
	a) Solve for IRR if PMT occurs at *end* of each cash flow period.	CPT %i
	b) Solve for IRR if PMT occurs at beginning of each cash flow period.	DUE %i

(Evaluating Investment Proposals–Continued)

Unequal Cash Flows

Concepts

When the cash flows vary from period to period, you must use an interpolation procedure to estimate the IRR. By trial and error, the interest rate that makes the net present value zero in the following equation is determined.

$$NPV = \sum_{j=1}^{N} CF_j \Big/ (1 + \%i/100)^{-j} - PV$$

Equation (11-8)

Solving for the IRR requires three steps. Step 1 is to find an interest rate that gives a negative net present value. Step 2 is to find an interest rate that gives a positive net present value. These negative and positive NPVs should be as small as possible. The third step is to solve the following interpolation equation.

$$\text{Approximate IRR} = \frac{\text{Positive NPV}(H\%i - L\%i)}{(\text{Positive NPV} - \text{Negative NPV})} + L\%i$$

Equation (11-9)

where:

L%i = Interest rate used to compute the positive net present value

Positive NPV = Positive NPV computed with the L%i

H%i = Interest rate used to compute the negative net present value

Negative NPV = Negative net present value with the H%i.

Note that if the cash flows change signs more than once, multiple IRRs may exist. One symptom of multiple IRRs is when the NPV increases as the interest rate increases or when the NPV decreases as the interest rate decreases, rather than the normal case when the NPV moves opposite to the interest rate.

Capital Budgeting Techniques

(Evaluating Investment Proposals–Continued)

Example

The Big Tex Boat Company is purchasing a new automated boat hull-making machine for $60,000. The after-tax cash flows occurring at the end of each year are:

Year	1	2	3	4	5
After-tax Cash flows	$25,400	$24,120	$27,160	$25,860	$32,560

The net present value is $22,949.02 at a hurdle rate of 18%. What is the approximate IRR?

First, a time-line diagram is developed for the after-tax cash flows.

```
60000    25400    24120    27160    25860    32560
  ↓        ↑        ↑        ↑        ↑        ↑
  0        1        2        3        4       N=5
```

Time-Line Diagram 11-8

Because the NPV at 18% is positive, the IRR is a higher interest rate. By using the NPV procedure for variable cash flows, a bracket is found with a positive NPV of $3996.62 at 30% and a negative NPV of −$1864.71 at 35%. Once a bracket is obtained with a small difference between the interest rates, the interpolation equation is solved.

(Evaluating Investment Proposals–Continued)

Calculator Solution

If the "DEC 2" indicator does not appear in the display, press 2nd Decimal before keying in the example.

Procedure	Press	Display
1. Clear calculator.	ON/C	**0** DEC 2 FIN
2. Enter positive NPV.	3996.22	**3996.22** DEC 2 FIN
3. Subtract negative NPV and store results.	☐ 1864.71 +/- ☐ STO	**5860.93** DEC 2 FIN
4. Subtract low interest rate from high interest rate and multiply by positive NPV.	35 ☐ 30 ☒ 3996.22 ☐	**19981.10** DEC 2 FIN
5. Divide by results of step 3.	☐ RCL ☐	**3.41** DEC 2 FIN
6. Add low interest rate to determine approximate IRR.	☐ 30 ☐	**33.41** DEC 2 FIN

The approximate IRR is 33.41% using the linear interpolation procedure.

Capital Budgeting Techniques

(Evaluating Investment Proposals–Continued)

Review

Equation Value	Meaning	Keystrokes
Inputs:		
a. Positive NPV – negative NPV	Subtract negative NPV from positive NPV.	PNPV ⊟ NNPV ± ⊟ STO
b. (H%i – L%i) × positive NPV	Difference between interest rates times positive NPV.	H%i ⊟ L%i ⊠ positive NP ⊟
c. (H%i – L%i) × (Positive NPV) Positive NPV – Negative NPV	Divide by results of step a.	÷ RCL
d. Approximate IRR	Add L%i.	⊞ L%i ⊟

(Evaluating Investment Proposals–Continued)

Profitability Index and Equivalent Annuity Value

Concepts

The profitability index, which is also called the benefit/cost ratio, shows the total present value as a percentage of cost using the equation:

$$\text{Profitability Index} = \frac{\text{Present Value of Net Future Cash Flows}}{\text{Initial Cost}}$$

Equation (11-10)

A profitability index greater than one indicates that the net present value is positive. An index less than one indicates a negative present value. When comparing two or more investments having the *same cost*, the investment with the largest profitability index should be selected.

The equivalent annuity value is a method to convert the net present value to equivalent equal cash flows. This is a measure that some managers find useful in evaluating capital budgeting projects. The equivalent annuity value is calculated using:

$$\text{Equivalent Annuity Value} = \text{NPV} \Big/ \left[\frac{1 - (1 + \%i/100)^{-N}}{\%i/100} \right]$$

Equation (11-11)

It is simply the equal cash flows at the end of each period that discount back at the hurdle rate to an amount equaling the net present value.

Capital Budgeting Techniques

(Evaluating Investment Proposals–Continued)

Example

The Big Tex Boat Company is evaluating a capital budgeting project costing $60,000. The project has a present value of $82,949.02 and a NPV of $22,949.02 with an 18% hurdle rate over the project's five-year life. What is the profitability index and the equivalent annuity value?

Calculator Solution

If the "DEC 2" indicator does not appear in the display, press [2nd] [Decimal] before keying in the example.

Procedure	Press	Display
1. Clear calculator and select finance mode.	[ON/C] [2nd] [FIN]	0 _{DEC 2}　　_{FIN}
2. Divide present value by cost to determine profitability index.	82949.02 [÷] 60000 [=]	1.38 _{DEC 2}　　_{FIN}
3. Enter number of cash flow periods.	5 [N]	5.00 _{DEC 2}　　_{FIN}
4. Enter hurdle rate per cash flow period.	18 [%i]	18.00 _{DEC 2}　　_{FIN}
5. Enter net present value.	22949.02 [PV]	22949.02 _{DEC 2}　　_{FIN}
6. Compute equivalent annuity factor.	[CPT] [PMT]	7338.59 _{DEC 2} _{ANN} _{FIN}

The project has a profitability index of 1.38 which means that for each dollar invested today, the project returned $1.38 in present value dollars. The excess equivalent annuity factor means the net present value of $22,949.02 is equivalent, using an 18% interest rate, to receiving $7338.59 at the end of each year for five years.

(Evaluating Investment Proposals–Continued)

Review

Be sure to clear the financial registers at the start of each problem by pressing `2nd` `FIN`.

Equation Value	Meaning	Keystrokes
Profitability Index		
a) Present Value		
Cost	Compute profitability index.	PV `÷` COST `=`
b) Equivalent annuity value		
Inputs:		
N	Number of cash flow periods.	`N`
%i	Hurdle rate.	`%i`
NPV	Net present value.	`PV`
Solution:	Compute equivalent annuity value.	`CPT` `PMT`

Capital Budgeting Techniques

Net Present Value versus Internal Rate of Return

This chapter discusses several project evaluation techniques for capital budgeting. Net present value is preferred over internal rate of return as an evaluation tool for several reasons. First, IRR is not additive. The IRRs of several projects cannot be added as can NPVs. Secondly, IRR does not allow for the relative size of the investment as does NPV. Thirdly, IRR is biased in favor of the shorter-lived project. Finally, multiple IRRs can exist when more than one sign change occurs in the cash flows. The NPV is unaffected. In summary, NPV is a superior evaluation technique to IRR.

Risk and Uncertainty in Cash Flows

Concepts

Previously it was assumed that all cash flows occur as predicted. In the real world, however, cash flows resulting from a new project are not known beforehand because of the risk associated with the project. Risk causes the actual cash flows to deviate from the forecasted amount. The riskiness or the variability of the possible outcomes can be assigned a probability. Since probability is discussed in detail in Chapter 4, the discussion is not repeated here. The three quantitative measures of risk—the expected value of the cash flows, the standard deviation of the cash flows, and the coefficient of variation—are included here.

Expected Value for Cash Flows

The expected value of a cash flow is computed with the following equation.

$$E(CF) = \sum_{i=1}^{N} (CF_i)P_{i/100}$$

Equation (11-12)

where:

CF$_i$ = value of the ith possible outcome

P$_i$ = probability as a percentage that the CF$_i$ will occur. The sum of $P_1 + P_2 + ... + P_x$ equals 100%.

N = number of possible outcomes.

The expected value of a cash flow is a weighted average value for the cash flow using the probabilities (P$_i$) as weights.

(Risk and Uncertainty in Cash Flows–Continued)

Standard Deviation

The standard deviation of a cash flow with discrete probabilities is computed using:

$$\sigma CF = \sqrt{\sum_{i=1}^{N} [CF_i - E(CF)]^2 P_i}$$

Equation (11-13)

Here the standard deviation is a measure of dispersion as discussed in Chapter 4. In addition, it is a measure of risk (variability) associated with the cash flow. The larger the standard deviation, the greater the risk.

Coefficient of Variation

Because the cash flows for different projects may differ in size, comparing the standard deviations can be misleading. This problem can be solved by expressing a project's cash flow standard deviation as a percentage of the expected value for the cash flow. The resulting value, the coefficient of variation, is a unitless value and allows comparison of risk among various projects.

The equation is:

$$\text{Coefficient of Variation (CV)} = \frac{\sigma CF}{E(CF)}$$

Equation (11-14)

The larger the coefficient of variation, the greater the risk.

The three quantities described above—expected value, standard deviation, and coefficient of variation—are computed on your calculator using the statistical keys. Probabilities as a percentage, along with the cash flow values, are entered using $\boxed{\Sigma+}$ and $\boxed{\text{FRQ}}$. $\boxed{\bar{x}}$ and $\boxed{\sigma n}$ directly calculate the expected value and the standard deviation. The following example illustrates the use of these keys.

(Risk and Uncertainty in Cash Flows–Continued)

Example

The JSA Computer Company is comparing two projects. Both projects require an initial investment of $60,000. Both have estimated lives of ten years. Project A has an expected value for each end-of-year cash flow equal to $12,000 and a net present value of $2500. The standard deviation for the end-of-year cash flow is $9000 with a .75 coefficient of variation. Project B has the following possible cash flows and probabilities that can occur at the end of each year for ten years.

Cash Flow (CF$_i$)	Probability (P$_i$)
$ 8000	20%
12000	30%
13000	30%
17000	20%

Compute the expected value, standard deviation, and coefficient of variation for Project B. Next, compute the present value of project B, and compare the two projects. Both projects have a 15% discount rate.

```
PV = 60000    E(CF) = ?        E(CF) = ?   E(CF) = ?
      ↓           ↑       . . .     ↑           ↑
      0           1                 9         N = 10
                      %i = 15
```
Time-Line Diagram 11-9

The unknown to solve for is E(CF), the expected value. The values needed are given: the total present value, PV = $60,000; the number of cash flow periods, N = 10; the discount rate, %i = 15.

Solving the problem requires two steps. First, the risk measures are determined in the statistical mode. Next, the net present value is computed in the finance mode using the techniques discussed previously.

Capital Budgeting Techniques

(Risk and Uncertainty in Cash Flows–Continued)

Calculator Solution

If the "DEC 2" indicator does not appear in the display, press [2nd] [Decimal] before keying in the example.

Procedure	Press	Display
1. Clear calculator and select *statistics mode*.	[ON/c] [2nd] [STAT]	0 DEC 2 STAT
A. Compute Expected Value		
2. Enter first possible cash flow.	8000 [FRQ]	Fr 00 DEC 2 STAT
3. Enter first probability.	20* [Σ+]	20.00 DEC 2 STAT
4. Enter second possible cash flow and probability.	12000 [FRQ] 30 [Σ+]	50.00 DEC 2 STAT
5. Repeat Step 4 for remaining possible cash flows.	13000 [FRQ] 30 [Σ+] 17000 [FRQ] 20 [Σ+]	100.00** DEC 2 STAT
6. Compute expected value and store.	[x̄] [STO]	12500.00 DEC 2 STAT
7. Compute standard deviation of discrete probability for cash flow.	[σn]	2872.28 DEC 2 STAT
8. Calculate coefficient of variation.	[÷] [RCL] [=]	0.23 DEC 2 STAT
B. Compute Net Present Value		
9. Clear calculator and select *finance mode*.	[ON/c] [2nd] [FIN]	0 DEC 2 FIN
10. Enter number of cash flows.	10 [N]	10.00 DEC 2 FIN

(continued)

(Risk and Uncertainty in Cash Flows–Continued)

(continued)

Procedure	Press	Display
11. Enter discount rate per payment period.	15 $\boxed{\%i}$	**15.00** DEC 2 FIN
12. Enter expected value of each end-of-period cash flow.	12500 $\boxed{PMT}$	**12500.00** DEC 2 ANN FIN
13. Compute present value of expected cash flows.	$\boxed{CPT}$ $\boxed{PV}$	**62734.61** DEC 2 ANN FIN
14. Subtract initial investment to determine net present value.	$\boxed{-}$ 60000 $\boxed{=}$	**2734.61** DEC 2 ANN FIN

*Note that the probability value is entered as a percentage and the accumulated probability is displayed as a percentage.

**After all possible cash flows are entered, the display shows 100.00 because the sum of all probabilities of the cash flows is 100%.

The pertinent values for the two projects are:

	Project A	**Project B**
Net present value	$2500	$2734.61
Expected value of end-of-year cash flow	$12000	$12500
Standard deviation	$9000	$2872.28
Coefficient of variation	.75	.23
Initial investment	$60000	$60000

Project B not only has the largest net present value and expected value of end-of-year cash flow, but is less risky because the coefficient of variation is lower than Project A's coefficient of variation.

Capital Budgeting Techniques

(Risk and Uncertainty in Cash Flows–Continued)

Review

Note that probabilities must be entered as percentages with this procedure.

Equation Value	Meaning	Keystrokes
A. Enter Data		
1. CF_1, P_1	First possible cash flow and probability.	CF_1 [FRQ] P_1 [Σ+]
2. CF_i, P_i	Subsequent possible cash flows and probabilities.	CF_i [FRQ] P_i [Σ+]
	Repeat Step 2 until all data is entered.	
B. E(CF)	Expected value of cash flow.	[x̄]
C. σ	Standard deviation.	[σn]
D. CV	Coefficient of variation.	[÷] E(CF) [=]

Chapter 12

COST OF CAPITAL

Cost of Capital

Contents

Introduction

In the capital budgeting chapter, analysis of investment is discussed assuming that a desired rate of return is given. This desired rate of return is an important element in ranking investment proposals. Many different terms, such as minimum desired rate of return, target rate, hurdle rate, and cost of capital, are used in describing this desired rate of return.

Cost of capital represents the rate of return that a company must earn on its investments to meet the required rate of return of the firm's investors. Cost of capital is a key factor for a firm when deciding what it has to pay for debt, preferred stock, retained earnings, and common stock.

Cost of capital is of great importance to a firm. First, it plays a vital role in the ranking of investment proposals. Secondly, cost of capital is different for different capital structures. The optimal capital structure is determined by finding the capital structure that minimizes the cost of capital.

Cost of capital is quite an involved subject. Because of the limited scope of this book, further details are not presented. However, many finance texts discuss this topic.

The discussion in this chapter starts with the methods of computation of the cost of the major sources of capital—debt (bonds), preferred stock, and common equity (common stock). These component costs are then combined into a weighted average cost of capital.

Cost of Debt (Bonds)

Concepts

One of the major ways a firm raises capital is to borrow money. The principal debt instrument is a bond which pays to a lender periodic interest payments and returns the principal at maturity. The valuation of a bond is discussed in Chapter 10, but that procedure is not appropriate (because taxes are omitted) for determining the cost of a new bond issue. Interest paid on debt is deductible, so the after-tax cost to the company is:

After-Tax Interest (AFI) = Interest Payment (1 − Tax Rate)
Equation (12-1)

Once the after-tax interest payment is determined, the cost can be found using the bond valuation equation (10-1) where the interest rate represents the cost. Using the terminology commonly associated with the cost of debt, the equation is:

$$NBV = AFI \left[\frac{1 - (1 + \%i/100)^{-N}}{\%i/100} \right] + Rd (1 + \%i/100)^{-N}$$

Equation (12-2)

where:

NBV = The net book value of bond;
        Par + Premium or Par − Discount
AFI = After-tax interest payment
Rd = Redemption value of bond
N = Number of interest payments
%i = Cost of bond issue as a percentage

(Cost of Debt (Bonds)–Continued)

Example

The Big Steer Company issues $2,000,000 in 20-year bonds. Each bond has a $1000 par value with 12% interest paid semiannually ($60 per $1000 bond). The bonds are sold with a yield to maturity of 12.51%. The net book value per bond after deducting the discount is $962.50. Assuming the tax rate is 35%, what is the cost of the bond issue to the company, assuming the bonds are held to maturity?

Calculator Solution

If the "DEC 2" indicator does not appear in the display, press [2nd] [Decimal] before keying in the example.

Procedure	Press	Display
1. Clear calculator and select finance mode.	[ON/C] [2nd] **FIN**	**0** DEC 2 FIN
2. Calculate after-tax amount and enter.	60 [−] 35 [%] [=]* [PMT]	**39.00** DEC 2 ANN FIN
3. Enter number of interest payments.	20 [×] 2 [=] [N]	**40.00** DEC 2 ANN FIN
4. Enter net book value.	962.50 [PV]	**962.50** DEC 2 ANN FIN
5. Enter redemption value.	1000 [FV]	**1000.00** DEC 2 ANN FIN
6. Compute bond cost per payment period.	[CPT] [%i]	**4.09** DEC 2 ANN FIN
7. Compute annual nominal interest cost and store.	[×] 2 [=] [STO]	**8.18** DEC 2 ANN FIN
8. Enter number of payments per year.	2 [2nd] **APR▶**	**2.00** DEC 2 ANN FIN
9. Recall annual nominal interest cost and compute cost as annual effective rate.	[RCL] [=]	**8.35** DEC 2 ANN FIN

*This is the same as 1 [−] 35 [%] [×] 60 [=].

(Cost of Debt (Bonds)–Continued)

The bond cost stated as an annual nominal interest rate is 8.18%, equivalent to an annual effective rate of 8.35%. The company's cost is lower than the yield to maturity of 12.51% because the interest payments are tax deductible.

Review

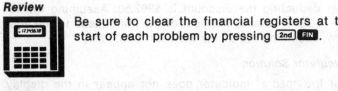

Be sure to clear the financial registers at the start of each problem by pressing ⟨2nd⟩⟨FIN⟩.

Equation Value	Meaning	Keystrokes
Inputs:		
$(1 - Tx) \times$ Interest Payment(IP)	After-tax cost of interest payment (AFI).	IP ⟨−⟩ Tx ⟨%⟩⟨=⟩⟨PMT⟩
N	Number of interest payments.	⟨N⟩
NBV	Net bond value.	⟨PV⟩
Rd	Redemption value.	⟨FV⟩
Solution:	Solve for cost per interest payment period.	⟨CPT⟩⟨%i⟩

Cost of Preferred Stock

Concepts

Another method of raising capital is to issue preferred stock. Preferred stock dividends are not tax deductible. They are generally assumed to remain constant and to be paid indefinitely.

Flotation costs affect the cost of issuing preferred stock. Flotation costs are the accounting, underwriting, legal, and other expenses required to issue the stock. These costs are usually estimated as a percentage of the new stock issue. The cost of issuing preferred stock is found using a perpetuity equation.

$$CP = \frac{100\,D}{P\,(1 - FC\%/100)}^{*} \qquad \textit{Equation (12-3)}$$

where:

    CP = Cost of preferred stock as a percentage

    D = Dollar amount of preferred stock

    P = Gross issue price per share

    FC% = Flotation costs as a percentage

*Reference: Weston, J. Fred and Eugene F. Brigham. *Essentials of Managerial Finance*. 7th Edition. Hinsdale, Illinois: The Dryden Press 1981, page 592.

Cost of Capital

(Cost of Preferred Stock–Continued)

Example

The Small Table Company issues 500,000 shares of preferred stock at $75 per share. The dividend paid each year is $7.50. Assuming the flotation costs are 1.5%, what does the stock cost the company?

Calculator Solution

If the "DEC 2" indicator does not appear in the display, press [2nd] [Decimal] before keying in the example.

Procedure	Press	Display
1. Clear calculator.	[ON/C]	**0** DEC 2 FIN
2. Calculate net share price and store.	75 [−] 1.5 [%] [=] * [STO]	**73.88** DEC 2 FIN
3. Multiply dividend by 100. Divide by net share price and calculate cost of preferred stock.	7.5 [×] 100 [÷] [RCL] [=]	**10.15** DEC 2 FIN

The preferred stock issue has a 10.15% cost.

*This is the same as 1 [−] 1.5 [%] [×] 75 [=].

(Cost of Preferred Stock–Continued)

Review

Equation Value	Meaning	Keystrokes
Inputs:		
P(1 – FC%/100)	Net dollar amount of stock.	P $\boxed{-}$ FC $\boxed{\%}$ $\boxed{=}$ $\boxed{\text{STO}}$
Solution:	Cost of preferred stock.	D $\boxed{\times}$ 100 $\boxed{\div}$ $\boxed{\text{RCL}}$ $\boxed{=}$

Cost of Equity (Common Stock)

Concepts

A firm can increase equity in two ways. One way is internally through retained earnings. The other method is externally through the sale of new common stock. Valuation of common stock from the investor's viewpoint is discussed in Chapter 10. Here the cost of common stock from the issuing company's viewpoint is described.

Because dividends are not tax deductible, the tax rate has no impact on the cost of common stock. The flotation costs do affect the cost of issuing common stock. These costs usually are estimated as a percentage of the new stock issue.

Many textbooks assume that dividends grow indefinitely at a constant rate. With this assumption, the cost of a new stock issue can be found using:

$$CS = \frac{100\,D}{P\,(1 - FC\%/100)} + GR\%^{*}$$

Equation (12-4)

where:

CS = Percentage cost of common stock

P = Gross issue price per share

D = Dollar amount per share of the first dividend

FC% = Flotation costs as a percentage of the new stock issue

GR% = Dividend constant growth rate as a percentage.

*Reference: Weston, J. Fred and Eugene F. Brigham. *Essentials of Managerial Finance*. 7th Edition. Hinsdale, Illinois: The Dryden Press 1981, page 599.

(Cost of Equity (Common Stock)–Continued)

Example

A $1,800,000 new stock issue at $10 per share with 2% flotation costs is planned by the New Tech Company. The first dividend paid is $0.85 per share and grows indefinitely at a 3% rate. What is the cost of the stock to the New Tech Company?

Calculator Solution

If the "DEC 2" indicator does not appear in the display, press 2nd Decimal before keying in the example.

Procedure	Press	Display
1. Clear calculator.	ON/c	0 DEC2 FIN
2. Calculate net share price and store.	10 ⊟ 2 % =* STO	9.80 DEC2 FIN
3. Multiply first dividend by 100 and divide by net share price.	.85 ⊠ 100 ⊞ RCL =	8.67 DEC2 FIN
4. Add constant growth percentage to calculate cost of new stock issue.	⊞ 3 =	11.67 DEC2 FIN

The company's cost for the new stock issue is 11.67%.

*This is the same as 1 ⊟ 2 % ⊠ 10 =.

Cost of Capital

(Cost of Equity (Common Stock)–Continued)

Review

Equation Value	Meaning	Keystroke
Inputs:		
P(1 – FC%/100)	Net dollar amount of stock.	P ⊟ FC %⁄ ⊟ STO
$\dfrac{100\ D}{P(1 - FC\%/100)}$	Percentage cost of first dividend.	D ⊠ 100 ⊞ RCL ⊟
Solution:	Cost of common stock.	⊞ GR% ⊟

Weighted Average Cost of Capital

Concepts

One method a firm may use when evaluating capital expenditure proposals is a weighted or overall cost of capital. The weighted cost of capital is calculated based on the proportions of debt and equity in the firm's target capital structure. A weighted average cost of capital can be computed using the following equation.

$$W_c = P_d C_d + P_e C_e \qquad \text{Equation (12-5)}$$

where:

W_c = Weighted average cost of capital

P_d = Proportion of debt in capital structure

C_d = Average cost of debt

P_e = Proportion of equity in capital structure

C_e = Average cost of equity.

A company can minimize its cost of capital by varying the proportion of debt and equity, as well as the average costs of debt and equity.

Example

The XYZ Company projects the cost of debt and equity capital for two situations. Which combination has the lowest weighted average cost of capital?

	Debt		Equity	
Alternative	P_d	C_d	P_e	C_e
A	.10	3.7	.90	11
B	.20	4.0	.80	11.5.

Cost of Capital

(Weighted Average Cost of Capital–Continued)

Calculator Solution

If the "DEC 2" indicator does not appear in the display, press (2nd) (Decimal) before keying in the example.

Procedure	Press	Display
1. Clear calculator and select finance mode.	(ON/c) (2nd) (FIN)	0
Alternative A		
2. Multiply proportion of debt by its cost and store.	.1 (X) 3.7 (=) (STO)	0.37
3. Multiply proportion of equity by its cost.	.9 (X) 11 (=)	9.90
4. Add results of Steps 2 and 3 to determine weighted average cost of capital.	(+) (RCL) (=)	10.27
Alternative B		
5. Multiply proportion of debt by its cost and store.	.2 (X) 4 (=) (STO)	0.80
6. Multiply proportion of equity by its cost.	.8 (X) 11.5 (=)	9.20
7. Add results of Steps 5 and 6 to determine weighted average cost of capital.	(+) (RCL) (=)	10.00

Alternative B gives the lower cost of capital of 10%, as compared to the alternative cost of capital of 10.27%.

Chapter 13
MANAGEMENT ACCOUNTING

Management Accounting

Contents

Introduction

This chapter contains a number of analysis techniques appropriate for managerial decision making. Cost estimating is discussed using the High Low method and regression analysis. The breakeven point and net income are estimated with cost-volume-profit analysis. An inventory planning model useful for estimating reorder quantities is discussed. Also included is a discussion of financial analysis techniques. The chapter ends with a discussion of estimating labor hours using learning curves.

Cost Classifications and Behavior

All organizations—manufacturing, retail, government units, hospitals—incur costs. The kinds of costs incurred and the way these costs are classified depends on the type of organization. There are two basic cost classifications—manufacturing and nonmanufacturing.

Manufacturing costs may be broken down into three parts—direct materials, direct labor, and manufacturing overhead. Direct materials are materials that can be identified with the product. Direct labor is work which is traceable to the creation of the product. Manufacturing overhead is all other manufacturing costs which cannot be classified as direct materials costs or direct labor costs.

Nonmanufacturing costs generally are divided as marketing or selling costs and administrative costs. Marketing or selling costs are those incurred in obtaining customer orders and getting the finished product to the customer. Administrative costs are those which cannot be classified as production or marketing, for example, general management costs.

Costs also may be classified as period and product costs. Period costs are identified with a time period. All nonmanufacturing costs are considered period costs on an income statement. Product costs "attach" to the goods as produced. All manufacturing costs are considered product costs. Product costs are treated as expenses when the product is sold rather than at the time costs are incurred.

Cost classifications for financial statements may not be the same classifications used for cost behavior. For cost behavior, costs may be divided into variable, fixed, and mixed (semi-variable). These categories are valid only if the range over which the costs are estimated is relatively small. This range is called the "relevant range", and the accountant assumes the costs are linear within the range limits.

(Cost Classifications and Behavior–Continued)

Costs that remain constant within the relevant range or over the time period being analyzed are called *fixed costs* (FC). Examples of fixed costs are rent, straight line depreciation, and salaries. Costs that vary in total as the activity level changes are called *variable costs* (VC). Examples of variable costs and activity levels are cost per labor hour, per unit of material, and per unit of product. Total variable costs can be shown as:

Total Variable Costs (TVC) = VC(x)

where:

VC = variable cost per unit of x

x = activity level

Combining fixed and variable costs results in a cost pattern called *mixed or semi-variable costs*. This is the relationship often shown for total costs, TC = FC + VC(x).

These three cost relationships are shown graphically in Figure 13-1.

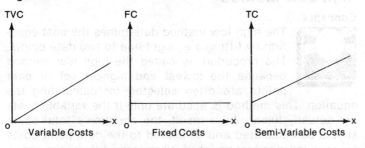

Figure 13-1. Cost Relationships

Manufacturing and period costs can be variable, fixed, or semi-variable. The cost behavior is independent of the classification of manufacturing or period costs.

Estimating Costs

Manufacturing overhead (manufacturing costs other than direct labor and materials) is composed of numerous items which often cannot be easily divided into fixed and variable costs. As a result, overhead costs are often estimated using either the "high low method" or linear regression.

Both methods are linear and are used to predict variable overhead and total costs. Two components of these methods are slope and intercept. The variable costs are equal to the slope. Fixed overhead, however, is not equal to the intercept unless the data set includes the overhead costs at a zero activity level. Nor are the methods valid for predictions outside the data set used for determining the equation. Linear regression is preferable to the high low method because the equation can be evaluated for accuracy. Either method is suitable for developing cost equations for cost-volume-profit analysis.

High Low Method

Concepts

The high low method determines the cost equation by fitting a straight line to two data points. The procedure is called the high low method because the lowest and highest set of data points are often selected for calculating the equation. This method is accurate only if the variable costs are actually linear. As a result, the equation's total costs should be calculated and compared to the data point costs for each independent variable. When large differences occur, linear regression or some other method should be employed for estimating overhead costs.

(Estimating Costs–Continued)

Many textbooks often show the slope as variable costs and the intercept as fixed costs. The following equations incorporate both terms. The equations used to compute the cost equation are:

$$\text{Variable costs (slope)} = VC = \frac{Y_H - Y_L}{X_H - X_L}$$

Equation (13-1)

$$\text{Fixed costs (intercept)} = FC = Y_H - VC(X_H)$$

Equation (13-2)

$$\text{Total Costs} = FC + VC(X) \qquad \text{Equation (13-3)}$$

where:

Y_H = cost value of high data point
X_H = activity level of high data point
Y_L = cost value of low data point
X_L = activity level of low data point
VC = variable costs

Example

The ABC company manufactures surgical instruments. They have determined that manufacturing overhead varies with direct labor hours. Selected labor hours and total overhead costs for several accounting periods are:

Overhead Costs	$39,500	$52,000	$58,250	$61,500
Labor Hours	10,000	14,000	16,000	18,000

Using the high low method, develop the overhead cost equation and predict overhead for 15,000 hours.

Management Accounting

(Estimating Costs–Continued)

The following inputs are given or must be calculated to solve the problem.

High data point	Low data point
$Y_H = 61500$	$Y_L = 39500$
$X_H = 18000$	$X_L = 10000$

$$\text{Variable costs (slope)} = VC = \frac{61500 - 39500}{18000 - 10000}$$

Fixed costs (intercept) = $FC = 61500 - A(18000)$

Calculator Solution

If the "DEC 2" indicator does not appear in the display, press [2nd][Decimal] before keying in the example.

Procedure	Press	Display
1. Clear calculator.	[ON/C]	**0**
2. Enter high and low hours.	18000 [−]	
	10000 [=][STO]	**8000.00**
3. Enter high and low costs.	61500 [−]	
	39500	**39500**
4. Calculate variable costs (slope).	[÷][RCL][=][STO]	**2.75**
5. Enter high hours and costs and calculate fixed costs (intercept).	[×] 18000	
	[+/−][+] 61500	
	[=]	**12000.00**
6. Predict total costs for 15,000 hours.		
a) Enter hours	15000 [×][RCL]	**2.75**
b) Enter fixed costs and calculate total costs	[+] 12000 [=]	**53250.00**

The total overhead equation is:
Total overhead costs = $12000 + 2.75(x)$.

(Estimating Costs–Continued)

The predicted overhead for 15,000 hours is $53,250. Variable overhead is $2.75 per direct labor hour. The intercept of $12,000 does not represent fixed costs because the data does not include overhead at zero hours. The equation is not completely accurate because at 14,000 hours overhead is estimated as $50,500, while actual overhead equals $52,000.

Review

Equation Value	Meaning	Keystroke
A. Solve for variable costs $\dfrac{Y_H - Y_L}{X_H - X_L}$	Variable costs (slope).	X_H ⊟ X_L ⊜ STO Y_H ⊟ Y_L ÷ RCL ⊜ STO
B. Solve for fixed costs $Y_H - VC(X_H)$	Fixed costs (intercept).	✕ X_H +/− + Y_H ⊜
C. Predict costs $FC + VC(x)$	Total costs for X hours.	X ✕ RCL + FC ⊜

(Estimating Costs–Continued)

Linear Regression

Concepts

Linear regression (also called least squares) is a statistical technique that fits a straight line to a set of data points. The resulting equation is linear in the form $Y = b + aX$ as shown below.

In the equation, a is the variable cost and X is the number of units. Intercept b represents the fixed cost only if the set of data points includes a zero value.

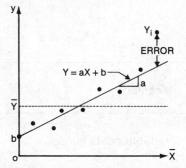

Figure 13-2. Linear Regression Analysis

The least squares linear regression analysis minimizes the sum of the squares of the variation of the Y values from the straight line of best fit.

Remember, it is not statistically valid to compute an X (independent) value on the basis of a Y (dependent) value or to compute a Y value on the basis of an X which is outside the range of entered X values. However, trend line analysis and forecasting calculations often use X values outside the relevant range to make predictions or estimations of probability about the future. When you perform such calculations, it is important to remember that the actual values probably will differ from the calculated values.

(Estimating Costs–Continued)

The general normal equations for determining the slope and intercept for linear regression are:

$$\Sigma XY = b\Sigma X + a\Sigma X^2$$

$$\Sigma Y = nb + a\,\Sigma X$$

These equations can be rewritten to determine the various values as shown below.

$$\text{Slope (a)} = \frac{N(\Sigma XY) - (\Sigma Y)(\Sigma X)}{N(\Sigma X^2) - (\Sigma X)^2}$$

Equation (13-4)

$$a = \frac{\dfrac{\Sigma XY}{N\overline{X}} - \overline{Y}}{\dfrac{\Sigma X^2}{N\overline{X}} - \overline{X}}$$

Equation (13-5)

$$Y - \text{intercept (b)} = \frac{\Sigma Y - a\Sigma X}{N}$$

$$= \overline{Y} - a\overline{X}$$

Equation (13-6)

where:
$\overline{X}$ is the mean $= \Sigma X/N$
$\overline{Y}$ is the mean $= \Sigma Y/N$

Equation (13-4) is changed to the form shown in equation (13-5) because it allows an easier solution on your calculator and avoids recording large numerical values.

(Estimating Costs–Continued)

Example

The Big Red Company controller has determined that as the number of direct labor hours increases, the company's manufacturing overhead costs also increase. The controller would like to predict the total overhead costs and the variable overhead costs within the normal production range of 4000 to 6000 hours. The following data is a monthly sample of the number of labor hours worked and the actual manufacturing overhead incurred during the last year.

Sample of Monthly Costs	Direct Labor Hours(X)	Manufacturing Overhead (Y)
1	4000	$21,050
2	5200	$25,820
3	6000	$28,150
4	5500	$26,585
5	4500	$23,595

With this data set, an overhead cost equation, the variable overhead rate per hour, and the total overhead for 5400 direct labor hours can be determined.

The following inputs are known or must be calculated to solve the problem.

X_i = 4000, 5200, 6000, 5500, 4500

Y_i = 21050, 25820, 28150, 26585, 23595

$N = 5$

$$\text{Variable costs per hour (a)} = \frac{\dfrac{\Sigma XY}{5\overline{X}} - \overline{Y}}{\dfrac{\Sigma X^2}{5\overline{X}} - \overline{X}}$$

Y-intercept (b) = $\overline{Y} - a\overline{X}$

Project overhead for 5400 hours = $b + a(5400)$

The problem is solved in six parts. Parts A and B compute $\overline{X}$, $\overline{Y}$, σ_x and σ_y (σ_x and σ_y are not needed here but are useful in the next problem). Part C computes $\Sigma XY/N$ and Part D com-

(Estimating Costs–Continued)

putes $\Sigma X^2/N$. Parts E and F compute the slope and intercept using equations (13-5) and (13-6). Be sure to press 2nd Decimal so that the full numeric value can be entered for the various terms calculated. (If the value calculated in Part C is in scientific notation, i.e. 1.5 08, enter the value in Part E as follows: 10 Y^x 8 X 1.5 =.)

Calculator Solution

If the "DEC 2" indicator appears in the display, press 2nd Decimal before keying in the example.

Procedure	Press	Display
1. Clear calculator and select statistics mode.	ON/c 2nd STAT	**0** STAT

A. *Calculate mean and standard deviation of labor hours*

2. Enter hours.	4000 Σ+	**1** STAT
	5200 Σ+	**2** STAT
	6000 Σ+	**3** STAT
	5500 Σ+	**4** STAT
	4500 Σ+	**5** STAT
3. Compute mean and record ($\overline{X}$).	$\overline{x}$	**5040** STAT
4. Compute standard deviation (σ_x) and record.	σn	**711.61787** STAT

B. *Calculate mean and standard deviation of overhead costs*

5. Clear statistics mode.	2nd STAT	**711.61787** STAT
6. Enter overhead costs.	21050 Σ+	**1** STAT
	25820 Σ+	**2** STAT
	28150 Σ+	**3** STAT
	26585 Σ+	**4** STAT
	23595 Σ+	**5** STAT

(continued)

(Estimating Costs–Continued)

(continued)

Procedure	Press	Display
7. Calculate mean ($\bar{Y}$) and record.	$\boxed{\bar{x}}$	**25040** _{STAT}
8. Calculate standard deviation (σ_y) and record.	$\boxed{\sigma n}$	**2476.9195** _{STAT}

C. *Calculate mean of ΣXY divided by N*

9. Clear statistics mode.	$\boxed{\text{2nd}}\ \boxed{\text{STAT}}$	**2476.9195** _{STAT}
10. Multiply hours by cost and enter.	4000 $\boxed{\times}$ 21050	
	$\boxed{=}\ \boxed{\Sigma+}$	**1** _{STAT}
	5200 $\boxed{\times}$ 25820	
	$\boxed{=}\ \boxed{\Sigma+}$	**2** _{STAT}
	6000 $\boxed{\times}$ 28150	
	$\boxed{=}\ \boxed{\Sigma+}$	**3** _{STAT}
	5500 $\boxed{\times}$ 26585	
	$\boxed{=}\ \boxed{\Sigma+}$	**4** _{STAT}
	4500 $\boxed{\times}$ 23595	
	$\boxed{=}\ \boxed{\Sigma+}$	**5** _{STAT}
11. Calculate mean ($\Sigma XY/N$) and divide by mean labor hours (Step 3) and record.	$\boxed{\bar{x}}\ \boxed{\div}$ 5040 $\boxed{=}$	**25387.262** _{STAT}

D. *Calculate mean of ΣX^2 divided by N*

12. Clear statistics mode.	$\boxed{\text{2nd}}\ \boxed{\text{STAT}}$	**25387.262** _{STAT}
13. Enter squared hours X_i^2.	4000	
	$\boxed{\text{2nd}}\ \boxed{x^2}\ \boxed{\Sigma+}$	**1** _{STAT}
	5200	
	$\boxed{\text{2nd}}\ \boxed{x^2}\ \boxed{\Sigma+}$	**2** _{STAT}
	6000	
	$\boxed{\text{2nd}}\ \boxed{x^2}\ \boxed{\Sigma+}$	**3** _{STAT}
	5500	
	$\boxed{\text{2nd}}\ \boxed{x^2}\ \boxed{\Sigma+}$	**4** _{STAT}
	4500	
	$\boxed{\text{2nd}}\ \boxed{x^2}\ \boxed{\Sigma+}$	**5** _{STAT}

(continued)

(Estimating Costs–Continued)

(continued)

Procedure	Press	Display
14. Calculate mean of squared hours.	$\overline{x}$	**25908000** _{STAT}
15. Divide by mean of X data points (Step 3).	÷ 5040 STO	**5040** _{STAT}

E. *Calculate slope*

16. Subtract mean of X data points and store.	− RCL = STO	**100.47619** _{STAT}
17. Enter results of Step 11.	25387.262	**25387.262** _{STAT}
18. Subtract mean of overhead costs ($\overline{Y}$) (Step 7) and calculate variable cost per hour (slope).	− 25040 ÷ RCL = STO	**3.4561621** _{STAT}

F. *Calculate Y-intercept*

19. Enter mean of hours ($\overline{X}$) (Step 3).	× 5040	5040 _{STAT}
20. Enter mean of overhead costs ($\overline{Y}$) (Step 7) and calculate Y-intercept.	− 25040 = +/−	**7620.9431** _{STAT}

Using the results for Y-intercept (Step 20) and slope (Step 18), the equation for manufacturing overhead is:

Overhead cost = 7620.94 + 3.46 (Direct Labor Hours).

The variable overhead rate is $3.46 per hour, and the Y-intercept is $7620.94.

(Estimating Costs–Continued)

Review

Equation Value	Meaning	Keystroke
A. Solve for $\overline{X}$ and σ_x		
X_i	Enter X data point.	X_i `Σ+`
$\overline{X}$	Mean of X data.	`x̄`
σ_x	Standard deviation of X data.	`σn`
B. Solve for $\overline{Y}$ and σ_y		
Y_i	Enter Y data points.	Y_i `Σ+`
$\overline{Y}$	Mean of Y data points.	`x̄`
σ_y	Standard deviation of Y data.	`σn`
C. Calculate $\Sigma XY/(N\overline{X})$		
$X_i\, Y_i$	Enter $X_i\, Y_i$.	X_i `×` Y_i `=` `Σ+`
$\Sigma XY/N$	Mean of ΣXY.	`x̄`
$\Sigma XY/(N\overline{X})$	Divide by mean of X data points (Step A).	`÷` $\overline{X}$ `=`
D. Calculate $\Sigma X^2/(N\overline{X})$		
X_i^2	Enter X_i^2.	X_i `2nd` `x²` `Σ+`
$\Sigma X^2/N$	Mean of ΣX^2.	`x̄`
$\Sigma X^2/(N\overline{X})$	Divide by mean of X data points.	`÷` $\overline{X}$ `=`

(continued)

(Estimating Costs–Continued)

(continued)

Equation Value	Meaning	Keystroke
E. Calculate slope (a)		
$\dfrac{\Sigma X^2}{N(\overline{X})} - \overline{X}$	Denominator term of equation (13-5).	$\boxed{-}\ \overline{X}$
		$\boxed{=}\boxed{STO}$
$\dfrac{\Sigma XY}{N\overline{X}} - \overline{Y}$	Calculate numerator term of equation (13-5).	
	Enter result of Step C.	$\Sigma XY/N\ \overline{X}$
		$\boxed{-}$
	Enter Y mean.	$\overline{Y}$
a	Calculate slope.	$\boxed{\div}\boxed{RCL}$
		$\boxed{=}\boxed{STO}$
F. Calculate y intercept		
$(a)\overline{X}$	Enter X data points mean.	$\boxed{\times}\ \overline{X}$
$b = \overline{Y} - a\overline{X}$	Enter Y data points and calculate Y-intercept.	$\boxed{-}\ \overline{Y}$
		$\boxed{=}\boxed{+/-}$

Going Further

After determining the regression equation, you can evaluate whether or not it can be used effectively for prediction or estimation purposes.

The coefficient of determination (r^2) is a measure of the "goodness of the fit" of the regression line to the data points. It measures the amount of variation removed when the regression line is computed. The closer r^2 is to one, the better the fit of the regression line.

Management Accounting

The square root of r^2 is called the *correlation coefficient*. It measures the strength of the linear relationship. The correlation coefficient value can range from -1 to $+1$. A positive correlation value means that as one variable increases the other variable also increases. A negative correlation value means that as one variable increases the other variable decreases. If the correlation coefficient is zero, the variables are uncorrelated.

The standard error of the regression line, $S_{y/x}$, indicates the possible errors between the predicted equation value and the actual results. The $S_{y/x}$ can be used to construct confidence limits for the regression equation. The standard error of the slope, s_a, evaluates the slope in the same manner as $S_{y/x}$ evaluates the total results. In general, a small $S_{y/x}$ and s_a relative to their expected values, y and a, is desired for predicting total and variable costs.

$$\text{correlation coeffient (r)} = a\left[\frac{\sigma x}{\sigma y}\right]$$

Equation (13-7)

$$\text{Index of determination} = r^2 \qquad \textit{Equation (13-8)}$$

standard error of the regression line

$$S_{Y/X} = [[(1 - r^2)\sigma_y{}^2]\,N/(N - 2)]^{1/2}$$

Equation (13-9)

standard error of the slope

$$s_a = \frac{S_{Y/X}}{[(\sigma x^2)N]^{1/2}}$$

Equation (13-10)

(Estimating Costs–Continued)

The keystroke sequences are shown below.

Equation Value	Meaning	Keystrokes

Execute Steps A through F in the regression sequence.

G. Calculate correlation coefficient and index of determination

σ_x/σ_y	Divide σ_x by σ_y.	σ_x ÷ σ_y
r	Calculate correlation coefficient.	X RCL =
r^2	Index of determination.	2nd x^2

H. Calculate standard error of regression line

$(1 - r^2)$	Subtract r^2 from one.	+/– + 1 =
$(1 - r^2)\sigma_y^2$	Multiply by squared standard error of y data point.	X σ_y 2nd x^2
$\left(\dfrac{N}{N-2}\right)$	Multiply by N and divide by $N - 2$.	X N ÷ (N – 2) =
$S_{y/x}$	Calculate standard error of regression line.	$\sqrt{x}$ STO

I. Calculate standard error of slope

$[\sigma_x^2 \, N]^{1/2}$	Enter standard error of X data points and number of observations.	σ_x 2nd x^2 X N = $\sqrt{x}$
s_a	Calculate standard error of slope.	÷ RCL = 1/x

J. Calculate Y for given X

X_i	Enter X value and slope.	X_i X a
Y	Enter Y-intercept and calculate predicted y value.	+ b =

(Estimating Costs–Continued)

If you had executed the keystrokes in this section for the previous example, the following information would be determined.

The correlation coefficient (0.99) is a value close to one; therefore, the equation is a good fit if the data points fall within the relevant range of 4000 to 6000 hours.

The value for the standard error of the regression line, $378.93, means the actual overhead costs are usually within the $2 \times \$378.93$ limits of the estimated costs. The smaller the standard error, the more accurate the estimate.

The standard error of the slope, $0.24, indicates that the actual variable overhead rate is usually within $2 \times \$0.24$ limits of the estimated slope. The smaller the s_a, the more accurate the estimate.

For 5400 hours of direct labor, the equation predicts a total overhead amount of $26,284.22. By applying the standard error of the regression line, the actual amount should fall within the range of $26,284.22 $\pm (2 \times \$378.93)$ or $25,526.36 to $27,042.08.

Cost-Volume-Profit Analysis

Concepts

Cost-volume-profit analysis discusses the interrelationships among the price of products, volume, variable costs, total fixed costs, and mix of the product sold. It is a valuable technique in estimating the breakeven point and sales level necessary to earn a specified income after taxes for a product. This model assumes linear values. As a result, the sales price per unit, variable cost per unit, fixed costs and sales mix all remain constant. The model also assumes that all units purchased or produced are sold. The model is shown graphically in Figure 13-3.

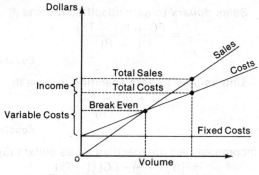

Figure 13-3. Cost-Volume-Profit

The *contribution margin* represents the percentage of sales remaining after covering the variable costs. The contribution margin first covers the fixed expenses and then results in profits for the company. Variable costs are expressed as a percentage of sales. For example, if variable costs are 40%, then $100 of sales incurs $40 of variable costs. Fixed costs, however, remain constant regardless of the sales level.

The sales level where total costs equal total sales is the *breakeven point*, as shown above. At the breakeven point the total contribution margin also equals the total fixed expenses. For sales above the breakeven point, net income increases by the unit contribution margin for each additional unit sold.

(Cost-Volume-Profit Analysis–Continued)

The general cost-volume-profit model is expressed as:

Sales = Variable expenses + Fixed expenses + Net Income

$$S = S \times R + FC + I/(1 - Tx)$$

Equation (13-11)

Contribution Margin $= 1 - R$

Equation (13-12)

Breakeven point in sales *dollars* $= FC/(1 - R)$

Equation (13-13)

Breakeven point in units $= FC/[SP(1 - R)]$

Equation (13-14)

Sales *dollars* to earn specified income (I)

$$= \frac{FC + I/(1 - TX)}{(1 - R)}$$

Equation (13-15)

Unit volume to earn specified income (I)

$$= \frac{FC + I/(1 - TX)}{SP(1 - R)}$$

Equation (13-16)

Income earned on specified sales dollars (S)

$$= [S(1 - R) - FC](1 - Tx)$$

Equation (13-17)

where:

S = sales dollars

R = ratio of total variable costs to total sales expressed as a decimal, or the ratio of unit variable costs to unit sale price expressed as a decimal

FC = total fixed costs in dollars

I = income after taxes in dollars

Tx = tax rate as a decimal

SP = unit sales price

(Cost-Volume-Profit Analysis–Continued)

Example

A model ship company sells its model kits for $20 each. Each kit has a variable cost of $15. The fixed costs are $30,000 per year. The company's tax rate is 40%. Assuming that all kits produced are sold and all costs remain constant, what sales volume (in dollars) must be generated to breakeven and to earn $6000 after taxes? What income after taxes is earned on $180,000 of sales?

The following inputs are given or must be calculated to solve the problem.

Ratio of variable costs to sales = 15/20 = .75

Total fixed costs = 30000

Tax rate = 40% = .40

Specified income = 6000

Specified sales = 180000

Breakeven point = 30000/(1 − .75)

Sales level to earn $6000 after taxes =
$$\frac{30000 \,-\, 6000/(1 \,-\, .4)}{(1 \,-\, .75)}$$

Income on $180,000 of sales = [180000 (1 − .75) − 30000] × (1 − .4)

Calculator Solution

If the "DEC 2" indicator does not appear in the display, press `2nd` `Decimal` before keying in the example.

Procedure	Press	Display
1. Clear calculator.	`ON/c`	**0** DEC 2 FIN
2. Calculate ratio of variable costs to sales.	15 `÷` 20 `=`	**0.75** DEC 2 FIN
3. Calculate contribution margin as decimal and store.	`+/−` `+` 1 `=` `STO`	**0.25** DEC 2 FIN

(continued)

(Cost-Volume-Profit Analysis–Continued)

(continued)

Procedure	Press	Display
4. Enter fixed costs and solve for breakeven point in sales dollars.	30000 $\div$ RCL $=$	**120000.00** <small>DEC 2 FIN</small>
5. Solve for sales to earn specified income.		
a) Enter tax rate	1 $-$ 40 $\%$ $=$	**0.60** <small>DEC 2 FIN</small>
b) Enter after tax income to calculate income before taxes	$1/x$ $\times$ 6000 $=$	**10000.00** <small>DEC 2 FIN</small>
c) Add fixed costs	$+$ 30000 $=$	**40000.00** <small>DEC 2 FIN</small>
d) Divide by contribution margin to determine sales necessary to earn $6000 after tax	$\div$ RCL $=$	**160000.00** <small>DEC 2 FIN</small>
6. Solve for income on specified sales.		
a) Enter sales and calculate contribution margin in dollars	180000 $\times$ RCL $=$	**45000.00** <small>DEC 2 FIN</small>
b) Subtract fixed costs to find income before taxes	$-$ 30000 $=$	**15000.00** <small>DEC 2 FIN</small>
c) Enter tax rate to determine after tax income	$-$ 40 $\%$ $=$	**9000.00** <small>DEC 2 FIN</small>

The company must have sales of $120,000 to breakeven and sales of $160,000 to earn $6000 after taxes. Sales of $180,000 earn $9000 after taxes.

(Cost-Volume-Profit Analysis–Continued)

Review

Equation Value	Meaning	Keystroke
A. Basic Inputs		
R	Variable costs (VC) divided by sales.	VC ➗ Sales ⊜
1 – R	Contribution margin as a percentage of sales.	⊬ ➕ 1 ⊜ STO
B. Solve for breakeven point in dollars		
FC/(1 – R)	Breakeven point.	FC ➗ RCL ⊜
C. Solve for sales to earn specified income		
1 – Tx	After-tax rate.	1 ➖ Tx % ⊜
I/(1 – Tx)	Before-tax income.	1/x ✕ I ⊜
FC + I/(1 – Tx)	Add fixed costs.	➕ FC ⊜
$\frac{FC + I/(1 - Tx)}{(1 - R)}$	Divide by contribution margin to determine sales.	➗ RCL ⊜
D. Income on specified sales		
S(1 – R)	Contribution margin in dollars.	S ✕ RCL ⊜
S(1 – R) – FC	Income before tax.	➖ FC ⊜
[S(1 – R) – FC] × (1 – Tx)	Income after tax.	➖ Tx % ⊜

Inventory Planning

Concepts

Inventory carried by a business incurs costs, both ordering costs and carrying costs. Ordering costs are those expenditures made each time inventory is ordered. They are shown as an expense on the income statement. Carrying costs are the costs of storing inventory, obsolescence, insurance, and taxes. One additional carrying cost is the interest lost by having money invested in the inventory. Planning requires minimizing the ordering costs and carrying costs. One model that minimizes these costs is the *Economic Order Quantity model (EOQ)*. The EOQ is the quantity which should be ordered to minimize inventory costs during a specified time period, assuming no stock outs. A stock out means that orders are received for items not currently in inventory. In addition, the number of times to order can be found by dividing the number of units to be used during the time period by the EOQ.

The equations for the EOQ model are:

$$EOQ = \sqrt{\left[\frac{2\,(P)(D)}{C}\right]}$$
Equation (13-18)

$$\text{Minimum costs for time period} = \sqrt{[2(P)(D)(C)]}$$
Equation (13-19)

$$\text{Number of times to order during period} = D/EOQ$$
Equation (13-20)

where:

EOQ = economic order quantity

P = cost of placing each purchase order

D = demand or total number of units used during time period

C = cost of carrying one unit in inventory for the time period

(Inventory Planning–Continued)

Example

The Slow Time Company makes fine clocks. A special gear is required to make their clocks. The company uses 40,000 of these gears per year. They incur a $12 cost each time a purchase order is prepared and mailed. The company estimates that carrying one gear in inventory for a year costs $0.015. What is the economic order quantity (EOQ), and what are the minimum annual inventory costs? How many times per year should gears be ordered?

The following inputs are given or must be calculated to solve the problem.

Cost of placing order (P) = 12
Annual demand (D) = 40000
Carrying cost (C) = 0.015

$$EOQ = \sqrt{\left[\frac{2(12)(40000)}{0.015} \right]}$$

Minimum costs = $\sqrt{[2(12)(40000)(0.015)]}$

Number of times to order = 40000/EOQ

Management Accounting

(Inventory Planning–Continued)

Calculator Solution

If the "DEC 2" indicator does not appear in the display, press ⟦2nd⟧ ⟦Decimal⟧ before keying in the example.

Procedure	Press	Display
1. Clear calculator.	⟦ON/C⟧	0 DEC 2 FIN
2. Enter order cost and demand and store results.	2 ⟦×⟧ 12 ⟦×⟧ 40000 ⟦=⟧⟦STO⟧	960000.00 DEC 2 FIN
3. Enter carrying costs and solve for EOQ.	⟦÷⟧ .015 ⟦=⟧⟦√x̄⟧	8000.00 DEC 2 FIN
4. Enter demand and solve for number of times to order per year.	⟦1/x⟧⟦×⟧ 40000 ⟦=⟧	5.00 DEC 2 FIN
5. Enter carrying costs and solve for minimum costs.	.015 ⟦×⟧⟦RCL⟧⟦=⟧⟦√x̄⟧	120.00 DEC 2 FIN

The economic order quantity is 8000 gears with a minimum annual inventory cost of $120. The company should order five times per year.

(Inventory Planning–Continued)

Review

Equation Value	Meaning	Keystroke
A. Basic Inputs		
2(P)(D)	2 × order cost × demand.	2 ⊠ P ⊠ D ⊜ STO
B. Solve for EOQ		
$\sqrt{\left[\dfrac{2(P)(D)}{C}\right]}$	EOQ.	÷ C ⊜ √x̄
C. Solve for number of times to order		
D/EOQ	Times to order.	1/x ⊠ D ⊜
D. Solve for minimum costs		
$\sqrt{[2(P)(D)(C)]}$	Minimum costs.	C ⊠ RCL ⊜ √x̄

Financial Analysis

Basic financial analysis techniques are discussed in this section. They are used widely in managerial and financial accounting and marketing. These techniques include: computing expenses as a percentage of sales, percentage change of actual to budget, mark-ups, and mark-downs. Because these techniques are relatively simple to calculate, the following examples show only the equation and sample problem.

Computing Expenses as a Percentage of Sales

Concepts

Computing expenses as a percentage of sales allows comparison of income statements from different reporting periods because the dollars are converted to percentages.

The equation used is:

$$percent = Expense/(Sales/100) \quad \textit{Equation (13-21)}$$

Computing expenses as a percentage of sales allows comparison of income statement and prior year statement.

Example

	Current Year	Prior Year
Sales	$25,000	$20,000
Cost of sales	− 15,000	− 12,400
Gross margin	10,000	7,600
Selling and administrative expenses	− 6,000	− 4,800
Net income	$4,000	$2,800

(Financial Analysis–Continued)

Calculator Solution

If the "DEC 2" indicator does not appear in the display, press 2nd Decimal before keying in the example.

Procedure	Press	Display
1. Clear calculator.	ON/c	**0** DEC 2 FIN
A. Current year statement		
2. Enter sales total and divide by 100. Store results.	25000 ÷ 100 = STO	**250.00** DEC 2 FIN
3. Enter cost of sales and calculate percentage of total sales.	15000 ÷ RCL =	**60.00** DEC 2 FIN
4. Enter gross margin.	10000 ÷ RCL =	**40.00** DEC 2 FIN
5. Enter selling and administrative expenses.	6000 ÷ RCL =	**24.00** DEC 2 FIN
6. Enter net income.	4000 ÷ RCL =	**16.00** DEC 2 FIN
B. Prior year statement		
7. Enter prior year's sales total and divide by 100. Store results.	20000 ÷ 100 = STO	**200.00** DEC 2 FIN
8. Enter cost of sales.	12400 ÷ RCL =	**62.00** DEC 2 FIN
9. Enter gross margin.	7600 ÷ RCL =	**38.00** DEC 2 FIN
10. Enter selling and administrative expense.	4800 ÷ RCL =	**24.00** DEC 2 FIN
11. Enter net income.	2800 ÷ RCL =	**14.00** DEC 2 FIN

FINANCE

(Financial Analysis–Continued)

Now the two years can be compared on a percentage basis.

	Current Year	Prior Year
Sales	100%	100%
Cost of sales	60%	62%
Gross margins	40%	38%
Selling and administrative expenses	24%	24%
Net income	16%	14%

By comparing the two statements, you see that the 2% increase in net income was the result of decreasing cost of sales by 2% in the current year.

Computing Percentage Change of Actual to Budget

Concepts

Computing the percentage change of actual to budget is a useful analysis technique. The degree of compliance with the budget is shown as a percentage using the following equation.

$$\Delta\% = \left[\frac{X_1 - X_2}{X_2} \right] 100$$

Equation (13-22)

The value X_1 is expressed as a percentage of the X_2 amount.

(Financial Analysis–Continued)

Example

The sales department of the ABC Company turned in the following budget summary for June's travel expenses.

Account	Actual	Budget
Airfare	$4800	$4000
Meals	$ 640	$ 600
Hotel	$1100	$1200
Car rental	$1050	$1000

Find the percentage change of actual expenses to budget expenses.

Calculator Solution

If the "DEC 2" indicator does not appear in the display, press [2nd] [Decimal] before keying in the example.

Procedure	Press	Display
1. Clear calculator.	[ON/C]	0
2. Enter actual airfare and budgeted airfare expense to compute percentage change.	4800 [2nd] [Δ%] 4000 [=]	20.00
3. Enter actual and budget amounts for meals.	640 [2nd] [Δ%] 600 [=]	6.67
4. Enter actual and budget amounts for hotel expenses.	1100 [2nd] [Δ%] 1200 [=]	−8.33
5. Enter actual and budget amounts for car rental.	1050 [2nd] [Δ%] 1000 [=]	5.00

(Financial Analysis–Continued)

The report is summarized as follows.

Account	Actual	Budget	Percentage Change of Actual to Budget
Airfare	$4800	$4000	20
Meals	$ 640	$ 600	6.67
Hotel	$1100	$1200	− 8.33
Car Rental	$1050	$1000	5

Hotel expenses were under budget by 8⅓%, while the other items were over budget.

Markups

A markup is a percentage of cost and is used widely in retail firms for computing prices. The examples below show you how to compute the three unknown values of a markup problem.

Solving for Price with a Markup
Concepts

The selling price determined by a markup on cost is computed using:

Selling price = (1 + markup %/100) Cost

Equation (13-23)

(Financial Analysis–Continued)

Example

The Small Town Store uses a 50% markup to price their appliances. A recent shipment of coffee makers had a unit cost of $9. What is the selling price?

Calculator Solution

If the "DEC 2" indicator does not appear in the display, press 2nd Decimal before keying in the example.

Procedure	Press	Display
1. Clear calculator.	ON/c	0 DEC 2 FIN
2. Add one and markup percentage.	1 + 50 % =	1.50 DEC 2 FIN
3. Multiply by cost to calculate selling price.	× 9 =	13.50 DEC 2 FIN

The coffee makers are priced at $13.50 each.

Solving for Cost Before Markup

Concepts

The cost before markup is found using:

Cost = selling price/(1 + Markup %/100)

Equation (13-24)

(Financial Analysis–Continued)

Example

The Blue Valley furniture store applies a 40% markup to their sofas. What is the cost of a sofa selling for $1120?

Calculator Solution

If the "DEC 2" indicator does not appear in the display, press [2nd] [Decimal] before keying in the example.

Procedure	Press	Display
1. Clear calculator.	[ON/C]	0
2. Add one and markup percentage.	1 [+] 40 [%] [=]	1.40
3. Divide by selling price and calculate reciprocal to compute cost.	[÷] 1120 [=] [1/x]	800.00

The Blue Valley store paid $800 for the sofa.

Solving for Markup Percentage

Concepts

The markup percentage is found using:

$$\text{markup \%} = (\text{selling price} - \text{cost})/\text{cost}$$

Equation (13-25)

(Financial Analysis–Continued)

Example

The Quiet Store is selling stero speakers for $49.95 each. The wholesale cost of the speakers was $35 each. What is the percentage of markup based on cost?

Calculator Solution

If the "DEC 2" indicator does not appear in the display, press [2nd] [Decimal] before keying in the example.

Procedure	Press	Display
1. Clear calculator.	[ON/C]	0
2. Enter selling price.	49.95	49.95
3. Enter cost.	[2nd] [Δ%] 35	35
4. Calculate percentage of markup on cost.	[=]	42.71

The markup on cost is about 43%.

Markdowns and Gross Profit Margins

A markdown is a percentage of selling price. This technique is often used by retail stores to adjust selling prices. This technique is called gross profit margin when used internally by companies to measure product profitability. The examples below show you how to compute the three unknown values of a markdown or gross profit margin problem.

(Financial Analysis–Continued)

Solving for Cost with a Markdown
Concepts

The cost after a markdown is found using:

Cost = Sales price (1 – markdown %/100)

Equation (13-26)

Example

The XYZ store sells a product for $25. What is the cost if the markdown or gross profit margin is 35%?

Calculator Solution

If the "DEC 2" indicator does not appear in the display, press `2nd` `Decimal` before keying in the example.

Procedure	Press	Display
1. Clear calculator.	`ON/C`	0 DEC 2 FIN
2. Enter sales price.	25	25 DEC 2 FIN
3. Subtract markdown % to determine cost.	`–` 35 `%` * `=`	 16.25 DEC 2 FIN

The unit cost is $16.25.

*The key sequence `–` 35 `%` is the same as multiplying by (1 – 35/100).

(Financial Analysis–Continued)

Solving for Markdown or Gross Profit Margin Percentage

Concepts

The markdown or gross profit margin percentage is found using:

$$\text{markdown \%} = \left[\frac{\text{selling price} - \text{cost}}{\text{selling price}} \right] \times 100$$

$$= \left[1 - \frac{\text{cost}}{\text{selling price}} \right] \times 100$$

Equation (13-27)

Example

The Big Store sells china that costs $40 for $65 per plate. What is the markdown percentage (gross profit margin)?

Calculator Solution

If the "DEC 2" indicator does not appear in the display, press 2nd Decimal before keying in the example.

Procedure	Press	Display
1. Clear calculator.	ON/c	0 DEC 2 FIN
2. Divide cost by selling price.	40 ÷ 65	65 DEC 2 FIN
3. Compute the markdown % (gross profit margin).	+/− + 1 ✕ 100 =	38.46 DEC 2 FIN

The markdown percentage (gross profit margin) is about 38%.

(Financial Analysis–Continued)

Solving for Sales Price with the Markdown (Gross Profit Margin) Given

Concepts

The sales price when the markdown (gross profit margin) and cost are known is found using:

Sales price = Cost/(1 – markdown %/100)

Equation (13-28)

Example

The Super Store manager wants to price products so that the markdown is 45%. A toaster costs $15. What is the selling price?

Calculator Solution

If the "DEC 2" indicator does not appear in the display, press [2nd] [Decimal] before keying in the example.

Procedure	Press	Display
1. Clear calculator.	[ON/C]	**0** DEC 2 FIN
2. Subtract markdown % from one.	1 [–] 45 [%] [=]	**0.55** DEC 2 FIN
3. Divide by cost and calculate reciprocal to compute selling price.	[÷] 15 [=] [1/x]	**27.27** DEC 2 FIN

The selling price should be $27.27 for each toaster.

Learning Curve Analysis

Concepts

Learning curve analysis is employed by companies producing groups of labor intensive products. Aircraft and electronic companies are examples of companies using such analysis. Learning curves are based on the assumption that the labor hours per unit decline as experience is gained in making the product. The learning curve model discussed here assumes that as the cumulative unit produced *doubles*, the *cumulative average* labor hours decline by a fixed percent. While there are several learning curve models, the Cumulative Average Model is used widely in business textbooks.

The learning curve $(y = ax^b)$ has many applications in modern business, such as scheduling production, projecting unit costs and labor hours, and setting cost and labor standards. The *average number* of labor hours needed to produce x cumulative units is found with the equation:

$$y = ax^b \qquad \textit{Equation (13-29)}$$

where:

y = average number of labor hours required to produce x cumulative units

a = labor hours required to produce the first unit

x = cumulative number of units produced

LR = learning rate as a percentage

b = learning rate factor expressed as b = ln(decimal learning rate)/ln(2)

ln = logarithm to the base e

(Learning Curve Analysis–Continued)

An 80% learning rate often is used in examples. It means that when production doubles, the cumulative average number of hours per unit is 80% of the previous average. The total number of hours required to produce x cumulative units is expressed as:

$$y(x) = x(ax^b) \qquad \text{Equation (13-30)}$$

while the incremental hours required to produce the xth unit are:

$$\text{Incremental hours} = (b + 1)\, ax^b$$

$$\text{Equation (13-31)}$$

Example

The FAP Electronic Company introduced a new game this year. Based on past experience with other games, they expect an 80% learning curve rate on the average cumulative labor hours. Twelve labor hours were required to make the first unit. With an 80% learning rate, calculate the following:

a) Average number of hours to produce 150 units

b) Incremental hours to produce the 150th unit

c) Total number of hours to produce 150 units

The following inputs are given or must be calculated to solve the problem.

Number of hours for producing first unit (a) = 12

Learning rate = 80

Learning rate factor (b) = ln(.8)/ln(2)

Number of cumulative units (x) = 150

Average hours to produce 150 units

(y) = 12(150^b)

Total hours to produce 150 units (xy) = 150(12)150^b

Incremental hours to produce 150th unit = (b + 1)(12) 150^b

(Learning Curve Analysis–Continued)

Calculator Solution

If the "DEC 2" indicator does not appear in the display, press 2nd Decimal before keying in the example.

Procedure	Press	Display
1. Clear calculator.	ON/C	0
2. Enter learning rate and calculate b.	80 % 2nd ln x ÷ 2 2nd ln x = STO	-0.32
3. Enter number of units and calculate x^b.	150 y^x RCL =	0.20
4. Enter hours for first unit and calculate average hours.	X 12 =	2.39
5. Calculate incremental hours to produce 150th unit.	EXC + 1 X RCL =	1.62
6. Enter number of units and calculate total hours.	150 X RCL =	358.70

The first 150 units will require 358.7 hours with an average of 2.39 hours per unit. The 150th unit will require 1.62 hours. These results are based on the *Cumulative Average* learning curve model.

(Learning Curve Analysis–Continued)

Review

Equation Value	Meaning	Keystroke
b	Learning rate factor.	LR `%` `2nd` `lnx` `÷` 2 `2nd` `lnx` `=` `STO`
ax^b	Average hours to produce x units.	x `yˣ` `RCL` `X` a `=`
$(b + 1)ax^b$	Incremental hours to produce xth unit.	`EXC` `+` 1 `X` `RCL` `=`
$x(ax^b)$	Total hours to produce x units.	x `X` `RCL` `=`

Chapter 14
FINANCIAL ACCOUNTING

Financial Accounting

Contents

Introduction

Three financial accounting applications are discussed in this chapter. The first topic is depreciation. Examples of four methods of calculating depreciation are given: straight-line, sum-of-the-years' digits, declining balance, and accelerated cost recovery. The next topic is leases in which the implicit interest rate, lease payment, and leasehold amortization are calculated. Bond amortization using the effective interest rate method is the final topic discussed.

Depreciation

One of the necessary calculations in the financial operation of almost every company, large or small, is depreciation of equipment and other assets. Depreciation is the allocation to future income periods of the asset's cost as an expense.

Prior to 1981, companies computed depreciation using traditional methods such as the straight-line method (SL), the sum-of-the-years' digits method (SYD), or the declining-balance method (DB). Combinations of these three methods and other depreciation methods were employed for both financial statements and income tax returns. In 1981, however, a new procedure is allowed for tax return depreciation calculation. This procedure is called the accelerated cost recovery system (ACRS) depreciation.

This section shows you how to calculate depreciation using one of the following methods: SL, SYD, DB, or ACRS. The procedures allow for partial-year depreciation when an asset is purchased during a fiscal year. The SL and SYD depreciation methods depreciate the asset for the remainder of the year of purchase with the difference recorded for one year beyond the asset's life.

(Depreciation–Continued)

Straight Line (SL) Depreciation
Concepts

The net depreciable asset value (Cost − Salvage) is allocated evenly during the asset's life using the straight-line method. When an asset is purchased during the year, the first whole year's depreciation is allocated between the first year and the year after the last year of the asset's life. The equations are:

$$\text{Dep/Yr} = \frac{\text{Cost} - \text{Salvage}}{\text{Life}} \qquad \textit{Equation (14-1)}$$

First partial year depreciation:

$$\text{Dep}_1 = \frac{\text{Months}}{12}(\text{Dep/Yr}) \qquad \textit{Equation (14-2)}$$

Last partial year depreciation:

$$\text{Dep}_N = \text{Dep/Yr} - \text{Dep}_1 \qquad \textit{Equation (14-3)}$$

(Depreciation–Continued)

Example

The ABC Company purchases a machine for $5000 that has a $750 salvage value with a five-year life. Nine months are depreciated during the first year. Compute the depreciation expense for each year using the straight-line method.

Calculator Solution

If the "DEC 2" indicator does not appear in the display, press 2nd Decimal before keying in the example.

Procedure	Press	Display
1. Clear calculator.	ON/c	**0** DEC 2 · FIN
2. Subtract salvage from cost to find depreciable value.	5000 − 750 =	**4250.00** DEC 2 · FIN
3. Divide by number of years to determine yearly depreciation and store.	÷ 5 = STO	**850.00** DEC 2 · FIN
4. Enter number of months of depreciation taken in first year and divide by 12.	9 ÷ 12 =	**0.75** DEC 2 · FIN
5. Calculate first partial year's depreciation.	× RCL =	**637.50** DEC 2 · FIN
6. Calculate final partial year's depreciation.	+/− + RCL =	**212.50** DEC 2 · FIN

The depreciation expense for the first nine months of year one is $637.50. The depreciation expense for years two, three, four, and five is $850. The depreciation expense for the final partial period, year six, is $212.50.

(Depreciation–Continued)

Review

Equation Value	Meaning	Keystrokes
Dep/Yr	Yearly depreciation.	Cost $\boxed{-}$ Salvage $\boxed{\div}$ Life $\boxed{=}$ $\boxed{\text{STO}}$
(Months/ 12)Dep	First partial year depreciation.	Months $\boxed{\div}$ 12 $\boxed{\times}$ $\boxed{\text{RCL}}$ $\boxed{=}$
Dep/Yr − Dep_1	Last partial year depreciation.	$\boxed{+/-}$ $\boxed{+}$ $\boxed{\text{RCL}}$ $\boxed{=}$

Sum-of-the-Years' Digits (SYD) Depreciation

Concepts

Because the contributions of an asset frequently are greater during the early years of its lifetime rather than the final years, it is often desirable to depreciate a larger amount of the costs of an asset during the early years. The sum-of-the-years'-digits method of calculating depreciation gives a greater depreciation in the early years of the lifetime of an asset than in the final years.

Financial Accounting

(Depreciation–Continued)

The depreciation expense using the SYD method is computed by multiplying the depreciable value (Cost (C) – Salvage (S)) and the ratio of the number of remaining periods to the sum of all years in the life, L, of the asset. The sum of the years is calculated using L(L + 1)/2. The standard equation for SYD depreciation when the asset has a whole first-year depreciation is:

$$\text{Yearly Depreciation Expense} = (L + 1 - j) \left[\frac{2(C - S)}{L(L + 1)} \right]$$

Equation (14-4)

where j is the year number for calculating the depreciation expense.

When the asset is purchased during a year, partial period depreciation is recorded for the first year. To avoid an awkward year-by-year allocation procedure, the following equation can be used to calculate the annual depreciation expense.

First partial-year's depreciation:

$$\text{Dep}_1 = L(M) \left[\frac{(C - S)}{6(L)(L + 1)} \right]$$

Equation (14-5)

Remaining year's depreciation:

$$\text{Dep}_j = [12(L + 2 - j) - M] \left[\frac{(C - S)}{6(L)(L + 1)} \right]$$

Equation (14-6)

where:

M = Months of depreciation taken in first year
j = Year number for calculating depreciation where j = 2, 3, ... L, L + 1
L = Depreciable life in years

(Depreciation–Continued)

The solutions for both procedures are shown below.

Example

The ABC Company purchases a machine for $5000 that has a $750 salvage value and a five-year life. Compute the depreciation expense for each year using the SYD method where a) a whole year is depreciated during year one and b) nine months are depreciated during year one.

Calculator Solution

If the "DEC 2" indicator does not appear in the display, press (2nd)(Decimal) before keying in the example.

Procedure	Press	Display
1. Clear calculator.	(ON/C)	0 DEC 2 FIN
A. Whole year depreciation		
2. Enter life of asset, calculate sum of years, and store.	5 (+) 1 (X) 5 (+) 2 (=)(STO)	15.00 DEC 2 FIN
3. Enter cost and salvage.	5000 (−) 750 (=)	4250.00 DEC 2 FIN
4. Divide depreciable value by sum of years and store.	(÷)(RCL)(=)(STO)	283.33 DEC 2 FIN
5. Enter asset life (L) and calculate depreciation expense for year one.	(X) 5 (=)	1416.67 DEC 2 FIN
6. Calculate remaining years depreciation expense.		
Year two	(−)(RCL)(=)	1133.33 DEC 2 FIN
Year three	(−)(RCL)(=)	850.00 DEC 2 FIN
Year four	(−)(RCL)(=)	566.67 DEC 2 FIN
Year five	(−)(RCL)(=)	283.33 DEC 2 FIN

(continued)

Financial Accounting

(Depreciation–Continued)

Procedure	Press	Display
B. Partial year's depreciation		
1. Enter life, calculate sum of years in months, and store.	5 ⊞ 1 ⊠ 5 ⊠ 6 ⊜ STO	**180.00** DEC 2 FIN
2. Enter cost and salvage.	5000 ⊟ 750 ⊜	**4250.00** DEC 2 FIN
3. Divide depreciable value by sum of years in months and store.	⊞ RCL ⊜ STO	**23.61** DEC 2 FIN
4. Multiply results of Step 3 by life in years (L) and number of depreciation months (M) in year one to calculate first year's depreciation.	⊠ 5 ⊠ 9 ⊜	**1062.50** DEC 2 FIN
5. Enter life (L) and months (M) to calculate second year's depreciation.	5 ⊠ 12 ⊟ 9 ⊠ RCL ⊜	**1204.17** DEC 2 FIN
6. Calculate factor.	EXC ⊠ 12 ⊜ EXC	**1204.17** DEC 2 FIN
7. Depreciation for remaining years.		
Year three	⊟ RCL ⊜	**920.83** DEC 2 FIN
Year four	⊟ RCL ⊜	**637.50** DEC 2 FIN
Year five	⊟ RCL ⊜	**354.17** DEC 2 FIN
Partial year six	⊟ RCL ⊜	**70.83** DEC 2 FIN

If a whole year is depreciated during year one, the annual depreciation expenses are $1416.67, $1133.33, $850.00, $566.67, and $283.33. But if only nine months are depreciated, then the depreciation expenses are $1062.50 for the first year with $1204.17, $920.83, $637.50, $354.17, and $70.83 for the remaining years.

Financial Accounting   **Chapter 14**

(Depreciation–Continued)

Review

Equation Value	Meaning	Keystroke
A. Whole Year Depreciation		
1. $L(L+1)/2$	Sum of digits for asset life.	L ⊞ 1 ⊠ L ⊟ 2 ⊜ STO
2. $C - S$	Depreciable value.	C ⊟ S ⊜
3. $\dfrac{(C-S)2}{L(L+1)}$	Factor.	⊟ RCL ⊜ STO
4. Dep_1	First year's depreciation.	⊠ L ⊜
5. Dep_2	Second year's depreciation.	⊟ RCL ⊜
6. Dep_j	Repeat Step 5 for each year's depreciation.	⊟ RCL ⊜
B. Partial First Year Depreciation		
1. $(L+1)(L)6$	Months in sum of years.	L ⊞ 1 ⊠ L ⊠ 6 ⊜ STO
2. $C - S$	Depreciable value.	C ⊟ S
3. $\dfrac{C-S}{(L+1)(L)6}$	Factor.	⊟ RCL ⊜ STO
4. Dep_1	First year's partial depreciation.	⊠ L ⊠ M ⊜
5. Dep_2	Second year's depreciation.	L ⊠ 12 ⊟ M ⊠ RCL ⊜
6. $\dfrac{C-S \times 12}{(L+1)(L)6}$ Factor.		EXC ⊠ 12 ⊜ EXC
7. Dep_3	Third year's depreciation.	⊟ RCL ⊜
8. Dep_j	Repeat Step 7 for remaining years.	⊟ RCL ⊜

(Depreciation–Continued)

Declining Balance (DB) Depreciation

Concepts

The declining-balance method of depreciation also gives a greater depreciation in the early years of the lifetime of an asset. This method of depreciation assumes that the depreciation expense is a constant percentage of the net book value. The depreciation expense each year is computed by multiplying the net book value (NBV) and a fixed percentage rate called the declining balance factor (DBF). The percentage is often 125%, 150%, or 200% of the straight-line rate. The net book value for the first year is the cost. The depreciation expense is subtracted from the net book value with the result becoming the new net book value. The cycle is repeated until the salvage value is reached. The general equation is:

$$\text{Dep} = (\text{NBV})\frac{\text{DBF}}{\text{L}} \qquad \textit{Equation (14-7)}$$

The first year's depreciation for a partial period with M months of depreciation is:

$$\text{Dep}_1 = \frac{\text{M}}{12}(\text{Cost})\frac{\text{DBF}}{\text{L}} \qquad \textit{Equation (14-8)}$$

This method has some features which should be noted. First, unlike straight-line or sum-of-the-years'-digits depreciation, this method does not stop depreciating at the end of the asset's life. Rather, the process is stopped when the net book value equals the salvage value. This may occur before or after the asset's life. If salvage is reached before the end of the asset's life, you have no problems. If salvage is computed beyond the asset's life, you should consider a switch to the straight-line method before the end of the asset's life.

(Depreciation–Continued)

Example

The ABC Company purchases a machine for $5000 that has a $750 salvage value with a five-year life. Nine months of depreciation are calculated during the first year. What are the annual depreciation expenses using the 200% declining-balance method?

Calculator Solution

If the "DEC 2" indicator does not appear in the display, press [2nd] [Decimal] before keying in the example.

Procedure	Press	Display
1. Clear calculator.	[ON/C]	**0** DEC 2 FIN
2. Divide declining-balance factor by life in years and store.	200 [÷] 5 [=] [STO]	**40.00** DEC 2 FIN
3. Calculate first partial-year depreciation. a. Multiply by cost to calculate depreciation for first calendar year.	[%] [×] 5000 [=]	**2000.00** DEC 2 FIN
b. Enter month and calculate partial-year depreciation.	[×] 9 [÷] 12 [=]	**1500.00** DEC 2 FIN
4. Calculate net book value at start of second year.	[+/-] [+] 5000 [=]	**3500.00** DEC 2 FIN
5. Calculate depreciation expense for second year.	[−] [RCL] [%]	**1400.00** DEC 2 FIN
6. Calculate net book value at end of second year.	[=]	**2100.00** DEC 2 FIN
7. Calculate depreciation expense for third year.	[−] [RCL] [%]	**840.00** DEC 2 FIN *(continued)*

(Depreciation–Continued)

(continued)

Procedure	Press	Display
8. Calculate net book value at end of third year.	$=$	**1260.00** DEC 2 FIN
9. Calculate depreciation expense for fourth year.	$-$ RCL $\%$	**504.00** DEC 2 FIN
10. Calculate net book value at end of fourth year.	$=$	**756.00** DEC 2 FIN
11. Calculate depreciation expense for fifth year.	$-$ 750 $=$	**6.00** DEC 2 FIN

The depreciation stops in year five with a depreciation expense of $6.00 because the net book value in year six is less than the $750 salvage value after depreciation is computed using the regular procedure.

Review

Equation Value	Meaning	Keystrokes
1. DBF/L	Fixed percentage depreciation rate.	DBF $\div$ L $=$ STO
2. Dep$_1$	First year's depreciation.	$\%$ $\times$ Cost $\times$ M $\div$ 12 $=$
3. NBV$_1$	Net book value at end of year one.	$+/-$ $+$ Cost $=$
4. Dep$_j$	Depreciation for year j.	$-$ RCL $\%$
5. NBV$_j$	Net book value for year j.	$=$
6.	Repeat steps 4 and 5 until salvage is reached.	

(Depreciation–Continued)

Accelerated Cost Recovery System (ACRS) Depreciation

Concepts

 The Economic Recovery Tax Act of 1981 provides a depreciation procedure called the accelerated cost recovery system (ACRS). This method uses declining-balance depreciation during the asset's early life with a switch to straight-line depreciation during the latter years. The ACRS method assumes all assets are depreciated one-half year during the year of acquisition and have a zero salvage value. A set of tables is provided to calculate the ACRS depreciation. The tables vary depending on the date of purchase. Two of these tables are reproduced below.

Assets purchased during 1981-1984

Applicable percentage per year

Life/years	1	2	3	4	5	6	7	8	9	10
3 years	25	38	37							
5 years	15	22	21	21	21					
10 years	8	14	12	10	10	10	9	9	9	9

Assets purchased in 1985

Applicable percentage per year

Life/years	1	2	3	4	5	6	7	8	9	10
3 years	29	47	24							
5 years	18	33	25	16	8					
10 years	9	19	16	14	12	10	8	6	4	2

The depreciation expense for each year is equal to the cost multiplied by the applicable percentage from the table.

(Depreciation–Continued)

Example

The ABC Company purchases a machine for $5000 in 1982. It qualifies for five-year ACRS depreciation. Compute the depreciation expense for the annual tax return.

Calculator Solution

If the "DEC 2" indicator does not appear in the display, press [2nd] [Decimal] before keying in the example.

Procedure	Press	Display
1. Clear calculator.	[ON/C]	**0** DEC 2 FIN
2. Store asset cost.	5000 [STO]	**5000.00** DEC 2 FIN
3. Enter percentage for year one and calculate depreciation.	[X] 15 [%][=]	**750.00** DEC 2 FIN
4. Enter percentage for year two and calculate depreciation.	[RCL][X] 22 [%][=]	**1100.00** DEC 2 FIN
5. Enter percentage for years three, four, and five; calculate depreciation.	[RCL][X] 21 [%][=]	**1050.00** DEC 2 FIN

The depreciation expenses for years one through five are $750, $1100, $1050, $1050, and $1050.

Leases

Leases normally involve an asset or land that is used by a person or company (lessee) and owned by another person or company (lessor). The lessee makes regular payments, usually at the *beginning* of each payment period. The value of the asset at the end of the lease period is called the *residual value* (FV). When the lease payments (PMT) are equal, a time-line diagram shows that the cash flow pattern is that of an annuity due with a balloon.

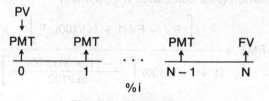

Time-Line Diagram 14-1

In this section you see how to solve for the lease payment and implicit interest rate as well as how to compute a leasehold amortization schedule. Note that the residual value must be less than the asset value or the lessor rather than the lessee is making payments.

(Leases–Continued)

Lease Payment

Concepts

 To compute the lease payment (PMT), you need to know the asset's cost or value (PV), the interest rate (%i), the number of payments (N), and the residual value (FV), which may be zero. The following equation for a present value annuity due, equation (9-8), calculates the payment.

$$PMT = \frac{\left[PV - FV(1 + \%i/100)^{-N} \right]}{(1 + \%iK/100) \left[\dfrac{1 - (1 + \%i/100)^{-N}}{\%i/100} \right]}$$

where:

  K = 1 for an annuity due (beginning-of-period payments).

  K = 0 for an ordinary annuity (end-of-period payments).

PV
↓
PMT = ?   PMT = ?   PMT = ?   FV
  ↑   ↑   . . .   ↑   ↑
  0   1   N − 1   N
                %i

Time-Line Diagram 14-2

(Leases–Continued)

Your calculator solves Equation (9-8) for the lease payment
as shown below.

Example

The JQ Company is leasing a machine with a current market value of $130,000 to the RO Com-
pany for three years. At the end of this time, the
machine's market value should be $90,000.
Lease payments are made at the beginning of
each month. If the JQ Company wants to earn an annual
return rate of 24% compounded monthly, how much is the
monthly payment?

Drawing the time-line diagram below gives all the inputs
necessary for computing the monthly payment.

PV = $130,000

PMT = ?   PMT = ?   PMT = ?   FV = $90,000

0   1   . . .   35   N = 36

%i = 24/12 = 2

Time-Line Diagram 14-3

The number of payments (N) is the years times the
payments per year (3 × 12). The interest rate (%i) is the annual
rate divided by the number of payments per year (24/12). The
residual value (FV) is $90,000 and the asset market value (PV)
is $130,000. The unknown to solve for is the lease payment
amount (PMT) as indicated by the question marks.

(Leases–Continued)

Calculator Solution

If the "DEC 2" indicator does not appear in the display, press 2nd Decimal before keying in the example.

Procedure	Press	Display
1. Clear calculator and select finance mode.	ON/C 2nd **FIN**	**0** DEC 2 FIN
2. Enter asset market value or cost.	130000 PV	**130000.00** DEC 2 FIN
3. Enter residual value.	90000 FV	**90000.00** DEC 2 FIN
4. Enter years and calculate total payments.	3 X 12 = N	**36.00** DEC 2 FIN
5. Enter annual interest rate and calculate rate per payment period.	24 ÷ 12 = %i	**2.00** DEC 2 FIN
6. Compute lease payment.	DUE PMT	**3303.25** DEC 2 ANN FIN

For the JQ Company to earn an annual interest rate of 24% compounded monthly, the RO Company must make monthly payments of $3303.25.

(Leases–Continued)

Review

Be sure to clear the financial registers at the start of each problem by pressing [2nd] [FIN].

Equation Value	Meaning	Keystrokes
Input:		
PV	Asset cost or market value.	[PV]
FV	Residual value.	[FV]
%i	Interest rate per period.	[%i]
N	Number of lease payments.	[N]
Solution:	Lease payment.	[DUE] [PMT]

(Leases–Continued)

Implicit Interest Rate

Concepts

The implicit interest rate is the interest rate that discounts the lease payments and residual value back to an amount equaling the asset's market value (PV). To compute the implicit interest rate, you need to know the asset's cost or market value (PV), the periodic lease payment (PMT), the number of lease payments (N), and the residual value (FV) which may be zero. The interest rate that balances equation (9-7) is the implicit interest rate.

$$PV = (1 + (\%i/100)\,K)\,PMT \left[\frac{1 - (1 + \%i/100)^{-N}}{\%i/100} \right]$$
$$+ FV(1 + \%i/100)^{-N}$$

where:

K = 1 for an annuity due (beginning-of-period payments).

K = 0 for an ordinary annuity (end-of-period payments).

Your calculator solves the above equation for the interest rate as shown below.

Example

The KK Company is leasing a machine with a current market value of $10,400 to the BG Company for 36 months. The BG Company pays $303.54 at the beginning of each month. If the asset has an assumed residual value of $3500, find the implicit interest rate compounded monthly and the annual effective rate.

PV = $10,400

PMT = $303.54 $303.54   . . . $303.54   FV = $3500

0   1   35   N = 36

%i = ?

Time-Line Diagram 14-4

(Leases–Continued)

The following inputs are given: number of payments, N = 36; asset market value, PV = 10,400; lease payment, PMT = 303.54; and residual value, FV = 3500. The unknown to solve for, as indicated by the question mark, is the interest rate.

Calculator Solution

If the "DEC 2" indicator does not appear in the display, press 2nd Decimal before keying in the example.

Procedure	Press	Display
1. Clear calculator and select finance mode.	ON/C 2nd **FIN**	**0** DEC 2 FIN
2. Enter asset market value or cost.	10400 PV	**10400.00** DEC 2 FIN
3. Enter periodic payment.	303.54 PMT	**303.54** DEC 2 ANN FIN
4. Enter number of payments.	36 N	**36.00** DEC 2 ANN FIN
5. Enter residual value.	3500 FV	**3500.00** DEC 2 ANN FIN
6. Compute implicit interest rate per payment period.	DUE %i	**1.58** DEC 2 ANN FIN
7. Multiply by number of payments per year to find annual nominal implicit interest rate and store.	✕ 12 = STO	**19.00** DEC 2 ANN FIN
8. Enter number of payments per year.	12 2nd APR▸	**12.00** DEC 2 ANN FIN
9. Compute equivalent annual effective rate.	RCL =	**20.75** DEC 2 ANN FIN

The annual implicit interest rate with monthly compounding is 19%, equivalent to a 20.75% annual effective interest rate.

(Leases–Continued)

Review

Be sure to clear the financial registers at the start of each problem by pressing ²ⁿᵈ FIN.

Equation Value	Meaning	Keystrokes
Inputs:		
PV	Asset market value.	PV
PMT	Periodic payment.	PMT
N	Number of payments.	N
FV	Residual value.	FV
Solution:	Implicit interest rate per payment period.	DUE %i

(Leases–Continued)

Leasehold Amortization
Concepts

Accountants require that certain types of leases be capitalized and amortized over the lease's term. Leasehold amortization requires determining the present value of the lease payments using an appropriate discount rate. This lease obligation is then amortized during the life of the lease. The lease payments are separated into two components—interest on the unpaid obligation (INT) and reduction of the lease obligation (PRIN).

The equations used to compute the amortization values for leases with $K = 1$ are:

$$BAL_M = \frac{PV(1 + \%i/100)^M}{(1 + \%iK/100)} - PMT \left[\frac{(1 + \%i/100)^M - 1}{\%i/100} \right]$$

Equation (14-9)

$$INT_N = (\%i/100)\,BAL_{M-1} \qquad \textit{Equation (14-10)}$$

$$PRIN_M = PMT - INT_M$$

Equation (14-11)

where:

M = Payment number
BAL_M = Balance after M payments
INT_M = Interest portion of Mth payment
$PRIN_M$ = Reduction of lease obligation for Mth payment
K = 0 for an ordinary annuity (end-of-period payments)
K = 1 for an annuity due (beginning-of-period payments)

NOTE: IF $K = 0$, $M = 1$, then $BAL_0 = PV$
IF $K = 1$, $M = 1$, then $BAL_0 = 0$

The following procedure assumes the lease payments occur at the beginning of each period. Substitute CPT for DUE in the procedure if payments occur at the end of each period.

Financial Accounting

(Leases–Continued)

Example

The ABC Company leases equipment for four years with a $6000 beginning-of-year payment. The present value of the lease using a 15% annual interest rate is $19,699.35. Prepare a leasehold amortization schedule for the equipment.

Calculator Solution

If the "DEC 2" indicator does not appear in the display, press `2nd` `Decimal` before keying in the example.

Procedure	Press	Display
1. Clear calculator and select finance mode.	`ON/c` `2nd` `FIN`	**0** <small>DEC 2 FIN</small>
2. Enter interest rate per payment period.	15 `%i`	**15.00** <small>DEC 2 FIN</small>
3. Enter periodic lease payment and store.	6000 `PMT` `STO`	**6000.00** <small>DEC 2 ANN FIN</small>
4. Enter present value of lease.	19699.35 `PV`	**19699.35** <small>DEC 2 ANN FIN</small>
5. Amortize first payment.		
a) Payment number	1	**1** <small>DEC 2 ANN FIN</small>
b) Interest portion	`DUE` `2nd` `INT`	**0** <small>DEC 2 ANN FIN</small>
c) Reduction of lease obligation	`+/−` `+` `RCL` `=`	**6000.00** <small>DEC 2 ANN FIN</small>
d) Enter payment number and compute balance after first payment	1 `DUE` `2nd` `BAL`	**13699.35** <small>DEC 2 ANN FIN</small>
6. Amortize second payment.		
a) Interest	2 `DUE` `2nd` `INT`	**2054.90** <small>DEC 2 ANN FIN</small>
b) Reduction of lease obligation	`+/−` `+` `RCL` `=`	**3945.10** <small>DEC 2 ANN FIN</small>
c) Balance	2 `DUE` `2nd` `BAL`	**9754.25** <small>DEC 2 ANN FIN</small>

(continued)

(Leases–Continued)

(continued)

Procedure	Press	Display
7. Amortize third payment.		
a) Interest	3 `DUE` `2nd` `INT`	**1463.14** <small>DEC 2 ANN FIN</small>
b) Reduction of lease obligation	`+/−` `+` `RCL` `=`	**4536.86** <small>DEC 2 ANN FIN</small>
c) Balance	3 `DUE` `2nd` `BAL`	**5217.39** <small>DEC 2 ANN FIN</small>
8. Amortize fourth payment.		
a) Interest	4 `DUE` `2nd` `INT`	**782.61** <small>DEC 2 ANN FIN</small>
b) Reduction of lease obligation	`+/−` `+` `RCL` `=`	**5217.39** <small>DEC 2 ANN FIN</small>
c) Balance	4 `DUE` `2nd` `BAL`	**− 0.0010409** <small>DEC 2 ANN FIN</small>

The small difference in the remaining balance is caused by the rounding of the payment to two decimal places.

(Leases–Continued)

Review

Be sure to clear the financial registers at the start of each problem by pressing 2nd FIN.

Equation Value	Meaning	Keystrokes
Inputs:		
%i	Interest rate per payment period.	%i
PMT	Enter lease payment and store.	PMT STO
PV	Present value of lease payments.	PV
Solution:		
INT_M	Enter payment number, M, and calculate interest portion.	M DUE 2nd INT
$PRIN_M$	Calculate reduction of lease obligation for Mth payment.	+/− + RCL =
BAL_M	Enter payment number, M, and calculate balance after payment.	M DUE 2nd BAL

(Leases–Continued)

Going Further with Leases

You can solve for the following lease values using the basic keystrokes shown below.

Solving for Present Value of Lease

General Equation (9-7)

$$PV = (1 + (\%i/100) K) \, PMT \left[\frac{1 - (1 + \%i/100)^{-N}}{\%i/100} \right]$$
$$+ FV (1 + \%i/100)^{-N}$$

where:

K = 1 for an annuity due (beginning-of-period payments).

K = 0 for an ordinary annuity (end-of-period payments).

Calculator Keys

Inputs: %i, PMT, FV, N

Solution: DUE PV

(Leases–Continued)

Solving for Residual Value of Lease

General Equation (9-9)

$$FV = PV(1 + \%i/100)^N - (1 + \%K/100)PMT$$
$$\times \left[\frac{(1 + \%i/100)^N - 1}{\%i/100} \right]$$

where:

K = 1 for an annuity due (beginning-of-period payments).

K = 0 for an ordinary annuity (end-of-period payments).

Calculator Keys

Inputs: %i, PMT, PV, N
Solution: DUE FV

Solving for Number of Lease Payments

General Equation (9-10)

$$N = \frac{\ln\left[\dfrac{\%i\,FV/100 - (1 + \%iK/100)\,PMT}{\%i\,PV/100 - (1 + \%iK/100)\,PMT} \right]}{\ln(1 + \%i/100)}$$

where:

K = 1 for an annuity due (beginning-of-period payments).

K = 0 for an ordinary annuity (end-of-period payments).

Calculator Keys

Inputs: PV, FV, %i, PMT
Solution: DUE N

Amortizing Bond Premium/Discount

Concepts

Accountants amortize bond premiums or discounts during the life of the bond. The effective interest method is the recommended procedure. This method assumes bond interest expense is computed using the effective interest rate per coupon period rather than the coupon rate. As a result, the interest expense is computed by multiplying the effective rate and the bond's net book value. The cash paid is computed by multiplying the periodic coupon rate and the bond's par value.

Any difference between the interest expense and cash payment is either bond premium or discount. Bond discount is added to the bond's net book value while bond premium is subtracted. After the last coupon payment, the bond's net book value equals its par value.

Because the bond premium or discount is amortized when coupon payments are made at the end of each period, the basic mortgage amortization equations, equations (14-9), (14-10), and (14-11), are used to calculate the amortization schedule when K = 0. The terminology is slightly different for amortizing bond premiums or discounts as shown below.

$$NBV = \frac{PV\,(1 + \%i/100)^M}{(1 + \%iK/100)} - PMT\left[\frac{(1 + \%i/100)^M - 1}{\%i/100}\right]$$

Equation (14-12)

$$INT_M = (\%i/100)\,NBV_{M-1}$$

Equation (14-13)

$$AMORT_M = PMT - INT_M$$

Equation (14-14)

where:

M = Coupon payment number
NBV_M = Net book value of bond after M payments
$\%i$ = Effective interest rate per coupon period
INT_M = Interest expense for Mth payment

(Amortizing Bond Premium/Discount–Continued)

PV = Present value of bond payments and redemption value one coupon period before the first coupon payment (initial net book value)

PMT = Periodic cash coupon payment

$AMORT_M$ = Amount of bond discount or premium amortized with Mth payment

K = 1 for an annuity due (beginning-of-period payments)

K = 0 for an ordinary annuity (end-of-period payments).

Note: IF K = 0, M = 1, then $BAL_0 = PV$

If K = 1, M = 1, then $BAL_0 = 0$

The calculator automatically computes the above values with the [2nd] [INT] and [2nd] [BAL] function keys.

Example

The Douglas RC Model Company issues $100,000 worth of bonds for $97,073.40. The bonds mature in 10 years and have semiannual interest payments equaling $5500. The yield to maturity on the bonds is 11.5%, which gives an effective interest rate per coupon period of 5.75%. Prepare a bond amortization schedule for the first two coupon payments and the final 20th payment. Bond discount is being amortized because the bonds sold for less than par value.

Calculator Solution

If the "DEC 2" indicator does not appear in the display, press [2nd] [Decimal] before keying in the example.

Procedure	Press	Display
1. Clear calculator and select finance mode.	[ON/c] [2nd] [FIN]	DEC 2 0 FIN
2. Enter initial net book value.	97073.4 [PV]	**97073.40** DEC 2 FIN
3. Enter effective interest rate per coupon period.	5.75 [%i]	**5.75** DEC 2 FIN

(continued)

(Amortizing Bond Premium/Discount–Continued)

(continued)

Procedure	Press	Display
4. Enter dollar amount of coupon period.	5500 [PMT][STO]	**5500.00** DEC 2 ANN FIN
5. Compute values for first coupon payment.		
a) Enter payment number	1	**1** DEC 2 ANN FIN
b) Compute interest expense for payment one	[CPT][2nd][INT]	**5581.72** DEC 2 ANN FIN
c) Compute amount of discount (premium) amortized for payment one	[−][RCL][=]	**81.72** DEC 2 ANN FIN
d) Enter payment number and compute net book value after first payment	1 [CPT][2nd][BAL]	**97155.12** DEC 2 ANN FIN
6. Compute values for second coupon payment.		
a) Interest expense	2 [CPT][2nd][INT]	**5586.42** DEC 2 ANN FIN
b) Discount (premium) amortized	[−][RCL][=]	**86.42** DEC 2 ANN FIN
c) Net book value	2 [CPT][2nd][BAL]	**97241.54** DEC 2 ANN FIN
7. Compute values for final payment (number 20).		
a) Interest expense	20 [CPT][2nd][INT]	**5736.41** DEC 2 ANN FIN
b) Discount (premium) amortized	[−][RCL][=]	**236.41** DEC 2 ANN FIN
c) Net book value	20 [CPT][2nd][BAL]	**99999.99** DEC 2 ANN FIN

The final net book value shows $99,999.99 instead of $100,000 because the original bond present value was rounded to two decimal places when entered. Bond premium is a negative value and bond discount a positive value in the keystroke sequence above.

(Amortizing Bond Premium/Discount–Continued)

Review

Be sure to clear the financial registers at the start of each problem by pressing [2nd] [FIN].

Equation Value	Meaning	Keystrokes
Inputs:		
PV	Bond net book value at time of issue.	[PV]
%i	Effective interest rate per coupon period (yield to maturity per period).	[%i]
PMT	Coupon payment.	[PMT] [STO]
Solution:		
INT_M	Interest expense for payment M.	M [CPT] [2nd] [INT]
$AMORT_M$	Amount of amortization for payment M (positive if discount, negative if premium).	[−] [RCL] [=]
NBV_M	Bond net book value after payment M.	M [CPT] [2nd] [BAL]

Chapter 15

MORTGAGE AND CONSUMER LOAN CALCULATIONS

Mortgage and Consumer Loan Calculations

Contents

Introduction

This chapter shows you how to compute the payment, yield, APR, and remaining balance for regular mortgages. Other mortgage values also are computed along with mortgage amortization. The calculation of loan payments in which the interest rate is an APR or an add-on rate is discussed. The final topic is the conversion of add-on interest rates to APR and vice-versa.

Mortgage and Consumer Loan Calculations

Regular Mortgages

The traditional mortgage instrument has a fixed number of equal payments and a constant interest rate. Payments are made at the end of each payment period, which is normally a month. The general time-line diagram for a regular mortgage shown below is that of a present value ordinary annuity. PMT is the equal payment amount, PV is the amount borrowed, N is the number of payments, and %i is the interest rate.

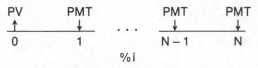

Time-Line Diagram 15-1

You can solve for any of the four values, PV, PMT, %i, or N, using the ordinary annuity procedure discussed in Chapter 8.

Some mortgages, on the other hand, have a balloon payment or an early payoff. Mortgages of this type have the following general time-line diagram. FV is the balloon or remaining balance, PMT is the equal payment amount, PV is the amount borrowed, N is the number of payments, and %i is the interest rate.

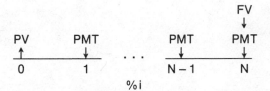

Time-Line Diagram 15-2

The FV in the diagram represents the remaining balance of the mortgage after N payments. The *total* final payment necessary to pay off the mortgage is the sum of the final regular payment and the remaining balance (PMT + FV).

This cash flow pattern is identical to the present value ordinary annuity with a balloon discussed in Chapter 9. You can solve directly for any of the five values (PV, PMT, %i, N, or FV).

(Regular Mortgages–Continued)

Solving for Payment

Concepts

Solving for the monthly payment of a regular mortgage is identical to computing the payment of a present value annuity as discussed in Chapter 8. The general time-line diagram is shown below. PV is the mortgage, N is the number of payments, %i is the interest rate, and payment is indicated by the question mark.

PV   PMT = ?   PMT = ?   PMT = ?

0   1   . . .   N − 1   N

%i

Time-Line Diagram 15-3

After the inputs are determined using the time-line diagram, equation (8-24) solves for the payment.

$$PMT = PV \Big/ \left[\frac{1 - (1 + \%i/100)^{-N}}{\%i/100} \right]$$

Example

The Double K Ranch has a $200,000 mortgage with the Small Town Bank. The mortgage has a twenty-year term with monthly payments. Assuming the annual interest rate is 15% compounded monthly, what is the monthly payment?

PV = 200000   PMT = ?   PMT = ?   PMT = ?

0   1   . . .   239   N = 240

%i = 15/12 = 1.25

Time-Line Diagram 15-4

(Regular Mortgages–Continued)

The number of payments (N) is found by multiplying the number of years and number of payments per year (20 × 12). The interest rate per payment period (%i) is calculated by dividing the annual rate by the number of payments per year (15/12). The mortgage amount (PV) is $200,000. The unknown to solve for is the monthly payment amount (PMT) as indicated by the question mark.

Calculator Solution

If the "DEC 2" indicator does not appear in the display, press [2nd] [Decimal] before keying in the example.

Procedure	Press	Display
1. Clear calculator and select finance mode.	[ON/C] [2nd] [FIN]	0
2. Enter mortgage amount.	200000 [PV]	200000.00
3. Calculate and enter interest rate per payment period.	15 [÷] 12 [=] [%i]	1.25
4. Calculate and enter number of payments.	20 [X] 12 [=] [N]	240.00
5. Compute monthly payment.	[CPT] [PMT]	2633.58

The monthly payment is $2633.58.

(Regular Mortgages–Continued)

Review

Be sure to clear your calculator by pressing [2nd] [FIN] before solving the problem.

Equation Value	Meaning	Keystroke
Inputs:		
PV	Mortgage amount.	[PV]
%i	Interest rate per payment period.	[%i]
N	Number of payments.	[N]
Solution:	Solve for payment.	[CPT] [PMT]

Solving for Remaining Balance (Balloon)

Concepts

Solving for the remaining balance of a regular mortgage is identical to computing the future value of a present value annuity with a balloon as discussed in Chapter 9. The general time-line diagram follows where FV is the remaining balance, PMT is the payment amount, PV is the mortgage amount, N is the number of payments, and %i is the interest rate.

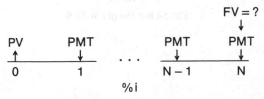

Time-Line Diagram 15-5

Mortgage and Consumer Loan Calculations

(Regular Mortgages–Continued)

After determining the inputs from the time-line diagram, equation (9-9) is solved for the remaining balance.

Remaining
Balance $(FV) = PV(1 + \%i/100)^N - (1 + \%iK/100)PMT$

$$\times \left[\frac{(1 + \%i/100)^N - 1}{\%i/100} \right]$$

where:

$K = 0$ for end-of-period payments (ordinary annuity)
$K = 1$ for beginning-of-period payments (annuity due)

You have a choice of two procedures on your calculator for computing the remaining balance. You may solve for FV, or you may solve for FV using [2nd] [BAL].

Example

The NXD Company has a mortgage with the Big South Bank for $175,000. The interest rate is 12% annually with monthly compounding. The monthly payments of $1800.07 are computed on a 30-year amortization schedule. What is the amount necessary to pay off the mortgage (remaining balance) after five years and after seven years?

```
                                                 FV = ?
                                                   ↓
PV = 175000  PMT = 1800.07    1800.07    1800.07
     ↑            ↓                 ↓          ↓
     0            1        . . .    59      N₁ = 60
                                    83      N₂ = 84
                    %i = 12/12 = 1
```

$PV = 175000$ $PMT = 1800.07$ 1800.07 1800.07
0 1 59 $N_1 = 60$
                          83 $N_2 = 84$
$\%i = 12/12 = 1$

Time-Line Diagram 15-6

(Regular Mortgages–Continued)

The total number of payments (N) is equal to the number of years multiplied by the number of payments per year (5 × 12 = 60 and 7 × 12 = 84). The interest rate per payment period (%i) is calculated by dividing the annual rate by the number of payments per year (12/12). The mortgage amount (PV) is $175,000 and the monthly payment (PMT) is $1800.07. The following procedure uses the [2nd] [BAL] key sequence for computing the remaining balance.

Calculator Solution

If the "DEC 2" indicator does not appear in the display, press [2nd] [Decimal] before keying in the example.

Procedure	Press	Display
1. Clear calculator and select finance mode.	[ON/C] [2nd] [FIN]	0
2. Calculate and enter interest rate per payment period.	12 [÷] 12 [=] [%i]	1.00
3. Enter amount of payment.	1800.07 [PMT]	1800.07
4. Enter amount borrowed.	175000 [PV]	175000.00
5. Enter number of payments made and compute balance after five years.	5 [X] 12 [=] [CPT] [2nd] [BAL]	170910.80
6. Enter number of payments and compute balance after seven years.	7 [X] 12 [=] [CPT] [2nd] [BAL]	168457.24

The balance after 60 payments is $170,910.80 and $168,457.24 after 84 payments. Remember, the remaining balance is computed immediately after the final payment and *does not include* the final payment.

(Regular Mortgages–Continued)

Review

Be sure to clear your calculator by pressing [2nd] [FIN] before solving the problem.

Equation Value	Meaning	Keystroke
A. Using [FV]		
Inputs:		
N	Number of payments made.	[N]
%i	Interest rate per payment period.	[%i]
PMT	Amount of payment.	[PMT]
PV	Amount borrowed.	[PV]
Solution:	Remaining balance.	[CPT] [FV]
B. Using [2nd] [BAL]		
Inputs:		
%i	Interest rate per payment period.	[%i]
PMT	Amount of payment.	[PMT]
PV	Amount borrowed.	[PV]
Solution:	Enter number of payment and compute remaining balance.	N [CPT] [2nd] [BAL]

Using the [2nd] [BAL] key sequence is probably the most convenient procedure because it does not alter the value stored in the [N] register.

(Regular Mortgages–Continued)

Solving for Yield and APR
Concepts

Computing the yield and APR (Annual Percentage Rate) requires finding the interest rate per payment period that makes the present value of the regular payments and balloon, if any, equal to the net cash borrowed or the mortgage value. The yield is based on the net cash received by the borrower, less points and fees, while APR is normally based on the mortgage amount. The yield and APR both have the same general time-line diagram. The difference between the two is the amount selected for present value. On the general time-line diagram below, FV is the remaining balance, PMT is the payment amount, PV is the mortgage amount or net cash borrowed, N is the number of payments, and %i is the yield or APR.

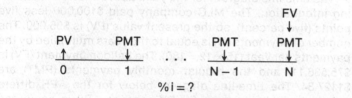

Time-Line Diagram 15-7

After determining the inputs from the time-line diagram, equation (9-7) is used to determine the interest rate. Because no direct solution for i exists, the calculator uses a mathematical trial and error process to balance the equation.

$$PV = (1 + (\%i/100) K) \, PMT \left[\frac{1 - (1 + \%i/100)^{-N}}{\%i/100} \right]$$
$$+ \, FV (1 + \%i/100)^{-N}$$

where:

K = 0 for end-of-period payments (ordinary annuity)
K = 1 for beginning-of-period payments (annuity due)

Mortgage and Consumer Loan Calculations

(Regular Mortgages–Continued)

Example

The MLC Financial Company recently made a $100,000 mortgage. The monthly payments of $1127.84 were computed on a 25-year amortization schedule, but the loan will be repaid after 15 years. The balloon is $75,536.11. The company charged five points on the loan. What are the yield and the APR on this mortgage?

$$FV = 75536.11$$
$$\downarrow$$

PV = 95000   PMT = 1127.84   1127.84   1127.84

0   1   . . .   179   N = 180

%i = ?

Time-Line Diagram 15-8

The time-line diagram for the yield above shows the following information. The MLC company paid $100,000 less five points (five percent), so the present value (PV) is $95,000. The number of payments (N) is equal to the years multiplied by the payments per year ($15 \times 12 = 180$). The balloon payment (FV) is $75,536.11, and the regular monthly payments (PMT) are $1127.84. The time-line diagram below for the APR differs only in the value entered for PV because APR is computed normally on the mortgage amount.

$$FV = 75536.11$$
$$\downarrow$$

PV = 100000 PMT = 1127.84   1127.84   1127.84

0   1   . . .   179   N = 180

%i = ?

Time-Line Diagram 15-9

(Regular Mortgages–Continued)

Calculator Solution

If the "DEC 2" indicator does not appear in the display, press `2nd` `Decimal` before keying in the example.

Procedure	Press	Display
1. Clear calculator and select finance mode.	`ON/C` `2nd` `FIN`	**0** DEC 2 FIN
A. Compute yield		
2. Enter mortgage amount. Subtract points and calculate net cash loaned.	100000 `−` 5 `%` `=` `PV`	**95000.00** DEC 2 FIN
3. Enter periodic payment.	1127.84 `PMT`	**1127.84** DEC 2 ANN FIN
4. Enter number of payments.	15 `X` 12 `=` `N`	**180.00** DEC 2 ANN FIN
5. Enter balloon, if any.	75536.11 `FV`	**75536.11** DEC 2 ANN FIN
6. Compute yield per payment period.	`CPT` `%i`	**1.15** DEC 2 ANN FIN
7. Enter number of payments per year and compute annual nominal yield.	`X` 12 `=`	**13.83** DEC 2 ANN FIN
B. Compute APR		
8. Enter amount of mortgage.	100000 `PV`	**100000.00** DEC 2 ANN FIN
9. Compute interest rate per payment period.	`CPT` `%i`	**1.08** DEC 2 ANN FIN
10. Enter number of payments per year and compute APR.	`X` 12 `=`	**13.00** DEC 2 ANN FIN

The MLC Financial Company used an APR of 13% to compute the payments, but because of the points charged, the yield is actually 13.83%.

(Regular Mortgages–Continued)

Review

Be sure to clear the calculator by pressing 2nd FIN before solving the problem.

Equation Value	Meaning	Keystrokes
Inputs:		
PV	Net cash loaned for yield or mortgage amount for APR.	PV
PMT	Periodic payment.	PMT
N	Number of payments.	N
FV	Balloon or payoff amount. If none, omit or enter zero.	FV
Solution:	a) Compute yield or APR depending on input for PV.	CPT %i
	b) Multiply by number of payments per year to find annual nominal rate.	X p/yr
		=

(Regular Mortgages–Continued)

Amortizing a Regular Mortgage

Concepts

Most, if not all regular mortgages are amortized with the amount of principal and interest in each payment calculated using compound interest. The amount of interest per payment is found by multiplying the beginning-of-period loan balance by the interest rate per payment period. The principal part of the payment is the difference between the payment amount and interest part of that payment. For end-of-period payments, the direct equations used are:

$$BAL_M = PV(1 + \%i/100)^M - PMT \left[\frac{(1 + \%i/100)^M - 1}{\%i/100} \right]$$

Equation (15-1)

$$INT_M = (\%i/100)\,BAL_{M-1}$$ *Equation (15-2)*

$$PRIN_M = PMT - INT_M$$ *Equation (15-3)*

where:

M = payment number
BAL_M = balance after M payments
INT_M = interest portion of Mth payment
$PRIN_M$ = principal portion of Mth payment
PMT = regular equal payment

Example

The XYZ Company has a 20-year $300,000 mortgage with end-of-month payments equaling $3950.37. The annual interest rate is 15% with monthly payments. Compute the monthly amortization for the first two payments and the accumulated interest and principal for the first three years.

(Regular Mortgages–Continued)

Calculator Solution

If the "DEC 2" indicator does not appear in the display, press [2nd] [Decimal] before keying in the example.

Procedure	Press	Display
1. Clear calculator and select finance mode.	[ON/C] [2nd] **FIN**	**0** DEC 2 FIN
2. Enter amount of mortgage.	300000 [PV]	**300000.00** DEC 2 FIN
3. Calculate and enter interest rate per payment period.	15 [÷] 12 [=] [%i]	**1.25** DEC 2 FIN
4. Enter periodic payment and store.	3950.37 [PMT] [STO]	**3950.37** DEC 2 ANN FIN

A. Monthly Principal, Interest, and Remaining Balance

5. Enter first payment number and compute interest portion of first payment.	1 [CPT] [2nd] **INT**	**3750.00** DEC 2 ANN FIN
6. Compute principal portion of first payment.	[+/−] [+] [RCL] [=]	**200.37** DEC 2 ANN FIN
7. Enter payment number and calculate balance after one payment.	1 [CPT] [2nd] **BAL**	**299799.63** DEC 2 ANN FIN

Repeat steps 5, 6, and 7 for each payment.

8. Enter payment number and compute interest for second payment.	2 [CPT] [2nd] **INT**	**3747.50** DEC 2 ANN FIN
9. Compute principal portion of payment.	[+/−] [+] [RCL] [=]	**202.87** DEC 2 ANN FIN
10. Enter payment number and compute remaining balance.	2 [CPT] [2nd] **BAL**	**299596.76** DEC 2 ANN FIN

(continued)

(Regular Mortgages–Continued)

(continued)

Procedure	Press	Display
B. Annual Interest and Principal		
11. Store amount borrowed.	300000 STO	**300000.00** DEC 2 ANN FIN
12. Calculate and record annual payments.	12 ⊠ 3950.37 ⊜	**47404.44** DEC 2 ANN FIN
13. Calculate balance after first year (12 payments).	12 CPT 2nd BAL	**297423.17** DEC 2 ANN FIN
14. Calculate principal paid during first year.	EXC ⊟ RCL ⊜	**2576.83** DEC 2 ANN FIN
15. Enter annual payment total and calculate interest.	+/− + 47404.44 ⊜	**44827.61** DEC 2 ANN FIN

Repeat steps 13, 14, and 15 for each subsequent year.

16. Calculate balance after two years (24 payments).	12 ⊠ 2 ⊜ CPT 2nd BAL	**294432.10** DEC 2 ANN FIN
17. Calculate principal paid during second year.	+/− + EXC ⊜	**2991.07** DEC 2 ANN FIN
18. Enter annual payment total and calculate interest.	+/− + 47404.44 ⊜	**44413.37** DEC 2 ANN FIN
19. Calculate balance after three years (36 payments).	12 ⊠ 3 ⊜ CPT 2nd BAL	**290960.21** DEC 2 ANN FIN
20. Calculate principal paid during third year.	+/− ⊟ EXC ⊜	**3471.90** DEC 2 ANN FIN
21. Enter annual payment total and calculate interest.	+/− + 47404.44 ⊜	**43932.54** DEC 2 ANN FIN

(Regular Mortgages–Continued)

The principal, interest, and remaining balance are:

	Principal	Interest	Remaining Balance
Payment 1	200.37	3750.00	299799.63
Payment 2	202.87	3747.50	299596.76
Year 1	2576.83	44827.61	297423.17
Year 2	2991.07	44413.37	294432.10
Year 3	3471.90	43932.54	290960.21

Review

Be sure to clear the calculator by pressing [2nd] [FIN] before solving the problem.

Equation Value	Meaning	Keystroke
A. Monthly Amortization		
Inputs:		
PV	Amount of loans.	[PV]
%i	Interest rate per payment period.	[%i]
PMT	Periodic payment and store.	[PMT] [STO]
Solution:	1. Enter payment number.	M
	2. Compute interest portion of Mth payment.	[CPT] [2nd] [INT]
	3. Compute principal portion of Mth payment.	[+/−] [+] [RCL] [=]
	4. Enter payment number and compute balance after Mth payment.	M [CPT] [2nd] [BAL]

Repeat steps 1, 2, 3, and 4 for each payment.

(continued)

(Regular Mortgages–Continued)

(continued)

Equation Value	Meaning	Keystroke
B. Accumulated Interest and Principal		
Inputs:		
PV	Amount of loan.	PV
%i	Interest rate per payment period.	%i
PMT	Periodic payment.	PMT
12 × PMT = AP	Calculate and record *annual* payment.	12 X PMT =
Solution:	1. Calculate and store balance at start of year.	
PV	a) First year	PV STO
BAL$_{M-12}$	b) Later year	(M − 12) CPT 2nd BAL STO
	2. Calculate balance after M payments.	M CPT 2nd BAL
	3. Calculate total principal paid.	+/− + EXC =
	4. Enter annual payment total and calculate interest.	+/− − AP =

Repeat steps 2, 3, and 4 for subsequent years.

Going Further With Mortgages

Level payments such as ordinary mortgages use the present value ordinary annuity with a balloon equations discussed in Chapter 9.

Mortgage and Consumer Loan Calculations

(Regular Mortgages–Continued)

Solving for Price to Pay for a Mortgage

General Equation (9-7)

$$PV = (1 + (\%i/100)\,K)\,PMT\left[\frac{1 - (1 + \%i/100)^{-N}}{\%i/100}\right]$$
$$+ FV(1 + \%i/100)^{-N}$$

where:

    K = 0 for end-of-period payments (ordinary annuity)

    K = 1 for beginning-of-period payments (annuity due)

Calculator Keys

    Inputs: [PMT] = Periodic payment

            [N] = Number of payments

            [FV] = Balloon payment, if any

            [%i] = Yield per payment period

    Solution: [CPT][PV]

Solving for Number of Payments

General Equation (9-10)

$$N = \frac{\ln\left[\dfrac{\%i\,FV/100 - (1 + \%iK/100)\,PMT}{\%i\,PV/100 - (1 + \%iK/100)\,PMT}\right]}{\ln(1 + \%i/100)}$$

where:

    K = 0 for end-of-period payments

    K = 1 for beginning-of-period payments

Calculator Keys

    Inputs: [PMT] = Periodic payment

            [PV] = Amount of mortgage

            [FV] = Balloon payment, if any

            [%i] = APR divided by number of payments per year

    Solution: [CPT][N]

Add-on Interest and APR

Federal regulations require lenders to quote interest rates as APR (Annual Percentage Rate). However, some states have usury laws stating interest rate ceilings in terms of add-on interest. Also, some lenders prefer to use add-on interest for computing payments. They convert the add-on rate to the APR for disclosure. This section of the chapter shows you how to compute a loan payment using add-on interest, calculate the equivalent APR, and convert an APR to an equivalent add-on interest rate.

Computing Payment and APR for an Add-on Interest Rate

Concepts

Computing the payment amount for an add-on interest rate (AOR) requires first determining the total interest rate. Add-on interest is equivalent to simple interest in that the interest paid is the add-on rate multiplied by the amount borrowed multiplied by the loan life. As a result, the add-on rate is paid over the loan life even though part of the principal is repaid with each payment. The equivalent APR is the interest rate that amortizes the loan using compound interest.

The total interest paid on a loan is calculated using:

$$\begin{array}{cccc} \text{Total Add-on} & \text{Amount} & \text{Add-on Rate} & \text{Number} \\ \text{Interest (AOI)} = \text{Borrowed (PV)} \times \text{Percentage (AOR)} \times \text{Years (Y)} \end{array}$$

Equation (15-4)

After determining the total interest, the payment is found using:

$$\text{PMT} = \frac{\text{Total Am Borrowed (PV)} + \text{Total Add-on Interest (AOI)}}{\text{Number of Payments (N)}}$$

Equation (15-5)

(Add-on Interest and APR–Continued)

Finally, the equivalent APR is computed by balancing the present value ordinary annuity equation (8-22).

$$PV = PMT \left[\frac{1 - (1 + \%i/100)^{-N}}{\%i/100} \right]$$

The %i multiplied by the number of payments per year is the APR.

Example

The XYZ Loan Company is loaning a consumer $2500 for three years. According to state law, the highest rate they can charge is 8% add-on. Assuming the 8% add-on rate, what is the total interest, monthly payment, and APR on the loan?

PV = 2500   PMT = ?   PMT = ?   PMT = ?

0   1   . . .   35   N = 36

%i = ?

Add-on Rate = 8%

Time-Line Diagram 15-10

The number of payments (N) is the loan life times the number of payments per year (p/yr) (3 × 12). The amount borrowed (PV) is $2500. The payment amount (PMT) is unknown as indicated by the question mark. The add-on rate is 8%. The APR must be calculated.

(Add-on Interest and APR–Continued)

Calculator Solution

If the "DEC 2" indicator does not appear in the display, press [2nd] [Decimal] before keying in the example.

Procedure	Press	Display
1. Clear calculator and select finance mode.	[ON/C] [2nd] **FIN**	**0** DEC 2 FIN
2. Enter amount borrowed.	2500 [PV]	**2500.00** DEC 2 FIN
3. Multiply by add-on percentage rate and number of years to calculate total add-on interest.	[X] 8 [%] [X] 3 [=]	**600.00** DEC 2 FIN
4. Add amount borrowed and divide by number of payments to calculate monthly payment.	[+] 2500 [÷] 36 [N] [=] [PMT]	**86.11** DEC 2 ANN FIN
5. Compute compound interest rate per month.	[CPT] [%i]	**1.21** DEC 2 ANN FIN
6. Multiply by number of payments per year to calculate ∧PR.	[X] 12 [=]	**14.55** DEC 2 ANN FIN

This loan has an $86.11 monthly payment, an APR of 14.55%, and total interest of $600.

(Add-on Interest and APR–Continued)

Review

Be sure to clear the calculator by pressing
[2nd] [FIN] before solving the problem.

Equation Value	Meaning	Keystroke
Inputs:		
1. PV × AOR × Y	Total Add-on Interest (AOI).	PV [PV] [X] AOR [%] [X] Y [=]
2. $\dfrac{PV + AOI}{N}$	Periodic payment.	[+] PV [÷] N [N] [=] [PMT]
3. APR	Interest rate per payment period.	[CPT] [%i]
Solution:	Multiply the %i by the number of payments per year (p/yr) to determine APR.	[X] p/yr [=]

(Add-on Interest and APR–Continued)

Computing Payment and Add-on Interest Rate for an APR

Concepts

Converting an APR to an add-on interest rate is the reverse of the previous example. First, the total interest is calculated as follows.

Total Interest (TI) = Number of payments (N)
× Payment (PMT) − Amount borrowed (PV)

Equation (15-6)

Secondly, the add-on interest percentage rate is calculated as follows.

Add-on Interest Rate (AOI) =

$$\frac{\text{Total interest}}{\text{Amount borrowed (PV)} \times \text{Years (Y)}} \times 100$$

Equation (15-7)

The payment amount is computed using the APR rate and the procedure described in Chapter 9 for the payment of a present value ordinary annuity.

(Add-on Interest and APR–Continued)

Example

You borrow $3000 for three years at 18% APR, compounded monthly, to be repaid monthly. What is the monthly payment and equivalent add-on interest rate?

PV = 3000   PMT = ?   PMT = ?   PMT = ?

```
↑            ↓         . . .    ↓          ↓
0            1                 35        N = 36
```

$\%i = 18/12 = 1.5$
Add-on Rate = ?

Time-Line Diagram 15-11

The number of payments (N) is equal to the loan life times the number of payments per year (3 × 12). The amount borrowed (PV) is $3000. After computing the payment (PMT), the equivalent add-on rate is calculated.

(Add-on Interest and APR–Continued)

Calculator Solution

If the "DEC 2" indicator does not appear in the display, press (2nd) (Decimal) before keying in the example.

Procedure	Press	Display
1. Clear calculator and select finance mode.	(ON/c) (2nd) **FIN**	0 _{DEC 2 FIN}
2. Calculate and enter number of payment.	3 (X) 12 (=) (N)	36.00 _{DEC 2 FIN}
3. Enter APR and divide by number of payments per year.	18 (÷) 12 (=) (%i)	1.50 _{DEC 2 FIN}
4. Enter amount borrowed and store.	3000 (PV) (STO)	3000.00 _{DEC 2 FIN}
5. Compute periodic payment.	(CPT) (PMT)	108.46 _{DEC 2 ANN FIN}
6. Enter number of payments and calculate total interest.	(X) 36 (—) (RCL) (=)	904.46 _{DEC 2 ANN FIN}
7. Divide by number of years and loan amount. Multiply by 100 to calculate add-on rate.	(÷) 3 (÷) (RCL) (X) 100 (=)	10.05 _{DEC 2 ANN FIN}

The monthly payments are $108.46 with total interest paid of $904.46. The 18% APR is equivalent to a 10.05% add-on interest rate.

Mortgage and Consumer Loan Calculations

(Add-on Interest and APR–Continued)

Review

Be sure to clear your calculator by pressing 2nd FIN before solving the problem.

Equation Value	Meaning	Keystroke
PMT × N − PV	Total Interest (TI).	PMT ☒ N ⊖ PV ⊜
÷ Y ÷ PV × 100	Add-on rate as a percentage.	⊙ Y ⊙ PV ☒ 100 ⊜

appendices

Appendix A—Financial Tables

Table A-1. $PVIF = (1 + \%i/100)^{-N}$

Number of Periods	2%	4%	6%	8%	10%	12%
1	.9804	.9615	.9434	.9259	.9091	.8929
2	.9612	.9246	.8900	.8573	.8264	.7972
3	.9423	.8890	.8396	.7938	.7513	.7118
4	.9238	.8548	.7921	.7350	.6830	.6355
5	.9057	.8219	.7473	.6806	.6209	.5674
6	.8880	.7903	.7050	.6302	.5645	.5066
7	.8706	.7599	.6651	.5835	.5132	.4523
8	.8535	.7307	.6274	.5403	.4665	.4039
9	.8368	.7026	.5919	.5002	.4241	.3606
10	.8203	.6756	.5584	.4632	.3855	.3220
11	.8043	.6496	.5268	.4289	.3505	.2875
12	.7885	.6246	.4970	.3971	.3186	.2567
13	.7730	.6006	.4688	.3677	.2897	.2292
14	.7579	.5775	.4423	.3405	.2633	.2046
15	.7430	.5553	.4173	.3152	.2394	.1827
16	.7284	.5339	.3936	.2919	.2176	.1631
17	.7142	.5134	.3714	.2703	.1978	.1456
18	.7002	.4936	.3503	.2502	.1799	.1300
19	.6864	.4746	.3305	.2317	.1635	.1161
20	.6730	.4564	.3118	.2145	.1486	.1037
21	.6598	.4388	.2942	.1987	.1351	.0926
22	.6468	.4220	.2775	.1839	.1228	.0826
23	.6342	.4057	.2618	.1703	.1117	.0738
24	.6217	.3901	.2470	.1577	.1015	.0659
25	.6095	.3751	.2330	.1460	.0923	.0588
26	.5976	.3607	.2198	.1352	.0839	.0525
27	.5859	.3468	.2074	.1252	.0763	.0469
28	.5744	.3335	.1956	.1159	.0693	.0419
29	.5631	.3207	.1846	.1073	.0630	.0374
30	.5521	.3083	.1741	.0994	.0573	.0334

(Appendix A-Financial Tables-Continued)

PVIF (Continued)

Number of Periods	14%	16%	18%	20%	22%	24%
1	.8772	.8621	.8475	.8333	.8197	.8065
2	.7695	.7432	.7182	.6944	.6719	.6504
3	.6750	.6407	.6086	.5787	.5507	.5245
4	.5921	.5523	.5158	.4823	.4514	.4230
5	.5194	.4761	.4371	.4019	.3700	.3411
6	.4556	.4104	.3704	.3349	.3033	.2751
7	.3996	.3538	.3139	.2791	.2486	.2218
8	.3506	.3050	.2660	.2326	.2038	.1789
9	.3075	.2630	.2255	.1938	.1670	.1443
10	.2697	.2267	.1911	.1615	.1369	.1164
11	.2366	.1954	.1619	.1346	.1122	.0938
12	.2076	.1685	.1372	.1122	.0920	.0757
13	.1821	.1452	.1163	.0935	.0754	.0610
14	.1597	.1252	.0985	.0779	.0618	.0492
15	.1401	.1079	.0835	.0649	.0507	.0397
16	.1229	.0930	.0708	.0541	.0415	.0320
17	.1078	.0802	.0600	.0451	.0340	.0258
18	.0946	.0691	.0508	.0376	.0279	.0208
19	.0829	.0596	.0431	.0313	.0229	.0168
20	.0728	.0514	.0365	.0261	.0187	.0135
21	.0638	.0443	.0309	.0217	.0154	.0109
22	.0560	.0382	.0262	.0181	.0126	.0088
23	.0491	.0329	.0222	.0151	.0103	.0071
24	.0431	.0284	.0188	.0126	.0085	.0057
25	.0378	.0245	.0160	.0105	.0069	.0046
26	.0331	.0211	.0135	.0087	.0057	.0037
27	.0291	.0182	.0115	.0073	.0047	.0030
28	.0255	.0157	.0097	.0067	.0038	.0024
29	.0224	.0135	.0082	.0051	.0031	.0020
30	.0196	.0116	.0070	.0042	.0026	.0016

(Appendix A-Financial Tables-Continued)

Table A-2. $PVIFA = \dfrac{1 - (1 + \%i/100)^{-N}}{\%i/100}$

Number of Periods	2%	4%	6%	8%	10%	12%
1	0.9804	0.9615	0.9434	0.9259	0.9091	0.8929
2	1.9416	1.8861	1.8334	1.7833	1.7355	1.6901
3	2.8839	2.7751	2.6730	2.5771	2.4869	2.4018
4	3.8077	3.6299	3.4651	3.3121	3.1699	3.0373
5	4.7135	4.4518	4.2124	3.9927	3.7908	3.6048
6	5.6014	5.2421	4.9173	4.6229	4.3553	4.1114
7	6.4720	6.0021	5.5824	5.2064	4.8684	4.5638
8	7.3255	6.7327	6.2098	5.7466	5.3349	4.9676
9	8.1622	7.4353	6.8017	6.2469	5.7590	5.3282
10	8.9826	8.1109	7.3601	6.7101	6.1446	5.6502
11	9.7868	8.7605	7.8869	7.1390	6.4951	5.9377
12	10.5753	9.3851	8.3838	7.5361	6.8137	6.1944
13	11.3484	9.9856	8.8527	7.9038	7.1034	6.4235
14	12.1062	10.5631	9.2950	8.2442	7.3667	6.6282
15	12.8493	11.1184	9.7122	8.5595	7.6061	6.8109
16	13.5777	11.6523	10.1059	8.8514	7.8237	6.9740
17	14.2919	12.1657	10.4773	9.1216	8.0216	7.1196
18	14.9920	12.6593	10.8276	9.3719	8.2014	7.2497
19	15.6785	13.1339	11.1581	9.6036	8.3649	7.3658
20	16.3514	13.5903	11.4699	9.8181	8.5136	7.4694
21	17.0112	14.0292	11.7641	10.0168	8.6487	7.5620
22	17.6580	14.4511	12.0416	10.2007	8.7715	7.6446
23	18.2922	14.8568	12.3034	10.3711	8.8832	7.7184
24	18.9139	15.2470	12.5504	10.5288	8.9847	7.7843
25	19.5235	15.6221	12.7834	10.6748	9.0770	7.8431
26	20.1210	15.9828	13.0032	10.8100	9.1609	7.8957
27	20.7069	16.3296	13.2105	10.9352	9.2372	7.9426
28	21.2813	16.6631	13.4062	11.0511	9.3066	7.9844
29	21.8444	16.9837	13.5907	11.1584	9.3696	8.0218
30	22.3965	17.2920	13.7648	11.2578	9.4269	8.0552

(Appendix A-Financial Tables-Continued)

PVIFA (Continued)

Number of Periods	14%	16%	18%	20%	22%	24%
1	0.8772	0.8621	0.8475	0.8333	0.8197	0.8065
2	1.6467	1.6052	1.5656	1.5278	1.4915	1.4568
3	2.3216	2.2459	2.1743	2.1065	2.0422	1.9813
4	2.9137	2.7982	2.6901	2.5887	2.4936	2.4043
5	3.4331	3.2743	3.1272	2.9906	2.8636	2.7454
6	3.8887	3.6847	3.4976	3.3255	3.1669	3.0205
7	4.2883	4.0386	3.8115	3.6046	3.4155	3.2423
8	4.6389	4.3436	4.0776	3.8372	3.6193	3.4212
9	4.9464	4.6065	4.3030	4.0310	3.7863	3.5655
10	5.2161	4.8332	4.4941	4.1925	3.9232	3.6819
11	5.4527	5.0286	4.6560	4.3271	4.0354	3.7757
12	5.6603	5.1971	4.7932	4.4392	4.1274	3.8514
13	5.8424	5.3423	4.9095	4.5327	4.2028	3.9124
14	6.0021	5.4675	5.0081	4.6106	4.2646	3.9616
15	6.1422	5.5755	5.0916	4.6755	4.3152	4.0013
16	6.2651	5.6685	5.1624	4.7296	4.3567	4.0333
17	6.3729	5.7487	5.2223	4.7746	4.3908	4.0591
18	6.4674	5.8178	5.2732	4.8122	4.4187	4.0799
19	6.5504	5.8775	5.3162	4.8435	4.4415	4.0967
20	6.6231	5.9288	5.3527	4.8696	4.4603	4.1103
21	6.6870	5.9731	5.3837	4.8913	4.4756	4.1212
22	6.7429	6.0113	5.4099	4.9094	4.4882	4.1300
23	6.7921	6.0442	5.4321	4.9245	4.4985	4.1371
24	6.8351	6.0726	5.4509	4.9371	4.5070	4.1428
25	6.8729	6.0971	5.4669	4.9476	4.5139	4.1474
26	6.9061	6.1182	5.4804	4.9563	4.5196	4.1511
27	6.9352	6.1364	5.4919	4.9636	4.5243	4.1542
28	6.9607	6.1520	5.5016	4.9697	4.5281	4.1566
29	6.9830	6.1656	5.5098	4.9747	4.5312	4.1585
30	7.0027	6.1772	5.5168	4.9789	4.5338	4.1601

Table A-3. $CVIF = (1 + \%i/100)^N$

Number of Periods	2%	4%	6%	8%	10%	12%
1	1.0200	1.0400	1.0600	1.0800	1.1000	1.1200
2	1.0404	1.0816	1.1236	1.1664	1.2100	1.2544
3	1.0612	1.1249	1.1910	1.2597	1.3310	1.4049
4	1.0824	1.1699	1.2625	1.3605	1.4641	1.5735
5	1.1041	1.2167	1.3382	1.4693	1.6105	1.7623
6	1.1262	1.2653	1.4185	1.5869	1.7716	1.9738
7	1.1487	1.3159	1.5036	1.7138	1.9487	2.2107
8	1.1717	1.3686	1.5938	1.8509	2.1436	2.4760
9	1.1951	1.4233	1.6895	1.9990	2.3579	2.7731
10	1.2190	1.4802	1.7908	2.1589	2.5937	3.1058
11	1.2434	1.5395	1.8983	2.3316	2.8531	3.4785
12	1.2682	1.6010	2.0122	2.5182	3.1384	3.8960
13	1.2936	1.6651	2.1329	2.7196	3.4523	4.3635
14	1.3195	1.7317	2.2609	2.9372	3.7975	4.8871
15	1.3459	1.8009	2.3966	3.1722	4.1772	5.4736
16	1.3728	1.8730	2.5404	3.4259	4.5950	6.1304
17	1.4002	1.9479	2.6928	3.7000	5.0545	6.8660
18	1.4282	2.0258	2.8543	3.9960	5.5599	7.6900
19	1.4568	2.1068	3.0256	4.3157	6.1159	8.6128
20	1.4859	2.1911	3.2071	4.6610	6.7275	9.6463
21	1.5157	2.2788	3.3996	5.0338	7.4002	10.8038
22	1.5460	2.3699	3.6035	5.4365	8.1403	12.1003
23	1.5769	2.4647	3.8197	5.8715	8.9543	13.5523
24	1.6084	2.5633	4.0489	6.3412	9.8497	15.1786
25	1.6406	2.6658	4.2919	6.8485	10.8347	17.0000
26	1.6734	2.7725	4.5494	7.3964	11.9182	19.0401
27	1.7069	2.8834	4.8223	7.9881	13.1100	21.3249
28	1.7410	2.9987	5.1117	8.6271	14.4210	23.8839
29	1.7758	3.1187	5.4184	9.3173	15.8631	26.7499
30	1.8114	3.2434	5.7435	10.0627	17.4494	29.9599

(Appendix A-Financial Tables-Continued)

CVIF (Continued)

Number of Periods	14%	16%	18%	20%	22%	24%
1	1.1400	1.1600	1.1800	1.2000	1.2200	1.2400
2	1.2996	1.3456	1.3924	1.4400	1.4884	1.5376
3	1.4815	1.5609	1.6430	1.7280	1.8158	1.9066
4	1.6890	1.8106	1.9388	2.0736	2.2153	2.3642
5	1.9254	2.1003	2.2878	2.4883	2.7027	2.9316
6	2.1950	2.4364	2.6996	2.9860	3.2973	3.6352
7	2.5023	2.8262	3.1855	3.5832	4.0227	4.5077
8	2.8526	3.2784	3.7589	4.2998	4.9077	5.5895
9	3.2519	3.8030	4.4355	5.1598	5.9874	6.9310
10	3.7072	4.4114	5.2338	6.1917	7.3046	8.5944
11	4.2262	5.1173	6.1759	7.4301	8.9117	10.6571
12	4.8179	5.9360	7.2876	8.9161	10.8722	13.2148
13	5.4924	6.8858	8.5994	10.6993	13.2641	16.3863
14	6.2613	7.9875	10.1472	12.8392	16.1822	20.3191
15	7.1379	9.2655	11.9737	15.4070	19.7423	25.1956
16	8.1372	10.7480	14.1290	18.4884	24.0856	31.2426
17	9.2765	12.4677	16.6722	22.1861	29.3844	38.7408
18	10.5752	14.4625	19.6733	26.6233	35.8490	48.0386
19	12.0557	16.7765	23.2144	31.9480	43.7358	59.5679
20	13.7435	19.4608	27.3930	38.3376	53.3576	73.8641
21	15.6676	22.5745	32.3238	46.0051	65.0963	91.5915
22	17.8610	26.1864	38.1421	55.2061	79.4175	113.5735
23	20.3616	30.3762	45.0076	66.2474	96.8894	140.8312
24	23.2122	35.2364	53.1090	79.4968	118.2050	174.6306
25	26.4619	40.8742	62.6686	95.3962	144.2101	216.5420
26	30.1666	47.4141	73.9490	114.4755	175.9364	268.5121
27	34.3899	55.0004	87.2598	137.3706	214.6424	332.9550
28	39.2045	63.8004	102.9666	164.8447	261.8637	412.8642
29	44.6931	74.0085	121.5005	197.8136	319.4737	511.9516
30	50.9502	85.8499	143.3706	237.3763	389.7579	634.8199

(Appendix A–Financial Tables–Continued)

Table A-4 CVIFA $= \dfrac{(1 + \%i/100)^N - 1}{\%i/100}$

Number of Periods	2%	4%	6%	8%	10%	12%
1	1.0000	1.0000	1.0000	1.0000	1.0000	1.0000
2	2.0200	2.0400	2.0600	2.0800	2.1000	2.1200
3	3.0604	3.1216	3.1836	3.2464	3.3100	3.3744
4	4.1216	4.2465	4.3746	4.5061	4.6410	4.7793
5	5.2040	5.4163	5.6371	5.8666	6.1051	6.3528
6	6.3081	6.6330	6.9753	7.3359	7.7156	8.1152
7	7.4343	7.8983	8.3938	8.9228	9.4872	10.0890
8	8.5830	9.2142	9.8975	10.6366	11.4359	12.2997
9	9.7546	10.5828	11.4913	12.4876	13.5795	14.7757
10	10.9497	12.0061	13.1808	14.4866	15.9374	17.5487
11	12.1687	13.4864	14.9716	16.6455	18.5312	20.6546
12	13.4121	15.0258	16.8699	18.9771	21.3843	24.1331
13	14.6803	16.6268	18.8821	21.4953	24.5227	28.0291
14	15.9739	18.2919	21.0151	24.2149	27.9750	32.3926
15	17.2934	20.0236	23.2760	27.1521	31.7725	37.2797
16	18.6393	21.8245	25.6725	30.3243	35.9497	42.7532
17	20.0121	23.6975	28.2129	33.7502	40.5447	48.8837
18	21.4121	25.6454	30.9057	37.4502	45.5992	55.7497
19	22.8406	27.6712	33.7600	41.4463	51.1591	63.4397
20	24.2974	29.7781	36.7856	45.7620	57.2750	72.0524
21	25.7833	31.9692	39.9927	50.4229	64.0025	81.6987
22	27.2990	34.2480	43.3923	55.4568	71.4027	92.5026
23	28.8450	36.6179	46.9958	60.8933	79.5430	104.6029
24	30.4219	39.0826	50.8156	66.7648	88.4973	118.1552
25	32.0303	41.6459	54.8645	73.1059	98.3471	133.3339
26	33.6709	44.3117	59.1564	79.9544	109.1818	150.3339
27	35.3443	47.0842	63.7058	87.3508	121.0999	169.3740
28	37.0512	49.9676	68.5281	95.3388	134.2099	190.6989
29	38.7922	52.9663	73.6398	103.9659	148.6309	214.5828
30	40.5681	56.0849	79.0582	113.2832	164.4940	241.3327

(Appendix A-Financial Tables-Continued)

CVIFA (Continued)

Number of Periods	14%	16%	18%	20%	22%	24%
1	1.0000	1.0000	1.0000	1.0000	1.0000	1.0000
2	2.1400	2.1600	2.1800	2.2000	2.2200	2.2400
3	3.4396	3.5056	3.5724	3.6400	3.7084	3.7776
4	4.9211	5.0665	5.2154	5.3680	5.5242	5.6842
5	6.6101	6.8771	7.1542	7.4416	7.7396	8.0484
6	8.5355	8.9775	9.4420	9.9299	10.4423	10.9801
7	10.7305	11.4139	12.1415	12.9159	13.7396	14.6153
8	13.2328	14.2401	15.3270	16.4991	17.7623	19.1229
9	16.0853	17.5185	19.0859	20.7989	22.6700	24.7125
10	19.3373	21.3215	23.5213	25.9587	28.6574	31.6434
11	23.0445	25.7329	28.7551	32.1504	35.9620	40.2379
12	27.2707	30.8502	34.9311	39.5805	44.8737	50.8950
13	32.0887	36.7862	42.2187	48.4966	55.7459	64.1097
14	37.5811	43.6720	50.8180	59.1959	69.0100	80.4961
15	43.8424	51.6595	60.9653	72.0351	85.1922	100.8151
16	50.9804	60.9250	72.9390	87.4421	104.9345	126.0108
17	59.1176	71.6730	87.0680	105.9306	129.0201	157.2534
18	68.3941	84.1407	103.7403	128.1167	158.4045	195.9942
19	78.9692	98.6032	123.4135	154.7400	194.2535	244.0328
20	91.0249	115.3797	146.6280	186.6880	237.9893	303.6006
21	104.7684	134.8405	174.0210	225.0256	291.3469	377.4648
22	120.4360	157.4150	206.3448	271.0307	356.4432	469.0563
23	138.2970	183.6014	244.4868	326.2369	435.8607	582.6298
24	158.6586	213.9776	289.4945	392.4842	532.7501	723.4610
25	181.8708	249.2140	342.6035	471.9811	650.9551	898.0916
26	208.3327	290.0883	405.2721	567.3773	795.1653	1114.6336
27	238.4993	337.5024	479.2211	681.8528	971.1016	1383.1457
28	272.8892	392.5028	566.4809	819.2233	1185.7440	1716.1007
29	312.0937	456.3032	669.4475	984.0680	1447.6077	2128.9648
30	356.7868	530.3117	790.9480	1181.8816	1767.0813	2640.9164

Appendix B—Statistical Information

Table B-1. Standard Normal Distribution

X	0.00	0.01	0.02	0.03	0.04
0.0	0.00000	0.00399	0.00798	0.01197	0.01595
0.1	0.03983	0.04280	0.04776	0.05172	0.05567
0.2	0.07926	0.08317	0.08706	0.09095	0.09483
0.3	0.11791	0.12172	0.12552	0.12930	0.13307
0.4	0.15542	0.15910	0.16276	0.16640	0.17003
0.5	0.19146	0.19497	0.19847	0.20194	0.20540
0.6	0.22575	0.22907	0.23237	0.23565	0.23891
0.7	0.25804	0.26115	0.26424	0.26730	0.27035
0.8	0.28814	0.29103	0.29389	0.29673	0.29955
0.9	0.31594	0.31859	0.32121	0.32381	0.32639
1.0	0.34134	0.34375	0.34614	0.34850	0.35083
1.1	0.36433	0.36650	0.36864	0.37076	0.37286
1.2	0.38493	0.38686	0.38877	0.39065	0.39251
1.3	0.40320	0.40490	0.40658	0.40824	0.40988
1.4	0.41924	0.42073	0.42220	0.42364	0.42507
1.5	0.43319	0.43448	0.43574	0.43699	0.43822
1.6	0.44520	0.44630	0.44738	0.44845	0.44950
1.7	0.45543	0.45637	0.45728	0.45818	0.45907
1.8	0.46407	0.46485	0.46562	0.46638	0.46712
1.9	0.47128	0.47193	0.47257	0.47320	0.47381
2.0	0.47725	0.47778	0.47831	0.47882	0.47932
2.1	0.48214	0.48257	0.48300	0.48341	0.49382
2.2	0.48610	0.48645	0.48679	0.48713	0.48745
2.3	0.48928	0.48956	0.48983	0.49010	0.49036
2.4	0.49180	0.49202	0.49224	0.49245	0.49266
2.5	0.49379	0.49396	0.49413	0.49430	0.49446
2.6	0.49534	0.49547	0.49560	0.49573	0.49585
2.7	0.49653	0.49664	0.49674	0.49683	0.49693
2.8	0.49744	0.49752	0.49760	0.49767	0.49774
2.9	0.49813	0.49819	0.49825	0.49831	0.49836
3.0	0.49865	0.49869	0.49874	0.49878	0.49882
3.1	0.49903	0.49906	0.49910	0.49913	0.49916
3.2	0.49931	0.49934	0.49936	0.49938	0.49940
3.3	0.49952	0.49953	0.49957	0.49957	0.49958
3.4	0.49966	0.49968	0.49969	0.49970	0.49971
3.5	0.49977	0.49978	0.49978	0.49979	0.49980
3.6	0.49984	0.49985	0.49985	0.49986	0.49986
3.7	0.49989	0.49990	0.49990	0.49991	0.49991
3.8	0.49993	0.49993	0.49993	0.49994	0.49994
3.9	0.49995	0.49995	0.49996	0.49996	0.49996

(Appendix B–Statistical Information–Continued)

Table B-1. Standard Normal Distribution, Continued

X	0.05	0.06	0.07	0.08	0.09
0.0	0.01994	0.02392	0.02790	0.03188	0.03586
0.1	0.05962	0.06356	0.06749	0.07142	0.07535
0.2	0.09871	0.10257	0.10642	0.11026	0.11409
0.3	0.13683	0.14058	0.14431	0.14803	0.15173
0.4	0.17364	0.17724	0.18082	0.18439	0.18793
0.5	0.20884	0.21226	0.21566	0.21904	0.22240
0.6	0.24215	0.24537	0.24857	0.25175	0.25490
0.7	0.27337	0.27637	0.27935	0.28230	0.28524
0.8	0.30234	0.30511	0.30785	0.31057	0.31327
0.9	0.32894	0.33147	0.33398	0.33646	0.33891
1.0	0.35314	0.35543	0.35769	0.35993	0.36214
1.1	0.37493	0.37698	0.37900	0.38100	0.38298
1.2	0.39435	0.39617	0.39796	0.39973	0.40147
1.3	0.41149	0.41309	0.41466	0.41621	0.41774
1.4	0.42647	0.42785	0.42922	0.43056	0.43189
1.5	0.43943	0.44062	0.44179	0.44295	0.44408
1.6	0.45053	0.45154	0.45254	0.45352	0.45449
1.7	0.45994	0.46080	0.46164	0.46246	0.46327
1.8	0.46784	0.46856	0.46926	0.46995	0.47062
1.9	0.47441	0.47500	0.47558	0.47615	0.47670
2.0	0.47982	0.48030	0.48077	0.48124	0.48169
2.1	0.48422	0.48461	0.48500	0.48537	0.48574
2.2	0.48778	0.48809	0.48840	0.48870	0.48899
2.3	0.49061	0.49086	0.49111	0.49134	0.49158
2.4	0.49286	0.49305	0.49324	0.49343	0.49361
2.5	0.49461	0.49477	0.49492	0.49506	0.49520
2.6	0.49598	0.49609	0.49621	0.49632	0.49643
2.7	0.49702	0.49711	0.49720	0.49728	0.49736
2.8	0.49781	0.49788	0.49795	0.49801	0.49807
2.9	0.49841	0.49846	0.49851	0.49856	0.49861
3.0	0.49886	0.49889	0.49893	0.49897	0.49900
3.1	0.49918	0.49921	0.49924	0.49926	0.49929
3.2	0.49942	0.49944	0.49946	0.49948	0.49950
3.3	0.49960	0.49961	0.49962	0.49964	0.49965
3.4	0.49972	0.49973	0.49974	0.49975	0.49976
3.5	0.49981	0.49981	0.49982	0.49983	0.49983
3.6	0.49987	0.49987	0.49988	0.49988	0.49989
3.7	0.49991	0.49992	0.49992	0.49992	0.49992
3.8	0.49994	0.49994	0.49995	0.49995	0.49995
3.9	0.49996	0.49996	0.49996	0.49997	0.49997

Table B-2. Random Digits

00	49487	52802	28667	62058	87822	14704	18519	17889	45869	14454
01	29480	91539	46317	84803	86056	62812	33584	70391	77749	64906
02	25252	97738	23901	11106	86864	55808	22557	23214	15021	54268
03	02431	42193	96960	19620	29188	05863	92900	06836	13433	21709
04	69414	89353	70724	67893	23218	72452	03095	68333	13751	37260
05	77285	35179	92042	67581	67673	68374	71115	98166	43352	06414
06	52852	11444	71868	34534	69124	02760	06406	95234	87995	78560
07	98740	98054	30195	09891	18453	79464	01156	95522	06884	55073
08	85022	58736	12138	35146	62085	36170	25433	80787	96496	40579
09	17778	03840	21636	56269	08149	19001	67367	13138	02400	89515
10	81833	93449	57781	94621	90998	37561	59688	93299	27726	82167
11	63789	54958	33167	10909	40343	81023	61590	44474	39810	10305
12	61840	81740	60986	12498	71546	42249	13812	59902	27864	21809
13	42243	10153	20891	90883	15782	98167	86837	99166	92143	82441
14	45236	09129	53031	12260	01278	14404	40969	33419	14188	69557
15	40338	42477	78804	36272	72053	07958	67158	60979	79891	92409
16	54050	71253	88789	98203	54999	96564	00789	68879	47134	83941
17	49158	20908	44859	29089	76130	51442	34453	98590	37353	61137
18	80958	03808	83655	18415	96563	43582	82207	53322	30419	64435
19	07636	04876	61063	57571	69434	14965	20911	73162	33576	52838
20	37227	80750	08261	97048	60438	75053	05939	34414	16685	32103
21	99460	45915	45637	41353	35335	69087	57536	68418	10247	93253
22	60248	75845	37296	33783	42393	28185	31880	00241	31642	37526
23	95076	79089	87380	28982	97750	82221	35584	27444	85793	69755
24	20944	97852	26586	32796	51513	47475	48621	20067	88975	39506
25	30458	49207	62358	41532	30057	53017	10375	97204	98675	77634
26	38905	91282	79309	49022	17405	18830	09186	07629	01785	78317
27	96545	15638	90114	93730	13741	70177	49175	42113	21600	69625
28	21944	28328	00692	89164	96025	01383	50252	67044	70596	58266
29	36910	71928	63327	00980	32154	46006	62289	28079	03076	15619

(continued)

(Appendix B–Statistical Information–Continued)

Table B-2. Random Digits (Continued)

30	48745	47626	28856	28382	60639	51370	70091	58261	70135	88259
31	32519	91993	59374	83994	59873	51217	62806	20028	26545	16820
32	75757	12965	29285	11481	31744	41754	24428	81819	02354	37895
33	07911	97756	89561	27464	25133	50026	16436	75846	83718	08533
34	89887	03328	76911	93168	56236	39056	67905	94933	05456	52347
35	30543	99488	75363	94187	32885	23887	10872	22793	26232	87356
36	68442	55201	33946	42495	28384	89889	50278	91985	58185	19124
37	22403	56698	88524	13692	55012	25343	76391	48029	72278	58586
38	70701	36907	51242	52083	43126	90379	60380	98513	85596	16528
39	69804	96122	42342	28467	79037	13218	63510	09071	52438	25840

(Appendix B–Statistical Information–Continued)

Table B-3. Student's t-Distribution Quantiles
(For Checking Upper or Lower Limits)

Degrees of Freedom	Cumulative Probability				
	90%	95%	97.5%	99%	99.5%
1	3.078	6.314	12.706	31.821	63.657
2	1.886	2.920	4.303	6.965	9.925
3	1.638	2.353	3.182	4.541	5.841
4	1.533	2.132	2.776	3.747	4.604
5	1.476	2.015	2.571	3.365	4.032
6	1.440	1.943	2.447	3.143	3.707
7	1.415	1.895	2.365	2.998	3.499
8	1.397	1.860	2.306	2.896	3.355
9	1.383	1.833	2.262	2.821	3.250
10	1.372	1.812	2.228	2.764	3.169
11	1.363	1.796	2.201	2.718	3.106
12	1.356	1.782	2.179	2.681	3.055
13	1.350	1.771	2.160	2.650	3.012
14	1.345	1.761	2.145	2.624	2.977
15	1.341	1.753	2.131	2.602	2.947
16	1.337	1.746	2.120	2.583	2.921
17	1.333	1.740	2.110	2.567	2.898
18	1.330	1.734	2.101	2.552	2.878
19	1.328	1.729	2.093	2.539	2.861
20	1.325	1.725	2.086	2.528	2.845
21	1.323	1.721	2.080	2.518	2.831
22	1.321	1.717	2.074	2.508	2.819
23	1.319	1.714	2.069	2.500	2.807
24	1.318	1.711	2.064	2.492	2.797
25	1.316	1.708	2.060	2.485	2.787
26	1.315	1.706	2.056	2.479	2.779
27	1.314	1.703	2.052	2.473	2.771
28	1.313	1.701	2.048	2.467	2.763
29	1.311	1.699	2.045	2.462	2.756
30	1.310	1.697	2.042	2.457	2.750
40	1.303	1.684	2.021	2.423	2.704
60	1.296	1.671	2.000	2.390	2.660
120	1.289	1.658	1.980	2.358	2.617
∞	1.282	1.645	1.960	2.326	2.576

Appendix C—Error Conditions

"Error" appears in the calculator display when an overflow or underflow occurs or when an improper operation is attempted. When the error condition occurs, no keyboard entry (except [OFF]) is accepted until [ON/C] is pressed. After you press [ON/C] to clear the error condition and all pending operations, determine what caused the error. Then enter the correct information.

The following sections list the circumstances which cause an error condition. The first section lists the general conditions which do not affect entered statistical or financial information. The second section lists errors occurring while entering financial information, while the third section lists errors occurring while entering statistical information.

Section 1—General Error Conditions

1. A number entry or calculation result in the display or memory is outside the range of $\pm 1 \times 10^{-99}$ to $\pm 9.9999999 \times 10^{99}$.
2. A number greater than 1×10^{99} multiplied by another number may cause an error condition.
3. The square root of a negative number is attempted.
4. A number is divided by zero.
5. One of the following is calculated: [2nd] [lnx] or [1/x] of zero or zero to the zero power.
6. A power or [2nd] [lnx] of a negative number is calculated.
7. The factorial of any number except a non-negative integer less than 70 is attempted.
8. A percent change in which the old value is equal to zero is calculated.
9. An argument outside the range given in Accuracy Information is used for the logarithmic function.

Section 2—Financial Error Conditions

1. The `CPT` or `DUE` key is followed by any key except `PV`, `FV`, `N`, `PMT`, `%i`, `2nd` `BAL`, `2nd` `INT`, `2nd` `APR▸`, or `2nd` `◂EFF`.
2. The `2nd` `RCL` key sequence is followed by a key other than `PV`, `FV`, `N`, `PMT`, `%i`, `CPT`, `DUE`, `2nd` `CPT`, or `2nd` `DUE`.
3. The calculation of financial unknowns is attempted before enough known variables are entered or is attempted when no solution exists.
4. A statistical key is pressed.
5. A financial value with a result greater than or equal to $\pm 1 \times 10^8$ (except for N) is calculated.
6. The balance or interest is computed for a payment number less than 1.
7. The `2nd` `APR▸` or `2nd` `◂EFF` key is used during computations in which the number of compounding periods per year is zero, the number of compounding periods per year is large, or %i is small.
8. The answer is less than or equal to -100% when %i is computed.
9. The calculation of N is attempted when PV = FV + PMT = PV $\times$ %i.

Section 3—Statistical Error Conditions

1. A financial key is pressed.
2. The `2nd` `RCL` key sequence is pressed.
3. Only one data point is used when calculating `σn-1`.
4. A data point is entered such that x $\leqslant \pm 1 \times 10^{-50}$ or x $\geqslant \pm 1 \times 10^{50}$.
5. A series of data points is entered such that the sum of the squares exceeds the upper or lower limit of the calculator.
6. More than 99,999 data points are entered.
7. Data points are removed using `2nd` `Σ−` or `FRQ` `2nd` `Σ−` to the extent that there are zero or fewer data points.
8. The `2nd` `x!` key is pressed after the `FRQ` key.

Appendix D—Accuracy Information

Each calculation produces an 11-digit result which is rounded to an 8-digit standard display. The 5/4 rounding technique used adds 1 to the least significant digit in the display if the next non-displayed digit is five or more. If this digit is less than five, no rounding occurs. In the absence of these extra digits, inaccurate results would frequently be displayed, such as

$$1 \div 3 \times 3 = 0.9999999$$

Because of rounding, the answer is given as 1, but is internally equal to 0.9999999999.

The higher order mathematical functions use iterative calculations. The cumulative error from these calculations in most cases is maintained beyond the 8-digit display so that no inaccuracy is displayed. Most calculations are accurate to ± 1 in the last displayed digit. There are a few instances in the solution of high order functions where display accuracy begins to deteriorate as the function approaches a discontinuous or undefined point.

The following gives the limits within which the display must be when calculating certain functions.

Function	Limit
ln x	$1 \times 10^{-99} \leqslant x < 1 \times 10^{100}$
e^x	$-227.95592 \leqslant x \leqslant 230.25850$
x!	$0 \leqslant x \leqslant 69$ where x is an integer
N	limited to four significant digits

Appendix E—Service Information

In Case of Difficulty

In the event that you have difficulty with your calculator, the following instructions will help you to analyze the problem. You may be able to correct your calculator problem without returning the unit to a service facility.

Symptom	Solution
Display is blank, shows erroneous results, flashes erratic numbers, or grows dim.	The battery may be discharged. Insert new batteries using the instructions in BATTERY REPLACEMENT.
Display shows erroneous results or error message.	Review the operating instructions, including the Error Conditions appendix to be certain that calculations were performed correctly.

Mailing Instructions

Enclose a written explanation of the problem with your calculator. Be sure to include your name and return address.

Wrap your calculator in tissue or similar soft packing material and enclose it in a strong, crushproof mailing carton. If you use the original display box for mailing, it cannot be returned to you.

To protect your calculator from theft, do not write "calculator" on the outside of the package. Send your calculator to the appropriate address listed in WARRANTY PERFORMANCE.

Texas Instruments strongly recommends that you insure the product for value prior to mailing.

(Appendix E–Service Information–Continued)

Battery Replacement

NOTE: The calculator cannot hold data in its user data memories or mode registers when the batteries are removed or become discharged.

The calculator uses 2 of any of the following batteries for up to 1000 hours of operation: Panasonic LR-44, Ray-O-Vac RW-82, Union Carbide (Eveready) A-76, or the equivalent. For up to 2500 hours of operation use Mallory 10L14, Union Carbide (Eveready) 357, Panasonic WL-14, Toshiba G-13, Ray-O-Vac RW-42, or the equivalent.

1. Turn off the calculator. Place a small screwdriver, paper clip, or other similar instrument into the slot and gently lift the battery cover.

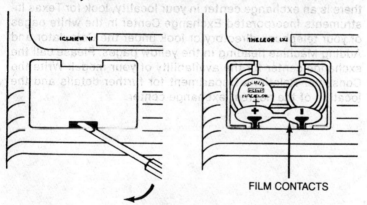

FILM CONTACTS

2. Remove the discharged batteries and install new ones as shown. Be careful not to crease the film contacts while installing the new batteries. Be sure the film contacts are positioned to lay on top of the batteries after the batteries are installed.
3. Replace the cover top edge first, then gently press until the bottom of the cover snaps into place.
4. Press [OFF], [ON/c], [STO], [2nd][FIN], and [2nd][STAT].

CAUTION: Do not incinerate the old batteries.

Calculator Exchange Centers

If your calculator requires service, instead of returning the unit to your dealer or to a service facility for repair, you may elect to exchange the calculator for a factory-rebuilt calculator of the same model (or equivalent model specified by TI) by bringing the calculator in person to one of the exchange centers which have been established across the United States. No charge will be made for the exchange with proof-of-purchase during the first 90 days. The exchanged unit will be in warranty for the remainder of the original warranty period or for 6 months, whichever is longer. A handling fee will be charged for exchange after 90 days from the date of purchase. Out-of-warranty exchanges will be charged at the rates in effect at the time of the exchange. To determine if there is an exchange center in your locality, look for Texas Instruments Incorporated Exchange Center in the white pages of your telephone directory or look under the Calculator and Adding Machine heading in the yellow pages. Please call the exchange center for the availability of your model. Write the Consumer Relations Department for further details and the location of the nearest exchange center.

(Appendix E–Service Information–Continued)

If You Need Service Information

If you need additional information about in-warranty or out-of-warranty service, write to:

Texas Instruments Consumer Relations
P.O. Box 53
Lubbock, Texas 79408

For Technical Assistance

For technical questions such as specific calculator applications, you can call (806) 747-3841. We regret that this is not a toll-free number, and we cannot accept collect calls. As an alternative, you can write to:

Texas Instruments Consumer Relations
P. O. Box 53
Lubbock, Texas 79408

California and Oregon: Consumers in California and Oregon may contact the following Texas Instruments offices for additional assistance or information.

Texas Instruments Consumer Service
831 South Douglas Street
El Segundo, California 90245
(213) 973-1803

Texas Instruments Consumer Service
6700 Southwest 105th St.
Kristin Square, Suite 110
Beaverton, Oregon 97005
(503) 643-6758

(Appendix E–Service Information–Continued)

Because of the number of suggestions which come to Texas Instruments from many sources, containing both new and old ideas, Texas Instruments will consider such suggestions only if they are freely given to Texas Instruments. It is the policy of Texas Instruments to refuse to receive any suggestions in confidence. Therefore, if you wish to share your suggestions with Texas Instruments, or if you wish us to review any calculator key sequence which you have developed, please include the following in your letter:

> "All of the information forwarded herewith is presented to Texas Instruments on a nonconfidential, nonobligatory basis; no relationship, confidential or otherwise, expressed or implied, is established with Texas Instruments by this presentation. Texas Instruments may use, copyright, distribute, publish, reproduce, or dispose of the information in any way without compensation to me."

ONE-YEAR LIMITED WARRANTY

THIS TEXAS INSTRUMENTS ELECTRONIC CALCULATOR WARRANTY EXTENDS TO THE ORIGINAL CONSUMER PURCHASER OF THE PRODUCT.

WARRANTY DURATION: This calculator is warranted to the original consumer purchaser for a period of one year from the original purchase date.

WARRANTY COVERAGE: This calculator is warranted against defective materials or workmanship. **THIS WARRANTY DOES NOT COVER BATTERIES AND IS VOID IF THE PRODUCT HAS BEEN DAMAGED BY ACCIDENT, UNREASONABLE USE, NEGLECT, IMPROPER SERVICE OR OTHER CAUSE NOT ARISING OUT OF DEFECTS IN MATERIAL OR WORKMANSHIP.**

(Appendix E–Service Information–Continued)

WARRANTY DISCLAIMERS: ANY IMPLIED WARRANTIES ARISING OUT OF THIS SALE, INCLUDING BUT NOT LIMITED TO THE IMPLIED WARRANTIES OF MERCHANTABILITY AND FITNESS FOR A PARTICULAR PURPOSE, ARE LIMITED IN DURATION TO THE ABOVE ONE YEAR PERIOD. TEXAS INSTRUMENTS SHALL NOT BE LIABLE FOR LOSS OF USE OF THE CALCULATOR OR OTHER INCIDENTAL OR CONSE- QUENTIAL COSTS, EXPENSES, OR DAMAGES INCURRED BY THE CONSUMER OR ANY OTHER USER. Some states do not allow the exclusion or limitation of implied warranties or consequential damages, so the above limitations or exclu- sions may not apply to you.

LEGAL REMEDIES: This warranty gives you specific legal rights, and you may also have other rights that vary from state to state.

WARRANTY PERFORMANCE: During the above one year war- ranty period your TI calculator will either be repaired or replaced with a reconditioned comparable model (at TI's op- tion) when the product is returned, postage prepaid, to a Texas Instruments Service Facility listed below. In the event of replacement with a reconditioned model, the replacement product will continue the warranty of the original calculator or 6 months, whichever is longer. Other than the postage re- quirement, no charge will be made for such repair, adjust- ment, and/or replacement.

(Appendix E-Service Information-Continued)

If the calculator is out of warranty, service rates in effect at the time of return will be charged. Please include information on the difficulty experienced with the calculator as well as return address information including name, address, city, state, and zip code. The shipment should be carefully packaged and adequately protected against shock and rough handling.

Texas Instruments Consumer Service Facilities

U. S. Residents:
Texas Instruments Service Facility
P. O. Box 2500
Lubbock, Texas 79408
Canadian customers only:
Geophysical Services Incorporated
41 Shelley Road
Richmond Hill, Ontario, Canada L4C5G4

NOTE: The P.O. Box number listed for the Lubbock Service facility is for United States parcel post shipments only. If you use another carrier, the street address is:

Texas Instruments Incorporated
2305 North University Avenue
Lubbock, TX 79415

Selected Bibliography

Brealey, Richard and Myers, Stewart. *Principles of Corporate Finance*. New York: McGraw-Hill, 1981.

Brueggeman, William B. and Stone, Leo D. *Real Estate Finance*. Seventh Edition. Homewood, Illinois: Richard D. Irwin, Inc., 1981.

Daniel, Wayne W. and Terrell, James C. *Business Statistics Basic Concepts and Methodology*. Second Edition. Dallas, Texas: Houghton Mifflin Company, 1979.

Folks, J. Leroy. *Ideas of Statistics*. Santa Barbara, California: J. Wiley and Sons, 1981.

Greynolds, Elbert B. Jr. and Stevens, Jan E. *Executive Calculator Guidebook*. Dallas: Texas Instruments, Inc., 1980.

Greynolds, Elbert B. Jr., Aronofsky, Julius S., and Frame, Robert J. *Financial Analysis Using Calculator: Time Value of Money*. New York: McGraw-Hill, 1980.

Horngren, Charles T. *Cost Accounting: A Managerial Emphasis*. Fifth Edition. Englewood Cliffs, New Jersey: Prentice-Hall, Inc., 1982.

Kieso, Donald E. and Weygandt, Jerry A. *Intermediate Accounting*. Third Edition. Santa Barbara, California: John Wiley and Sons, 1980.

Mendenhall, William. *Introduction to Probability and Statistics*. Fifth Edition. North Scituate, Massachusetts: Duxbury Press, 1979.

"The Learning Curve as a Production Tool." *Harvard Business Review*, January-February 1954, pp 87-97.

Van Horne, James C. *Financial Management and Policy*. Fifth Edition. Englewood Cliffs, New Jersey: Prentice-Hall, Inc., 1980.

Waller, Ray A. *Statistics: An Introduction to Numerical Reasoning*. Holden-Day Inc., 1979.

Weston J. Fred and Brigham, Eugene F. *Managerial Finance*. Seventh Edition. Hinsdale, Illinois: The Dryden Press, 1981.

(continued)

NOTES

NOTES

NOTES

NOTES

NOTES

NOTES

NOTES

NOTES